W9-AGV-449

NUMERICAL METHODS
IN ENGINEERING

PRENTICE-HALL CIVIL ENGINEERING
AND ENGINEERING MECHANICS SERIES

N. M. Newmark, *Editor*

NUMERICAL METHODS

IN ENGINEERING

Mario G. Salvadori

ASSOCIATE PROFESSOR OF CIVIL ENGINEERING

COLUMBIA UNIVERSITY

WITH A COLLECTION OF PROBLEMS BY

Melvin L. Baron

RESEARCH ASSOCIATE, COLUMBIA UNIVERSITY

New York PRENTICE-HALL, INC. 1952

To my father

RICCARDO SALVADORI

The interest of the applied mathematician and of the scientist in numerical methods has grown considerably during the last decades for many reasons. Electric desk calculators, mass-produced at reasonable prices, and electronic super-computers of the digital and the analogue type make possible today computations which could not have been tackled a few years ago. Technical problems, for which an analytical solution is unobtainable, more complicated and more numerous than ever, require an immediate answer, while technical personnel capable of working out complex analytical problems is scarce. The numerical approach permits the use of workers with a limited knowledge of mathematics.

These conditions explain the popularity of numerical methods, and indicate the increasing need for personnel with numerical skills and for courses on numerical methods in our colleges and universities.

This book has evolved from a set of mimeographed lecture notes used in a one-semester course offered in the School of Engineering at Columbia University. The course is the last of a sequence of five inaugurated by the author twelve years ago in order to widen the mathematical background of undergraduate and graduate students and to fill the gap between a knowledge of theoretical mathematics and the technique of solving physical problems by mathematical methods.

It would be obviously impossible to encompass the whole wide and growing field of numerical methods in a book of moderate size. It is the purpose of this presentation to introduce both the student and the practicing scientist, and in particular the engineer, to those elementary techniques which are needed more often in the solution of technical problems. The book is therefore addressed to students of engineering, physics, chemistry, mathematics, and to any individual desiring to become acquainted with numerical methods in order to apply them in his professional work. It is assumed that the reader has a knowledge of the calculus and a smattering of differential equations.

The five chapters of the book deal with:

1. The solution of algebraic equations of high degree and of simultaneous linear algebraic equations.

2. The elementary theory of finite differences and its application to numerical differentiation, integration, interpolation, and extrapolation.

3. The solution of ordinary initial-value problems.

4. The solution of ordinary boundary and characteristic-value problems.

5. The solution of problems involving partial differential equations of the boundary, characteristic, and mixed types.

In the presentation of the material, finite difference theory is made the unifying basis of all the numerical techniques. This makes the treatment of the various subjects economical and avoids unnecessary repetition. It also allows a simple evaluation of errors throughout the book and, perhaps for the first time, the systematic use of efficient extrapolation procedures.

The various numerical techniques are either introduced by, or applied to, a simple illustrative problem taken from the various fields of engineering, (mechanics, strength of materials, electricity, elasticity, plasticity, heat flow, vibrations, elastic stability, etc.) in order to give as wide a range of applications as possible within the limits of space and prerequisites. But the reader does not need to be familiar with the particular field of knowledge involved in the illustrative problem to grasp the meaning of the numerical technique.

The choice of techniques was based upon their simplicity and efficiency: some have been known for over two centuries; others have been advanced in the recent past. The numerical tools to which these techniques can be applied are, usually, the electric desk calculator and, in many cases, the slide rule. Modern electronic calculators, to which most of these techniques can also obviously be applied, are not mentioned since their theory constitutes an entire new field of applied mathematics.

The problems at the end of each chapter are essentially of two types: purely numerical exercises and applied problems. Many of the numerical exercises represent actual physical problems and can be interpreted analogically in a variety of ways. The mathematical formulation of the applied problems is given or can be derived from the text or from the numerous references in the footnotes. Answers are given to alternate problems and to all problems whose answers are of general interest.

Melvin L. Baron undertook, under my supervision, the painstaking and laborious task of assembling and solving the 400 problems contained in this book. He also checked the problems in the text and drew sketches for the figures. I am glad to express here my deep appreciation for his efficient efforts.

The books and individuals from which I have learned numerical mathematics are too many to be listed here, but I take this opportunity to express my gratitude to Prof. Mauro Picone, Director of the Istituto Nazionale per le Applicazioni del Calcolo (the national Italian computational laboratory, seat of the recently established International Center of Mechanical Calculus), who first taught me the love of numbers while I was his student at the University of Rome 20 years ago.

I am indebted to my friends and colleagues: Prof. R. J. Schwarz, for his critical reading of the manuscript, and Prof. F. H. Lee, for the care he gave to the drawing of the figures.

Mrs. P. Arno Moriarty has given renewed proof of her exceptional skill in typing the manuscript.

MARIO G. SALVADORI

New York, N. Y.

Note: The following books are referred to in the footnotes by their abbreviated titles. The latter two volumes are to be published in the near future.

Engineering Problems for *The Mathematical Solution of Engineering Problems,* by M. G. Salvadori and K. S. Miller, McGraw-Hill Book Co., New York, 1948.

Differential Equations for *Differential Equations in Engineering Problems,* by M. G. Salvadori and R. J. Schwarz, Prentice-Hall, Inc., New York.

Partial Differential Equations for *Partial Differential Equations in Engineering Problems,* by K. S. Miller, Prentice-Hall, Inc., New York.

CONTENTS

CHAPTER I:

THE PRACTICAL SOLUTION OF ALGEBRAIC AND
TRANSCENDENTAL EQUATIONS................... 1

1.1 Introduction... 1
1.2 Real Roots of Algebraic Equations.................... 1
1.3 Complex Roots of Algebraic Equations................ 8
1.4 Transcendental Equations............................ 13
1.5 Linear Simultaneous Algebraic Equations.............. 16
1.6 Gauss's Scheme...................................... 17
1.7 Matrices and Determinants........................... 20
1.8 Cholesky's Scheme................................... 23
1.9 The Gauss-Seidel Iteration Method................... 28
1.10 Solution of Linear Equations by Relaxation........... 31

CHAPTER II:

FINITE DIFFERENCES AND THEIR APPLICATIONS.. 45

2.1 Introduction... 45
2.2 Interpolating Parabolas.............................. 46
2.3 Taylor Series Expansions............................. 48
2.4 Backward Differences................................. 51
2.5 Forward Differences.................................. 58
2.6 Gregory-Newton Interpolation Formulas............... 61
2.7 Central Differences.................................. 63
2.8 Numerical Integration................................ 70
2.9 Richardson's Extrapolations.......................... 75

CHAPTER III:

THE NUMERICAL INTEGRATION OF INITIAL VALUE
PROBLEMS... 91

3.1 Introduction... 91
3.2 Starting the Solution of First-Order Equations.......... 91

xi

3.3 Starting the Solution of Higher-Order Equations........ 97
3.4 Adams' Method..................................... 101
3.5 The Runge-Fox Method for Linear Equations.......... 104
3.6 The Solution of Simultaneous First-Order Equations.... 108
3.7 The Adams-Störmer Method for Second-Order Equations 109
3.8 Fox's Methods for Second-Order Linear Equations...... 113
3.9 Accumulation of Error in Step-by-Step Integration...... 121

CHAPTER IV:

THE NUMERICAL INTEGRATION OF ORDINARY
BOUNDARY VALUE PROBLEMS.................... 133

4.1 Boundary Value Problems........................... 133
4.2 Step-by-Step Integration of Boundary Value Problems.. 134
4.3 Solution of Second Order Problems by Central Differences 135
4.4 Improvement of Solution by Corrections.............. 140
4.5 Improvement of Solution by Extrapolation............ 145
4.6 Solution of Higher Order Problems by Central Differences 148
4.7 Solution of Characteristic Value Problems............. 151
4.8 The Use of Unevenly Spaced Pivotal Points........... 155

CHAPTER V:

THE NUMERICAL SOLUTION OF PARTIAL DIFFER-
ENTIAL EQUATIONS............................... 167

5.1 Partial Difference Operators in Cartesian Coordinates... 167
5.2 Numerical Double Integration....................... 172
5.3 The Solution of Laplace's Equation by Iteration........ 178
5.4 Solution of Laplace's Equation by Relaxation........... 181
5.5 Solution of Poisson's Equation by Relaxation.......... 182
5.6 Elastic Torsion.................................... 188
5.7 Solution of a Problem in Plastic Torsion by Relaxation.. 191
5.8 A Boundary Value Problem Involving $\nabla^4 z$.............. 199

Contents   xiii

5.9 Two-dimensional Characteristic Value Problems........ 202
5.10 The Solution of Partial Differential Equations by Separation of the Variables and Finite Differences............ 208
5.11 Membrane Vibrations................................ 210
5.12 Pivotal Points Near Curved Boundaries................ 213
5.13 A Transient Problem in Two-dimensional Heat Flow.... 217
5.14 The Laplacian Operator in Skew Coordinates........... 220
5.15 The Laplacian Operator in Polar Coordinates.......... 224
5.16 The Laplacian Operator in Triangular Coordinates...... 229

INDEX... 253

CHAPTER I

The Practical Solution of Algebraic and Transcendental Equations

1.1 Introduction

The solution of algebraic and transcendental equations, and of systems of simultaneous linear equations, is one of the numerical tasks encountered most frequently in applied mathematics. Although many methods have been devised to obtain these solutions, and some of them are extremely ingenious from a theoretical viewpoint, the task of solving equations remains burdensome.

In what follows, methods are presented for the evaluation of the real and complex roots of algebraic equations of high degree, of real roots of transcendental equations, and of roots of simultaneous linear algebraic equations. These procedures are well adapted to slide-rule use and to use on desk electric calculators. They allow an accuracy of 5 to 10 significant figures and the solution of systems of between 40 and 100 simultaneous linear equations. Modern electronic calculators may extend considerably the use of these methods.

The general procedures outlined below attempt to combine various methods so as to reduce the amount of labor involved in the solution, but the reader may prefer other classical procedures or formulas since the choice of method is often a matter of training and personal preference.

1.2 Real Roots of Algebraic Equations

An algebraic equation of degree n has n roots, some of which may be real and different or real and repeated, and the rest of which appear in couples of complex conjugate numbers.

In solving an algebraic equation of high degree it is advisable to locate first its real roots, in order of decreasing absolute value.

This is best done by trial and error, evaluating remainders by synthetic division.

The possible number of positive and negative roots may be determined by Descartes' rule of sign: *the number of positive roots is equal to the number of sign changes in the coefficients of the equation (or less than that by an even number); the number of negative roots is equal to the number of sign repetitions in the coefficients (or less than that by an even number).*   Zero coefficients are ignored in this count.

Given an equation

$$f(x) = x^n + a_{n-1}x^{n-1} + \ldots + a_1x + a_0 = 0,^* \qquad (1.2.1)$$

its largest root may frequently be approximated by the root of the linear equation

$$x + a_{n-1} = 0 \qquad (1.2.2)$$

or by the root larger in absolute value of the quadratic equation

$$x^2 + a_{n-1}x + a_{n-2} = 0. \qquad (1.2.3)$$

Whenever the largest root of Eq. (1.2.1) is much larger than all the others in absolute value, these approximations are accurate.

The smallest root of Eq. (1.2.1) may similarly be approximated by the root of the equation

$$a_1x + a_0 = 0 \qquad (1.2.4)$$

or by the smaller root in absolute value of the quadratic equation

$$a_2x^2 + a_1x + a_0 = 0, \qquad (1.2.5)$$

whenever the smallest root is much smaller than the others.

A general procedure for the location of real roots will now be applied to the equation

$$y = f(x) = x^3 - 12.2x^2 + 7.45x + 42 = 0, \qquad (a)$$

which, by Descartes' rule of signs, may have either two positive roots or none, and only one negative root.

---

* The coefficient a_n of x^n is usually reduced to unity by division of the equation by a_n.

An approximate value of the largest root is given by the equation

$$x - 12.2 = 0$$

or by the equation
$$x^2 - 12.2x + 7.45 = 0.$$

The first equation gives $x_1 = 12.2$; the second gives

$$x_1 = 6.1 + \sqrt{(6.1)^2 - 7.45} = 11.55,$$

if the $+$ sign is chosen in front of the square root to obtain the larger root. Applying synthetic division with a trial value $x_1 = 12,*$ we obtain

	1	-12.2	7.45	42
12		12.0	-2.40	60.6
	1	-0.2	5.05	$\lfloor 102.6$

The magnitude of the remainder may lead the reader to believe that 12 is a poor approximation to x_1. This is not so, because *whenever a root is much larger than unity, the remainder is sensitive to changes in the value of the root.* In fact a second trial with $x_1 = 10$ gives

	1	-12.2	7.45	42
10		10.0	-22.00	-145.50
	1	-2.2	-14.55	$\lfloor -103.50$

The values $x = 12$ and $x = 10$ approximate the root from above and from below, respectively, and a better approximation may be obtained by *linear interpolation.* The intersection with the x-axis $(y = 0)$ of the straight line

$$\frac{x - x_1}{y - y_1} = \frac{x_2 - x_1}{y_2 - y_1}$$

connecting the two points $P_1(x_1,y_1)$ and $P_2(x_2,y_2)$:

$$x_3 = \frac{x_1 y_2 - x_2 y_1}{y_2 - y_1} \tag{1.2.6}$$

* The coefficients of the powers of x not appearing in the equation must be labeled zero in the synthetic division scheme.

gives the value of the linearly interpolated approximation x_3 (Fig. 1.1).   The right side of Eq. (1.2.6) can be evaluated by a single machine operation.   An application of Eq. (1.2.6) to the approximations $x_1 = 12$, $y_1 = 103$, and $x_2 = 10$, $y_2 = -103$ gives

$$x_3 = \frac{12(-103) - 10(103)}{-103 - 103} = 11,$$

and synthetic division gives a remainder $y_3 = -21.25$.   We can

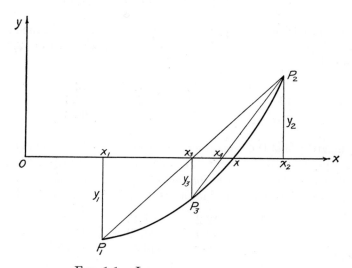

FIG. 1.1.   LINEAR INTERPOLATION.

now interpolate linearly between 11 and 12, obtaining $x_4 = 11.17$ with a remainder of -3.55, and a final guess 11.20 gives

	1	-12.2	7.45	42	
11.20		11.2	-11.20	-42.0	(b)
	1	-1.0	-3.75	0	

which shows $x = 11.2$ to be the required root.

Alternatively, and usually with definite advantage, one may use Newton's method of tangents (Fig. 1.2) to improve the first approximation to the root.*   Applying synthetic division *twice in succes-*

---

* See, for instance, *Engineering Problems*, p. 107.

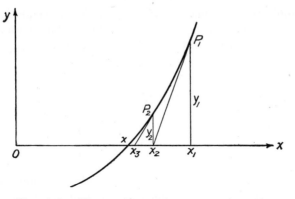

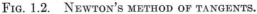

Fig. 1.2.   Newton's method of tangents.

sion, we obtain directly $f(x_n)$ *and* $f'(x_n)$ *and compute*

$$x_{n+1} = x_n - \frac{f(x_n)}{f'(x_n)}. \tag{1.2.7}$$

Thus with $x_1 = 12$ we obtain in two steps:

	1	−12.2	7.45	42
$x_1 = 12$		12.0	−2.40	61
	1	− 0.2	5.05	$\vert 103 = f(x_1)$
$x_1 = 12$		12.0	142	
	1	11.8	$\vert 147 = f'(x_1)$	

$$x_2 = 12 - \frac{103}{147} = 12 - 0.7 = 11.3.$$

Using the newly found value $x_2 = 11.3$, we have:

	1	−12.2	7.45	42.0
$x_2 = 11.3$		11.3	−10.17	−30.7
	1	− 0.9	− 2.72	$\vert 11.3 = f(x_2)$
$x_2 = 11.3$		11.3	117.52	
	1	10.4	$\vert 114.80 = f'(x_2)$	

$$x_3 = 11.3 - \frac{11}{115} = 11.3 - 0.1 = 11.2,$$

which is the value of the root obtained before.

One of the principal advantages of synthetic division lies in the fact that it gives directly the coefficients of the *reduced equation*, whose roots are the remaining roots of the original equation.   Thus synthetic division of Eq. (a) by $x - 11.2$ gives the quadratic whose coefficients appear in the last row of scheme (b):

$$x^2 - x - 3.75 = 0,$$

which may be solved by formula, giving the other two roots of Eq. (a):

$$x = 0.5 \pm \sqrt{0.25 + 3.75} = \left\{ \begin{array}{l} +2.5 \\ -1.5. \end{array} \right.$$

In order to avoid the high sensitivity of the remainder to changes in the root when the root is much larger than 1, we may use *backward synthetic division*, as illustrated in the following scheme:

$$
\begin{array}{r|rrrr}
 & 1 & -12.2 & 7.45 & 42 \\
x_1 = 12 & & 11.29 & -10.95 & -42 \\
\hline
 & 11.29 & -0.91 & -3.50 & \underline{}0 \\
\end{array}
$$

Starting with an *assumed* zero remainder, the value -42, which makes the remainder equal to zero, is divided by the approximate root 12, giving -3.50.   The number appearing under 7.45 must give -3.50 when added to 7.45; hence it equals $-3.50 -7.45 = -10.95$.   The number -0.91 is the quotient $-10.95/12$, and 11.29 is the difference $-0.91 - (-12.2)$.   This last result would check the assumed value of the root if correct.   It is seen that the difference between the assumed value and the value obtained by backward substitution is not large, indicating that 12 is not far from the root.   We try in the same manner $x_2 = 11$:

$$
\begin{array}{r|rrrr}
 & 1 & -12.2 & 7.45 & 42 \\
x_2 = 11 & & 11.18 & -11.27 & -42 \\
\hline
 & 11.18 & -1.02 & -3.82 & \underline{}0 \\
\end{array}
$$

The error in the first trial was $12 - 11.29 = +0.71$; the error in the second trial is $11 - 11.18 = -0.18$ and a single, linear interpolation gives:

$$x = \frac{12(-0.18) - 11(0.71)}{-0.18 - 0.71} = 11.20.$$

Generalizing the results of the present example, the m real roots of any algebraic equation may be obtained one at a time, using synthetic division by $(x - x_1)$, $(x - x_2)$, . . . , $(x - x_m)$, to any required accuracy.

Particular care must be taken in evaluating real roots if two roots are almost equal, that is, if the equation has an almost repeated root. A root *repeated k times* is a root of the equation $f(x) = 0$ and of its first $k - 1$ derivatives. For example, using synthetic division by $x - 3$ on the equation

$$x^3 - 5x^2 + 3x + 9 = 0,$$

we find that:

$$
\begin{array}{rrrrl}
 & 1 & -5 & 3 & 9 \\
3 & & 3 & -6 & -9 \\
\cline{2-5}
 & 1 & -2 & -3 & \;0 = f(3) \\
3 & & 3 & 3 & \\
\cline{2-4}
 & 1 & 1 & \;0 = f'(3) &
\end{array}
$$

and hence that $x = 3$ is a double root.

Whenever $f'(x)$ is very small in the neighborhood of a root $\bar{x}$, Eq. (1.2.7) becomes extremely sensitive to changes in x. In this case it is practical to evaluate first the root a of $f'(x) = 0$ near the root $\bar{x}$, to compute $f''(a)$, and to expand $f(x)$ in a Taylor series around $x = a$, neglecting terms of order higher than the third:

$$f(x) = f(a) + f'(a)(x - a) + \tfrac{1}{2}f''(a)(x - a)^2 + \ldots$$
$$\doteq f(a) + \tfrac{1}{2}f''(a)(x - a)^2.$$

To find the roots of $f(x)$ near $x = a$, we solve the quadratic equation

$$f(a) + \tfrac{1}{2}f''(a)(x - a)^2 = 0,$$

obtaining
$$x_{1,2} = a \pm \sqrt{\frac{-f(a)}{\tfrac{1}{2}f''(a)}}. \qquad (1.2.8)$$

For example, using synthetic division with $x = 1$ on the equation

$$x^3 - x^2 - 1.01x + 0.99 = 0,$$

we obtain:

$$
\begin{array}{rrrrl}
 & 1 & -1 & -1.01 & 0.99 \\
1 & & 1 & 0 & -1.01 \\
\cline{2-5}
 & 1 & 0 & -1.01 & \;-0.02 = f(1) \\
1 & & 1 & 1.00 & \\
\cline{2-4}
 & 1 & 1 & \;-0.01 = f'(1). &
\end{array}
$$

Since $f'(1)$ is small, we solve first the equation

$$f'(x) = 3x^2 - 2x - 1.01 = 0,$$

starting with $x = 1$:

	3	-2	-1.01
1		3	1.00
	3	1	$\boxed{-0.01} = f'(1)$
1		3	
	3	$\boxed{4} = f''(1)$	

and obtain the root

$$a = 1 - \frac{-0.01}{4} = 1.0025.$$

Evaluating $f(a)$ and $f''(a)$ by successive application of synthetic division,* we obtain:

	1	-1	-1.01	0.990
$a = 1.0025$		1.0025	0.0025	-1.010
	1	0.0025	-1.0075	$\boxed{-0.020} = f(a)$
$a = 1.0025$		1.0025	1.0075	
	1	1.0050	$\boxed{0} = f'(a)$	
$a = 1.0025$		1.0025		
	1	$\boxed{2.0075} = \frac{1}{2}f''(a),$		

and applying Eq. (1.2.8)

$$x_{1,2} = 1.0025 \pm \sqrt{-\frac{-0.020}{2.0075}} = \begin{cases} 1.102 \\ 0.903. \end{cases}$$

The true roots are 1.10 and 0.90.

Once all the real roots have been divided out of the equation, the last reduced equation contains only pairs of complex conjugate roots.

1.3 Complex Roots of Algebraic Equations

When the reduced equation is a quadratic, the two complex conjugate roots are immediately obtained by formula. When the reduced equation is of fourth, sixth, or even higher degree, it is convenient to isolate in the equation the quadratic factors which are

---

* Applying n times successively synthetic division to an equation $f(x) = 0$ with $x = a$, one obtains the values of $f(a), f'(a), 1/2!f''(a), \ldots, 1/n!f^{(n)}(a)$.

responsible for each pair of complex conjugate roots. This can be done again by synthetic division of the equation by trial quadratic factors until the remainder, which is a binomial $s_1 x + s_0$, becomes equal to zero or very small.

A first approximation to the quadratic factor responsible for the roots of largest modulus in Eq. (1.2.1) is the factor

$$x^2 + a_{n-1}x + a_{n-2}, \qquad (1.3.1)$$

while a first approximation to the quadratic factor responsible for the roots of smallest modulus is

$$a_2 x^2 + a_1 x + a_0$$

or

$$x^2 + \frac{a_1}{a_2}x + \frac{a_0}{a_2}, \qquad (1.3.2)$$

where the a's are now the coefficients of the reduced equation.

Table 1.1

Synthetic Division by $x^2 + px + q$

$$f(x) = x^n + a_{n-1}x^{n-1} + a_{n-2}x^{n-2} + \ldots + a_1 x + a_0$$

$$= (x^2 + px + q)(x^{n-2} + s_{n-1}x^{n-3} + s_{n-2}x^{n-4} + \ldots$$

$$+ s_3 x + s_2) + \frac{s_1 x + s_0}{f(x)}$$

1	1	a_{n-1}	a_{n-2}	a_{n-3}	. . .	a_2	a_1	a_0
$-p$		$-p \cdot 1$	$-ps_{n-1}$	$-ps_{n-2}$	. . .	$-ps_3$	$-ps_2$	
$-q$			$-q \cdot 1$	$-qs_{n-1}$	. . .	$-qs_4$	$-qs_3$	$-qs_2$
	1	s_{n-1}	s_{n-2}	s_{n-3}	. . .	s_2	s_1	s_0

In order to reduce the linear remainder $s_1 x + s_0$ to zero, we may either proceed by trial and error or by iteration. Both processes will be demonstrated on the following fourth-degree equation:

$$f(x) = x^4 + 27.4x^3 + 307.44x^2 - 873.7x + 1503.11 = 0. \quad \text{(a)}$$

An approximation to the smaller quadratic factor of this equation is given by

$$x^2 - \frac{873.7}{307.44}x + \frac{1503.11}{307.44} = x^2 - 2.84x + 4.89 \doteq x^2 - 3x + 5.$$

To evaluate the remainder due to the factor $x^2 + px + q$, we use first the scheme of synthetic division of Table 1.1, where

$$s_{n-1} = a_{n-1} - p, \qquad s_{n-2} = a_{n-2} - ps_{n-1} - q, \ \ldots$$

With an approximate factor $x^2 - 3x + 5$, this scheme applied to Eq. (a) with rounded-off coefficients gives:

1	1	27.4	307	-874	1503
3		3.0	91.2	1179.6	
-5			-5.0	-152.0	-1966
	1	30.4	393.2	153.6	$-\ 463$

(b)

The remainder is $153.6x - 463$, and the quotient is $x^2 + 30.4x + 393.2$. We try division by $x^2 - 2x + 5$, obtaining:

1	1	27.4	307	-874	1503
2		2.0	58.8	721.6	
-5			-5.0	-147.0	-1804
	1	29.4	360.8	-299.4	$-\ 301$

The coefficient s_1 of x in the remainder has changed sign, and the constant s_0 is slightly reduced in value. We try division by $x^2 - 3x + 4$:

1	1	27.4	307	-874	1503
3		3.0	91.2	1182.6	
-4			-4.0	-121.6	-1576.8
	1	30.4	394.2	187.0	$-\ 73.8$

The coefficient s_1 is now positive and larger than in the first trial, and the constant s_0 is smaller. We divide by $x^2 - 2.5x + 4$, obtaining a remainder of $-49.1x - 8.2$, while a final guess $x^2 - 2.6x + 3.9$ gives a remainder of $0.2x + 17$, which may be considered small, and a quotient $x^2 + 30x + 381.10$. The four roots of Eq. (a) are thus approximately:

$$x_{1,2} = 1.3 \pm \sqrt{(1.3)^2 - 3.9} = 1.3 \pm 1.49i,$$

$$x_{3,4} = -15 \pm \sqrt{(15)^2 - 381.10} = -15 \pm 12.5i.$$

The correct values of the roots are $x_{1,2} = 1.3 \pm 1.5i$ and $x_{3,4} = -15 \pm 12.5i$.

The *iteration process of Friedman** (which is faster than the better-known Lin's process) eliminates the necessity of guesses, but may converge very slowly or may not converge at all. In general, it is advisable to work by iteration and trial and error at the same time.

The Friedman procedure consists in dividing the left-hand member $f(x)$ of the equation by a trial quadratic factor *in descending powers of x*, as was done before, and in obtaining an improved factor by division of $f(x)$ by the quotient of the previous division, both arranged *in ascending powers of x*. The remainders of these divisions are not computed, since they are not needed if the process converges.

Thus, starting with the trial factor $x^2 - 3x + 5$ and dividing $f(x)$ in descending powers, we obtain [scheme (b), p. 10] the quotient

$$x^2 + 30.4x + 393.2 = 393.2\,(1 + 0.077x + 0.0025x^2).$$

Division of

$$f(x) = 1503.11 - 873.7x + 307.44x^2 + 27.4x^3 + x^4$$

by

$$1 + 0.077x + 0.0025x^2$$

(division in ascending powers) gives by the scheme of Table 1.1:

1	1503.11	−873.70	307.44
−0.077		−115.74	76.19
−0.0025			−3.76
	1503.11	−989.44	379.87

that is, a quotient

$$1503.11 - 989.44x + 379.87x^2 = 379.87\,(x^2 - 2.60x + 3.78).$$

Repeating these two operations once more and assembling the two divisions in a single table, with the division in descending powers

---

* B. Friedman, "Note on Approximating Complex Zeros of a Polynomial," *Communications on Pure and Applied Mathematics*, **II**, 195 (June–September 1949).

on the left and the division in ascending powers on the right, we obtain:

1	1	27.4	307.44	307.44	−873.70	1503.11	1
2.6		2.6	78.00	· 77.96	−118.14		−0.0786
−3.78			−3.78	−3.94			−0.00262
	1	30.0	381.66*	381.46*	−991.84	1503.11	

that is, a quotient

$$x^2 + 30x + 381.66 = 381.66(1 + 0.0786x + 0.00262x^2)$$

for the division in descending powers, and a quotient

$$381.46x^2 - 991.84x + 1503.11 = 381.46(x^2 - 2.60x + 3.94)$$

for the division in ascending powers. The near equality of the starred numbers indicates that the process converges and that the two factors of the equation are approximately $x^2 - 2.6x + 3.94$, and $x^2 + 30x + 381.66$, whose roots are

$$x_{1,2} = -1.3 \pm 1.5i, \qquad x_{3,4} = -15 \pm 12.5i.$$

These factors are correct to the number of figures computed.

The largest quadratic factor may be evaluated by the Friedman procedure starting with a division in ascending powers rather than with a division in descending powers. Thus, given

$$f(x) = x^6 - 11x^5 + 89x^4 + 89x^3 + 89x^2 + 88x + 100 = 0,$$

dividing in ascending powers by $x^2 - 11x + 89 = 89(1 - 0.12x + 0.011x^2)$, we obtain the quotient $100(1 + x + x^2 + x^3 + x^4)$, and dividing $f(x)$ in descending powers by $x^4 + x^3 + x^2 + x + 1$, we obtain the quotient $x^2 - 12x + 100$, whose roots $6 \pm 8i$ are exact roots of $f(x) = 0$. The divisions in ascending and descending powers appear on the left and right side, respectively, of the following scheme:

1	100	88	89	89	89	89	−11	1	1
0.12		12	12	12	12	12	− 1		−1
−0.011			−1	−1	−1	−1			−1
	100	100	100	100	100	100	−12	1	

Repeated complex roots occur seldom in practical problems and are evaluated by trial and error, since the iteration process converges very slowly (if at all) in this case.

"Squaring the roots," or *Graeffe's method*,* is frequently more cumbersome than the methods outlined above, particularly in connection with complex roots, but is widely used.

Once all the roots x_i of an algebraic equation have been obtained, the results of the solution may be checked by means of *Newton's relations:*

$$\sum_{i=1}^{n} x_i = -\frac{a_{n-1}}{a_n} \tag{1.3.3}$$

$$x_1 \cdot x_2 \cdot x_3 \cdot \ \ldots \ \cdot x_n = (-1)^n \frac{a_0}{a_n}. \tag{1.3.4}$$

For example, in Eq. (a) of this section:

$$\sum_{i=1}^{4} x_i = (1.3 + 1.49i) + (1.3 - 1.49i) + (-15 + 12.5i)$$
$$+ (-15 - 12.5i) = -27.4$$

$$x_1 \cdot x_2 \cdot x_3 \cdot x_4 = 1491,$$

indicating that the imaginary parts of the roots are probably slightly inaccurate.

1.4   Transcendental Equations

Any nonalgebraic equation is called a *transcendental equation.* A transcendental equation may have a finite or an infinite number of roots, and may have no real roots at all. For example, the equation

$$\sin x = 2$$

has no real roots (Fig. 1.3) but an infinity of complex roots; the equation

$$\sin x = \tfrac{1}{2}$$

---

* This method is explained in detail in J. B. Scarborough, *Numerical Mathematical Analysis*, Johns Hopkins Press, Baltimore, 1930, pp. 198 ff., and in R. E. Doughterty and E. G. Keller, *Mathematics of Modern Engineering*, John Wiley & Sons, Inc., New York, 1936, pp. 98 ff.

has an infinite number of real roots (Fig. 1.3); the equation

$$\sin x = \tfrac{1}{2}x$$

has three real roots (Fig. 1.3).

Once a root of a transcendental equation has been approximated from above and below, either graphically or by trial and error, linear

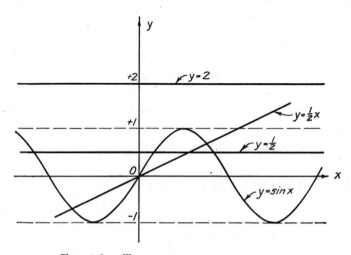

FIG. 1.3.   TRANSCENDENTAL EQUATIONS.

interpolation can be used to improve the value of the root by use of Eq. (1.2.6).   For example, the equation

$$y = f(x) = e^x - 3x = 0 \qquad\qquad \text{(a)}$$

has two real roots, one of which lies between 0.4 and 0.9 (Fig. 1.4).

With $x_1 = 0.9$, $y_1 = -0.24$ and $x_2 = 0.4$, $y_2 = 0.29$,   Eq. (1.2.6) gives:

$$x_3 = \frac{0.9(0.29) - 0.4(-0.24)}{0.29 - (-0.24)} = 0.67$$

and $y_3 = -0.06$.   Proceeding in the same way we obtain successively: $x_4 = 0.627$, $y_4 = -0.009$ and $x_5 = 0.619$, $y_5 = 0.00001$.

Alternatively, by Newton's method we have

$$f(x) = e^x - 3x, \qquad f'(x) = e^x - 3$$

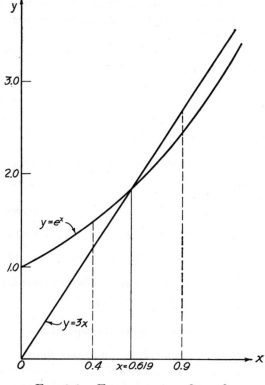

FIG. 1.4.   EQUATION $e^x - 3x = 0$.

and, starting at $x = 0.9$ with $f'(0.9) = -0.54$,

$$x_1 = 0.9 - \frac{-0.24}{-0.54} = 0.455; \quad f(x_1) = 0.21; \quad f'(x_1) = -1.42$$

$$x_2 = 0.455 - \frac{0.21}{-1.42} = 0.603; \quad f(x_2) = 0.019; \quad f'(x_2) = -1.17$$

$$x_3 = 0.603 - \frac{0.019}{-1.17} = 0.614; \quad f(x_3) = 0.0058; \quad f'(x_3) = -1.15$$

$$x_4 = 0.614 - \frac{0.0058}{-1.15} = 0.619; \quad f(x_4) = 0.00001.$$

Another method for the determination of the real roots of a transcendental equation, *which does not converge in all cases*, consists in expanding the functions appearing in the equation into power series (whenever possible) and in solving the algebraic equations obtained by cutting the series off after 2, 3, . . . , n terms.

For example, the expansion of the left-hand member of Eq. (a) gives:

$$f(x) = e^x - 3x = \left(1 + x + \frac{x^2}{2} + \frac{x^3}{6} + \frac{x^4}{24} + \ldots \right) - 3x$$

$$= 1 - 2x + \frac{x^2}{2} + \frac{x^3}{6} + \frac{x^4}{24} + \ldots,$$

and the successive algebraic equations with their lower root are:

$1 - 2x = 0$	$x_1 = 0.5$
$x^2 - 4x + 2 = 0$	$x_1 = 0.586$
$x^3 + 3x^2 - 12x + 6 = 0$	$x_1 = 0.613$
$x^4 + 4x^3 + 12x^2 - 48x + 24 = 0$	$x_1 = 0.618.$

This method may become advantageous when the first few roots of a transcendental equation must be determined.

1.5   Linear Simultaneous Algebraic Equations

The solution of systems of simultaneous linear equations is among the most important and most frequently encountered problems of numerical mathematics. A large number of methods has been proposed to perform the task, and various special computers (of the digital and the analogue type) are now available to solve equations.

The four methods presented here are all well adapted to use on either calculator or slide rule and have the following properties:

1. *Gauss's scheme* is a perfectly general systematic procedure for the elimination of the unknowns, particularly adapted to slide-rule use and easily remembered.

2. *Cholesky's scheme* is a perfectly general systematic procedure for the elimination of the unknowns, well adapted to machine calculations.

3. *Gauss-Seidel's iteration method* is a process of successive approximations applicable to certain types of equations and well adapted to machine computations.

4. *Relaxation* is a method of successive approximations applicable to a large variety of equations and well adapted to slide-rule use.

All these methods will be illustrated by means of examples in the following sections.

1.6 Gauss's Scheme*

Gauss's elimination scheme is applied in Table 1.2 to the following system:†

Eqs.	x_1	x_2	x_3	x_4	c
I	2	2	4	-2	10
II	1	3	2	1	17
III	3	1	3	1	18
IV	1	3	4	2	27

(1.6.1)

in which, for example, Eq. (I) reads

$$2x_1 + 2x_2 + 4x_3 - 2x_4 = 10.‡$$

Table 1.2 is self-explanatory, except for the numbers r and the column S. The numbers r are ratios of coefficients obtained as follows: r_2 is the ratio of the encircled coefficient 1 of x_1 in row 2 to the boxed coefficient 2 of x_1 in row 1; r_3 is the ratio of the encircled coefficient 3 of x_1 in row 5 to the boxed coefficient 2 of x_1 in row 1; r'_3 is the ratio of the encircled coefficient -2 of x_2 in row 7 to the boxed coefficient 2 of x_2 in row 4, etc. The column S is used as a check: it contains the sum of all the coefficients and the constant of each row, and is operated upon as any other number of the same row. Once the number S of a given row has been obtained by the operations indicated in the explanation column, it must check with the sum of all the numbers of that row. The use of a sum check

---

* Gauss's scheme is also known in the United States under the name of Doolittle's method.

† This example, entirely solvable by integers, is taken from Sec. 4.3 of *Engineering Problems,* and was suggested by Dr. V. P. Jensen, to whom the author is indebted.

‡ The constants c are always written as the right-hand members of the equations.

Table 1.2

Gauss's Scheme

Rows	r	x_1	x_2	x_3	x_4	c	S	Explanations
(1)		[2]	2	4	−2	10	16	(I)
2	$r_2 = \frac{1}{2}$	(1)	3	2	1	17	24	(II)
3		−1	−1	−2	1	−5	−8	$-r_2 \times (1)$
(4)		0	[2]	0	2	12	16	(2) + (3)
5	$r_3 = \frac{3}{2}$	(3)	1	3	1	18	26	(III)
6		−3	−3	−6	3	−15	−24	$-r_3 \times (1)$
7	$r'_3 = -\frac{2}{2}$	0	(−2)	−3	4	3	2	(5) + (6)
8			2	0	2	12	16	$-r'_3 \times (4)$
(9)			0	[−3]	6	15	18	(7) + (8)
10	$r_4 = \frac{1}{2}$	(1)	3	4	2	27	37	(IV)
11		−1	−1	−2	1	−5	−8	$-r_4 \times (1)$
12	$r'_4 = \frac{2}{2}$	0	(2)	2	3	22	29	(10) + (11)
13			−2	0	−2	−12	−16	$-r'_4 \times (4)$
14	$r_4'' = \dfrac{2}{-3}$		0	(2)	1	10	13	(12) + (13)
15				−2	4	10	12	$-r_4'' \times (9)$
(16)				0	[5]	20	25	(14) + (15)
17	Const. c_i	10	12	15	20			
18	$-x_4 a_{i4}$	8	−8	−24	20	$x_4 = \frac{20}{5} = 4$		
19	$-x_3 a_{i3}$	−12	0	−9	$x_3 = (-9)/(-3) = 3$			
20	$-x_2 a_{i2}$	−4	4	$x_2 = \frac{4}{2} = 2$				
21	$(i = 1,4,9,16)$	2	$x_1 = \frac{2}{2} = 1$					

column is imperative as soon as the number of the unknowns is higher than 4.   The roots are obtained from the equations appearing in the rows of the scheme labeled n^2 (1,4,9,16), which contain, respectively, 4, 3, 2, 1 unknowns, by back substitution starting from the last equation.   Thus

Row 16:	$5x_4 = 20$	$x_4 = 4$
Row 9:	$-3x_3 + 6x_4 = 15$	$x_3 = 3$
Row 4:	$2x_2 + 0x_3 + 2x_4 = 12$	$x_2 = 2$
Row 1:	$2x_1 + 2x_2 + 4x_3 - 2x_4 = 10$	$x_1 = 1^*$

In the solution by Gauss's scheme of two or more systems having the same coefficients of the unknowns but different values of the constants c, only the columns c and S of the scheme must be evaluated for each system, since the other columns of the scheme remain unchanged.   It is possible to use this important property of the scheme to evaluate additional figures in the roots with little additional labor.   To this purpose one evaluates the left-hand members c' of the equations for the obtained values of the roots, and computes the differences e between the constants c and c'.   Using the e as new constants, one evaluates the new values of the unknowns x', which, added to the old values of the unknowns, give improved values $x + x'$ of the roots of the original system.†

For example, assuming that an evaluation of the roots of the following system (a) to two significant figures gives $x_1 = 1.60$,

Eqs.	x_1	x_2	x_3	c	
I	1	2	1	6.00	(a)
II	2	1	1	6.11	
III	1	1	2	5.73	

---

* These operations can also be performed as indicated in the lower part of Table 1.2.

† See, for example, *Engineering Problems*, pp. 129 ff.

$x_2 = 1.50$, $x_3 = 1.30$, we compute

$$e_1 = 6.00 - (1.60 + 2 \cdot 1.50 + 1.30) = 0.10$$

$$e_2 = 6.11 - (2 \cdot 1.60 + 1.50 + 1.30) = 0.11$$

$$e_3 = 5.73 - (1.60 + 1.50 + 2 \cdot 1.30) = 0.03$$

and solve the system of so-called *error equations:*

Eqs.	x'_1	x'_2	x'_3	e
I	1	2	1	0.10
II	2	1	1	0.11
III	1	1	2	0.03

obtaining $x'_1 = 0.05$, $x'_2 = 0.04$, $x'_3 = -0.03$. The improved roots

$$x_1 = 1.60 + 0.05 = 1.65$$

$$x_2 = 1.50 + 0.04 = 1.54$$

$$x_3 = 1.30 - 0.03 = 1.27$$

are, in this case, the true roots of the original system (a).

1.7   Matrices and Determinants

A rectangular array of numbers with m rows and n columns is called an m by n *matrix*, and is indicated by a capital letter. The array

$$A = \begin{bmatrix} 2 & 1 & 3 \\ 3 & 2 & 1 \end{bmatrix}$$

is a 2 by 3 matrix. The element of A located at the ith row and the jth column is indicated by a_{ij}. An n by n matrix is called a *square matrix*. The elements a_{ii} constitute the *main diagonal* of a square matrix. The determinant of the elements of a square matrix A is called the determinant of A, and is indicated by $|A|$. A square matrix with zeros below its main diagonal is called an *upper triangular matrix;* a square matrix with zeros above its main diagonal is called a *lower triangular matrix* and will be indicated by L. A square matrix with ones on and zeros below the main diagonal is called a *unit upper triangular matrix*, and will be indicated by T.

An n by 1 matrix is called a *column*. A *zero matrix* has all its elements equal to zero. The *unit matrix* is a square matrix with ones on its main diagonal and zeros everywhere else.

Two matrices A and B are equal if and only if each a_{ij} equals the corresponding b_{ij}.

A matrix C is the *sum* of two matrices A and B if $c_{ij} = a_{ij} + b_{ij}$.

A matrix C is called the *product* AB (or the result of *premultiplying* B by A) if:

$$c_{ij} = \sum_{k=1}^{n} a_{ik}b_{kj}, \tag{1.7.1}$$

where n is the number of columns of A and of rows of B.

The product AB is hence obtained by "rows into columns" multiplication, and, in general, is different from the product BA (when this product exists). The product AB exists only if the number of columns of A equals the number of rows of B. For example, given:

$$A = \begin{bmatrix} 2 & 1 \\ 1 & 3 \end{bmatrix} \qquad B = \begin{bmatrix} 2 & 1 & 1 \\ 1 & 2 & 1 \end{bmatrix},$$

the product AB equals:

$$AB = \begin{bmatrix} 2 & 1 \\ 1 & 3 \end{bmatrix}\begin{bmatrix} 2 & 1 & 1 \\ 1 & 2 & 1 \end{bmatrix}$$

$$= \begin{bmatrix} (2 \cdot 2 + 1 \cdot 1) & (2 \cdot 1 + 1 \cdot 2) & (2 \cdot 1 + 1 \cdot 1) \\ (1 \cdot 2 + 3 \cdot 1) & (1 \cdot 1 + 3 \cdot 2) & (1 \cdot 1 + 3 \cdot 1) \end{bmatrix}$$

$$= \begin{bmatrix} 5 & 4 & 3 \\ 5 & 7 & 4 \end{bmatrix} = C.$$

The determinant of the product of two square matrices is equal to the product of the determinants of the matrices. For example, with

$$A = \begin{bmatrix} 2 & 1 \\ 1 & 2 \end{bmatrix}; \quad B = \begin{bmatrix} 1 & 3 \\ 2 & 1 \end{bmatrix}; \quad C = AB = \begin{bmatrix} 4 & 7 \\ 5 & 5 \end{bmatrix};$$

$$|A| = 3; \quad |B| = -5,$$

the determinant of C equals:

$$|C| = |A||B| = (3)(-5) = -15.^*$$

The most efficient method of evaluating a numerical (or literal) determinant

$$D_n = \begin{vmatrix} a_{11} & a_{12} & a_{13} & \cdots & a_{1n} \\ a_{21} & a_{22} & a_{23} & \cdots & a_{2n} \\ \cdots & \cdots & \cdots & \cdots & \cdots \\ \cdots & \cdots & \cdots & \cdots & \cdots \\ a_{n1} & a_{n2} & a_{n3} & \cdots & a_{nn} \end{vmatrix}$$

is, in general, by *pivotal condensation*, according to the following scheme,† in which each element is evaluated by means of a second order determinant:

$$D_n = \frac{1}{a_{11}{}^{n-2}} \begin{vmatrix} \begin{vmatrix} a_{11} & a_{12} \\ a_{21} & a_{22} \end{vmatrix} & \begin{vmatrix} a_{11} & a_{13} \\ a_{21} & a_{23} \end{vmatrix} & \cdots & \begin{vmatrix} a_{11} & a_{1n} \\ a_{21} & a_{2n} \end{vmatrix} \\ \begin{vmatrix} a_{11} & a_{12} \\ a_{31} & a_{32} \end{vmatrix} & \begin{vmatrix} a_{11} & a_{13} \\ a_{31} & a_{33} \end{vmatrix} & \cdots & \begin{vmatrix} a_{11} & a_{1n} \\ a_{31} & a_{3n} \end{vmatrix} \\ \cdots & \cdots & \cdots & \cdots \\ \cdots & \cdots & \cdots & \cdots \\ \begin{vmatrix} a_{11} & a_{12} \\ a_{n1} & a_{n2} \end{vmatrix} & \begin{vmatrix} a_{11} & a_{13} \\ a_{n1} & a_{n3} \end{vmatrix} & \cdots & \begin{vmatrix} a_{11} & a_{1n} \\ a_{n1} & a_{nn} \end{vmatrix} \end{vmatrix} \qquad (1.7.2)$$

For example:

$$\begin{vmatrix} 2 & 1 & 2 & 1 \\ 1 & 1 & 1 & 2 \\ 2 & 1 & 1 & 1 \\ 1 & 2 & 1 & 2 \end{vmatrix} = \frac{1}{2^{4-2}} \begin{vmatrix} 1 & 0 & 3 \\ 0 & -2 & 0 \\ 3 & 0 & 3 \end{vmatrix} =$$

$$= \frac{1}{4} \cdot \frac{1}{1^{3-2}} \begin{vmatrix} -2 & 0 \\ 0 & -6 \end{vmatrix} = \frac{1}{4} \cdot \frac{1}{1} \cdot 12 = 3.$$

---

* For a complete treatment of the algebra of matrices see, for instance, A. C. Aitken, *Determinants and Matrices*, Oliver and Boyd, London, 1939, or any book on advanced algebra.

† See, for example, *Engineering Problems*, pp. 121 ff.

Remembering the rule for matric multiplication, a system of, say, three simultaneous equations:

$$a_{11}x_1 + a_{12}x_2 + a_{13}x_3 = c_1$$

$$a_{21}x_1 + a_{22}x_2 + a_{23}x_3 = c_2$$

$$a_{31}x_1 + a_{32}x_2 + a_{33}x_3 = c_3$$

may be written in matric form as:

$$\begin{bmatrix} a_{11} & a_{12} & a_{13} \\ a_{21} & a_{22} & a_{23} \\ a_{31} & a_{32} & a_{33} \end{bmatrix} \begin{bmatrix} x_1 \\ x_2 \\ x_3 \end{bmatrix} = \begin{bmatrix} c_1 \\ c_2 \\ c_3 \end{bmatrix}$$

or simply as: $$AX = C.$$

The matrix $A = [a_{ij}]$ is called the matrix of the system, the columns $X = [x_i]$ and $C = [c_i]$ the columns of the unknowns and of the constants, respectively.

The fundamental step in any method of solution of simultaneous equations by elimination consists in reducing the system to unit upper triangular form:

$$\begin{bmatrix} 1 & t_{12} & t_{13} \\ 0 & 1 & t_{23} \\ 0 & 0 & 1 \end{bmatrix} \begin{bmatrix} x_1 \\ x_2 \\ x_3 \end{bmatrix} = \begin{bmatrix} k_1 \\ k_2 \\ k_3 \end{bmatrix}$$

or: $$TX = K,$$

since the system

$$x_1 + t_{12}x_2 + t_{13}x_3 = k_1$$

$$x_2 + t_{23}x_2 = k_2$$

$$x_3 = k_3$$

can be immediately solved by "back substitution."

1.8   Cholesky's Scheme*

Cholesky's method is conveniently presented in matric form since it consists essentially in determining an auxiliary matrix L of

---

* Cholesky's method was used by A. L. Cholesky in France before 1916 in connection with symmetrical systems, was given in matric form in Poland by Th. Banachiewicz in 1938, rediscovered and adapted to machine computations in the United States by P. D. Crout in 1941, studied again in England by A. M. Turing in 1948 and in Germany by A. Zurmühl in 1949.

the lower triangular type capable of reducing the original system $AX - C = 0$ to the unit triangular form $TX - K = 0$.

To this purpose let us assume that the system to be solved has been reduced to the unit triangular form $TX - K = 0$ and that premultiplication of this equation by a lower triangular matrix L will return it to its original form:

$$L(TX - K) = AX - C = 0.$$

This implies the two matric equations:

$$LT = A \qquad LK = C$$

Remembering the rule for matric multiplication, these matric equations allow the determination of L, T, and K in a very simple manner.* In fact, writing these equations out in explicit form and adding the column C to A, and the column K to T for compactness, these equations become for the case of a three-equation system:

$$
\begin{bmatrix} [A] & & & [C] \\ a_{11} & a_{12} & a_{13} & c_1 \\ a_{21} & a_{22} & a_{23} & c_2 \\ a_{31} & a_{32} & a_{33} & c_3 \end{bmatrix}
=
\begin{bmatrix} [L] & & \\ l_{11} & 0 & 0 \\ l_{21} & l_{22} & 0 \\ l_{31} & l_{32} & l_{33} \end{bmatrix}
\begin{bmatrix} [T] & & [K] \\ 1 & t_{12} & t_{13} & k_1 \\ 0 & 1 & t_{23} & k_2 \\ 0 & 0 & 1 & k_3 \end{bmatrix},
$$

from which the following equations are obtained for the elements of L, T, and K:

1. $$a_{i1} = l_{i1} \times 1 + l_{i2} \times 0 + l_{i3} \times 0 = l_{i1},$$

that is, the first column of L is identical with the first column of A.

2. $$a_{1j} = l_{11}t_{1j} + 0 \times t_{2j} + 0 \times t_{3j} = l_{11}t_{1j} = a_{11}t_{1j},$$

that is, the first row of T equals the first row of A divided by a_{11}.

3. $$a_{22} = l_{21}t_{12} + l_{22} \times 1 \quad \therefore \quad l_{22} = a_{22} - l_{21}t_{12}$$

$$a_{23} = l_{21}t_{13} + l_{22}t_{23} \quad \therefore \quad t_{23} = (a_{23} - l_{21}t_{13})/l_{22}$$

$$a_{32} = l_{31}t_{12} + l_{32} \times 1 \quad \therefore \quad l_{32} = a_{32} - l_{31}t_{12}$$

$$c_2 = l_{21}k_1 + l_{22}k_2 \quad \therefore \quad k_2 = (c_2 - l_{21}k_1)/l_{22}$$

and so forth.

* The procedure used to obtain L, T, and K shows that these three matrices are uniquely determined once A and C are known.

In this manner the elements of L, T, and K are obtained successively in terms of previously determined elements, *proceeding horizontally from l_{22} on.*

The general formulas for the computations are:

$$l_{ij} = a_{ij} - \sum_{r=1}^{j-1} l_{ir} t_{rj}, \qquad l_{i1} = a_{i1} \tag{1.8.1}$$

$$t_{ij} = \frac{1}{l_{ii}} \left[a_{ij} - \sum_{r=1}^{j-1} l_{ir} t_{rj} \right], \qquad t_{1j} = \frac{a_{1j}}{a_{11}}, \overset{*}{} \tag{1.8.2}$$

where for simplicity $a_{i,n+1} = c_i$ and $t_{i,n+1} = k_i$ and $n + 1$ indicates the last column of the *augmented* matrices $A + C$ and $T + K$.

It is seen from Eqs (1.8.1) and (1.8.2) that, if A is *symmetrical* $(a_{ij} = a_{ji})$,

$$l_{ij} = t_{ji} \times l_{ii} \quad (i,j = 1,2, \ldots, n-1; i \neq j), \tag{1.8.3}$$

and hence the elements of L below the main diagonal are obtained as an intermediate step in the computation of the t_{ij}.

The operations in Eqs. (1.8.1) and (1.8.2) can be performed on a calculating machine without writing any of the intermediate steps, that is, *each element l_{ij}, t_{ij} is obtained in a single machine operation.* This makes Cholesky's method the simplest and fastest among known elimination methods. Counting only multiplications, divisions,† and recording of numbers, the Gauss elimination process applied to a system of n equations requires $\frac{1}{3} n^3 +$ (a number of the order of n^2) operations, while Cholesky's method requires $n^2 +$ (a number of the order of n) operations. For example, for the case of $n = 10$ equations, Gauss's scheme requires approximately $\frac{10^3}{3} + 10^2 = 433$ operations, versus only $10^2 + 10 = 110$ operations required by Cholesky's.

The time involved in solving a system of n equations by Cholesky's method is of the order of $0.001n^4$ hours. Thus a system of 10 equations can easily be solved in approximately 10 hours.

---

* It may be noticed here that, since $A = LT$, $|A| = |L||T|$ and hence, if $|A|$ is different from zero, both $|L|$ and $|T|$ must be different from zero. But the determinant of a triangular matrix equals the product of its main diagonal elements. Hence $l_{ii} \neq 0$ and the divisions indicated in Eqs. (1.8.2) are always possible.

† A division is counted as two multiplications in this count.

The number of figures lost in the computations varies from system to system, but statistically is of the order of $0.3n$. Thus a system of 10 equations should be solved carrying 3 more significant figures than those required in the roots.

In Table 1.3 the system (1.6.1) is solved by Cholesky's method as follows. Write the first column of L which equals the first column of A [2,1,3,1], and the first row of the augmented matrix

Table 1.3

Cholesky's Scheme

i	A				C		L				T				K	
j	1	2	3	4	5	6	1	2	3	4	1	2	3	4	5	6
	x_1	x_2	x_3	x_4	c	S					x_1	x_2	x_3	x_4	$k.$	S
1	2	2	4	-2	10	16	2	0	0	0	1	1	2	-1	5	8
2	1	3	2	1	17	24	1	2	0	0	0	1	0	1	6	8
3	3	1	3	1	18	26	3	-2	-3	0	0	0	1	-2	-5	-6
4	1	3	4	2	27	37	1	2	2	5	0	0	0	1	4	5
5	7	9	13	2	72	S	7	2	-1	5						

$T + K$ which equals the first row of the augmented matrix $A + C$ divided by $a_{11} = 2$ and hence equals $[1,1,2,-1,5]$. Compute l_{22} by equating a_{22} to the row-into-column product of the second row of L by the second column of T:

$$3 = 1 \cdot 1 + l_{22} \cdot 1 + 0 \cdot 0 + 0 \cdot 0 \qquad \therefore \quad l_{22} = 2,$$

or directly by using Eq. (1.8.1). Compute t_{23}, the first unknown element of the second row of T, by equating a_{23} to the product of the second row of L by the third column of T:

$$a_{23} = 2 = 1 \cdot 2 + 2 \cdot t_{23} + 0 \cdot 1 + 0 \cdot 0 \qquad \therefore \quad t_{23} = 0,$$

or directly by Eq. (1.8.2).

Compute t_{24} by the same procedure:

$$a_{24} = 1 = 1 \cdot (-1) + 2 \cdot t_{24} + 0 \cdot t_{34} + 0 \cdot t_{44} \qquad \therefore \quad t_{24} = 1,$$

and evaluate next $t_{25} = k_2$:

$$a_{25} = c_2 = 17 = 1 \cdot 5 + 2 \cdot t_{25} + 0 \cdot t_{35} + 0 \cdot t_{45}$$

$$\therefore \quad t_{25} = k_2 = 6.$$

All the other elements of L and T are similarly computed. Check columns S may be carried in the augmented matrices $A + C$ and $T + K$, as well as check rows S' in the matrices A and L. These columns (and rows) are operated upon as the columns (and rows)

Table 1.4

Cholesky's Condensed Scheme

	A				C		L and T				K	
$\begin{smallmatrix}&j\\i&\end{smallmatrix}$	1	2	3	4	5	6	1	2	3	4	5	6
	x_1	x_2	x_3	x_4	c	S	x_1	x_2	x_3	x_4	k	S
1	2	2	4	-2	10	16	2	1	2	-1	5	8
2	1	3	2	1	17	24	1	2	0	1	6	8
3	3	1	3	1	18	26	3	-2	-3	-2	-5	-6
4	1	3	4	2	27	37	1	2	2	5	4	5
5	7	9	13	2	72	S'	7	2	-1	5		

of the corresponding matrices, and must check with the sums of the elements in the same column (or row.)

Additional columns C and K may be used in the solution of a set of systems having the same matrix of coefficients and different columns of constants.

As soon as the method is clearly understood, the two triangular matrices L and T may be written as a single square matrix, since the main diagonal elements of T are all unity. This gives the condensed solution of Table 1.4.

The values of the x_j are obtained from the triangular system $TX = K$ by back substitution, as follows:

Row 4 $x_4 = 4$

Row 3 $x_3 - 2 \cdot 4 = -5$ $\therefore$ $x_3 = 3$

Row 2 $x_2 + 0x_3 + x_4 = 6$ $\therefore$ $x_2 = 2$

Row 1 $x_1 + x_2 + 2x_3 - x_4 = 5$ $\therefore$ $x_1 = 1.$

Table 1.5 illustrates the solution of a symmetric system of three equations, which is simplified by the use of Eq. (1.8.3).

Table 1.5

Cholesky's Scheme for Symmetrical Matrices

	A			C	S	L			T			K	S
$\diagdown j$ $\quad i$	1	2	3	4	5	1	2	3	1	2	3	4	5
1	2	2	4	8	16	2	0	0	1	1	2	4	8
2	2	1	2	5	10	2	-1	0	0	1	2	3	6
3	4	2	3	9	18	4	-2	-1	0	0	1	1	2
4	8	5	9	22	S'	8	-3	-1					

(1) $l_{22} = 1 - 2 = -1;$

(2) $t_{23} = (2 - 2 \cdot 2)/(-1) = -2/-1 = l_{32}/-1 = 2;$

(3) $t_{24} = (5 - 2 \cdot 4)/(-1) = l_{42}/-1 = 3;$

(3a) $t_{25} = (10 - 2 \cdot 8)/(-1) = 6;$

(4) $l_{32} = -2;$

(4a) $l_{42} = -3;$

(5) $l_{33} = 3 - 4 \cdot 2 + 2 \cdot 2 = -1;$

(6) $t_{34} = (9 - 4 \cdot 4 + 2 \cdot 3)/(-1) = l_{43}/-1 = 1;$

(6a) $t_{35} = (18 - 4 \cdot 8 + 2 \cdot 6)/(-1) = 2.$

$x_3 = 1; x_2 = 3 - 2 \cdot 1 = 1; x_1 = 4 - 2 \cdot 1 - 1 \cdot 1 = 1.$

1.9   The Gauss-Seidel Iteration Method

A system of simultaneous linear equations is called *diagonal* when in each equation the coefficient of a *different* unknown is greater in absolute value than the sum of the absolute values of the other coefficients. The large coefficient is usually located in the main diagonal position a_{ii}. Many of the systems stemming from physical problems are of the diagonal type.

Diagonal systems have the fundamental property of being solvable by methods of successive approximations, among which the *Gauss-Seidel iterative process* presents great advantages of simplicity. To apply the Gauss method, solve each equation of the system for the unknown with the largest coefficient:

$$x_1 = b_{12}x_2 + b_{13}x_3 + \ldots + b_{1n}x_n + k_1$$
$$x_2 = b_{21}x_1 + b_{23}x_3 + \ldots + b_{2n}x_n + k_2$$
$$\cdot \ \cdot$$
$$x_n = b_{n1}x_1 + b_{n2}x_2 + \ldots + b_{n,n-1}x_{n-1} + k_n$$

$$(1.9.1)$$

and substitute in the right-hand members of Eqs. (1.9.1) any initial values $x_j^{(0)}$ for the unknowns, thus obtaining new values $x_j^{(1)}$ in the left-hand members. Substitute the new values $x_j^{(1)}$ in the right-hand members of the equations, obtaining improved values $x_j^{(2)}$ and continue the process until $x_j^{(m)}$ is equal to $x_j^{(m+1)}$ within the required accuracy. The $x_j^{(m)}$ are the roots of the system.

In the Gauss method each approximation of a root is obtained by means of a single machine operation, and errors do not impair the convergence of the process, since they are equivalent to a new set of starting values; the method, if convergent, converges *whatever* the starting values. If the last available approximation of the unknowns is used in the right-hand members of Eqs. (1.9.1), as suggested by Seidel, the rapidity of convergence of the method is greatly increased. Any guess which may accelerate the convergence is permissible at any stage of the process.

As an example of application of the Gauss-Seidel iteration method, consider the system

Eqs.	x_1	x_2	x_3	c
I	10	1	1	12
II	2	10	1	13
III	2	2	10	14

which, when "ready for iteration" in the form (1.9.1), becomes:

$$x_1 = 1.2 - 0.1x_2 - 0.1x_3$$

$$x_2 = 1.3 - 0.2x_1 - 0.1x_3$$

$$x_3 = 1.4 - 0.2x_1 - 0.2x_2.$$

Starting with $x_2 = x_3 = 0$, the first equation gives $x_1 = 1.2$. With $x_1 = 1.2$ and $x_3 = 0$, the second equation gives $x_2 = 1.3 - 0.2 \cdot 1.2 = 1.16$, and with $x_1 = 1.2$ and $x_2 = 1.16$, the third equation gives $x_3 = 1.40 - 0.2 \cdot 1.2 - 0.2 \cdot 1.16 = 0.92$. Returning

Table 1.6

n	1	2	3	4
x_1	1.20	0.99	1.00	1.00
x_2	1.16	1.01	1.00	
x_3	0.92	1.00	1.00	

Table 1.7

	I	II	III
x_1	1	−0.2	−0.2
x_2	−0.1	1	−0.2
x_3	−0.1	−0.1	1
c	1.20	1.30	1.40
	(1.20)	−0.24	−0.24
	−0.12	(1.16)	−0.24
	−0.09	−0.09	(0.92)
	(0.99)	−0.20	−0.20
	−0.10	(1.01)	−0.20
	−0.10	−0.10	(1.00)
	(1.00)	−0.20	−0.20
	−0.10	(1.00)	−0.20
	−0.10	−0.10	(1.00)
	(1.00)		

to the first equation with $x_2 = 1.16$ and $x_3 = 0.92$, we obtain $x_1 = 0.99$, and repeating the process, we have the results of Table 1.6.

When the computations are carried out on the slide rule, they are conveniently organized as in Table 1.7, in which equations (1.9.1) are written vertically.

1.10   Solution of Linear Equations by Relaxation

Relaxation is a method for the solution of linear algebraic equations by successive approximations in which the mathematical skill and the physical intuition of the computer may be used in an infinite variety of ways to accelerate the convergence of the process. Relaxation owes its name and its deserved popularity to the labors of Southwell and his school.*

Consider a system "ready for relaxation" with the main diagonal coefficients equal to -1 and the constants k *at the left-hand members of the equations:*

$$-x_1 + b_{12}x_2 + b_{13}x_3 + \ldots + b_{1n}x_n + k_1 = 0$$

$$b_{21}x_1 - x_2 + b_{23}x_3 + \ldots + b_{2n}x_n + k_2 = 0 \quad (1.10.1)$$

$$\cdots \cdots \cdots \cdots \cdots \cdots \cdots \cdots$$

$$b_{n1}x_1 + b_{n2}x_2 + b_{n3}x_3 + \ldots - x_n + k_n = 0$$

and indicate by R_i (*residuals*) the value of the left-hand member of the ith equation for an assumed set of starting values $x_j^{(0)}$:

$$-x_1^{(0)} + b_{12}x_2^{(0)} + b_{13}x_3^{(0)} + \ldots + b_{1n}x_n^{(0)} + k_1 = R_1$$

$$b_{21}x_1^{(0)} - x_2^{(0)} + b_{23}x_3^{(0)} + \ldots + b_{2n}x_n^{(0)} + k_2 = R_2 \quad (1.10.2)$$

$$\cdots \cdots \cdots \cdots \cdots \cdots \cdots \cdots$$

$$b_{n1}x_1^{(0)} + b_{n2}x_2^{(0)} + b_{n3}x_3^{(0)} + \ldots - x_n^{(0)} + k_n = R_n.$$

The relaxation procedure consists in changing the starting values of the unknowns, *one or more at a time*, until all the R_i become negligible.   For this purpose note that, if a given $x_j^{(0)}$, say $x_k^{(0)}$, is

---

* See R. V. Southwell, *Relaxation Methods in Theoretical Physics*, Oxford University Press, London, 1946; also R. V. Southwell, *Relaxation Methods in Engineering Science*, Oxford University Press, London, 1940.

changed by an amount δx_k, then R_k changes by $-\delta x_k$, while the other R_i change by $b_{ik}\delta x_k$. Hence to reduce a given R_i, say R_k, to zero, we change $x_k^{(0)}$ by $\delta x_k = R_k$. In so doing, the other R_i will also change and must be reduced to zero one by one by suitable changes δx_j. It is convenient to eliminate the largest residual appearing in the system at any stage in the process.

This procedure is conveniently carried out in tabular form by writing the initial value of each unknown $x_j^{(0)}$ and its successive changes δx_j in a column, and the residuals in another column (usually to the right of the x_j column); thus the relaxation table has two columns for each unknown. When the residuals have vanished to the degree of accuracy required, the sum of $x_j^{(0)}$ and of all the changes δx_j gives the value of the unknown x_j.

Consider, for example, the system:

Eqs.	x_1	x_2	x_3	c
I	10	-2	-2	6
II	-1	10	-2	7
III	-1	-1	10	8

(a)

which, when ready for relaxation [Eqs. (1.10.1)], becomes:

Eqs.	x_1	x_2	x_3	k
I	-1	0.2	0.2	0.6
II	0.1	-1	0.2	0.7
III	0.1	0.1	-1	0.8

(b)

Using the starting values $x_1^{(0)} = x_2^{(0)} = x_3^{(0)} = 0$, the corresponding residuals are

$$R_1 = 0.60 \qquad R_2 = 0.70 \qquad R_3 = 0.80.$$

The initial values $x_j^{(0)}$ and the residuals appear, respectively, in the columns x_j and R_i in the first row of Table 1.8. The largest residual $R_3 = 0.80$ is first reduced to zero by a change $\delta x_3 = 0.80$, which introduces a change $b_{23}\delta x_3 = 0.2 \cdot 0.80 = 0.16$ in R_2 and a change $b_{13}\delta x_3 = 0.2 \cdot 0.80 = 0.16$ in R_1. The new residuals are now $R_1 = 0.60 + 0.16 = 0.76$, $R_2 = 0.70 + 0.16 = 0.86$, and $R_3 = 0.80 - 0.80 = 0$. The largest residual $R_2 = 0.86$ is now wiped out by means of a change $\delta x_2 = 0.86$, introducing changes $\delta R_3 = b_{32}\delta x_2 = 0.1 \cdot 0.86 = 0.09$ and $\delta R_1 = b_{12}\delta x_2 = 0.2 \cdot 0.86 = 0.17$. The residuals at this stage are $R_1 = 0.76 + 0.17 = 0.93$, $R_2 = 0$, and

Table 1.8

x_1	R_1	x_2	R_2	x_3	R_3
0	0.60	0	.0.70	0	0.80
	0.16		0.16	0.80	−0.80
	0.76	0.86	0.86		0
	0.17		−0.86		0.09
0.93	0.93		0		0.09
	−0.93		0.09		0.09
	0		0.09	0.18	0.18
	0.04		0.04		−0.18
	0.04	0.13	0.13		0
	0.03		−0.13		0.01
0.07	0.07		0		0.01
	−0.07		0.01		0.01
	0		0.01	0.02	0.02
	0		0		−0.02
	0	0.01	0.01		0
	0		−0.01		0.
1.00	0	1.00	0	1.00	0

$R_3 = 0 + 0.09 = 0.09$. We now wipe out R_1 by means of a change $\delta x_1 = 0.93$, introducing new changes $\delta R_2 = b_{21}\delta x_1 = 0.1 \cdot 0.93 = 0.09$, $\delta R_3 = b_{31}\delta x_1 = 0.1 \cdot 0.93 = 0.09$. The process is repeated until the residuals are reduced to one unit in the last significant figure, and the value of x_j is the sum of all the figures in the x_j column:

$$x_1 = 0.93 + 0.07 = 1.00$$

$$x_2 = 0.86 + 0.13 + 0.01 = 1.00$$

$$x_3 = 0.80 + 0.18 + 0.02 = 1.00.$$

The results can be (*and should be*) checked by substitution in the original equations.

In practice, the changes in the residuals are added directly to the residuals without writing them down, and the scheme takes the more compact form of Table 1.9, in which all numbers are multiplied by 100 to avoid the use of the decimal point.

Table 1.9

x_1	R_1	x_2	R_2	x_3	R_3
0	60	0	70	0	80
	76	86	86	80	9
93	93		9	18	18
	4	13	13		1
7	7	1	1	2	2
100		100		100	

In order to show additional characteristic features of the relaxation technique, we shall solve the following system (c), which is ready for relaxation, and represents a physical problem dealt with in Chapter IV (see p. 135 ff):

v_1	v_2	v_3	k	
-1	0.3951	0	0.2695	(c)
0.3556	-1	0.3556	0.4763	
0	0.3232	-1	1.0717	

In a first approximation, the coefficients b_{ij} may be rounded off to one or two figures, since the errors thus introduced may always be wiped out by relaxation of the more accurate residuals computed by means of the complete coefficients. Thus, to obtain a solution with 1 per cent accuracy, we round off the coefficients and the constants of (c) to two figures, using the relaxation table:

v_1	v_2	v_3	k	B	
-1	0.40	0	0.27	-0.60	(d)
0.36	-1	0.36	0.48	-0.28	
0	0.32	-1	1.07	-0.68	

The assumed starting values are:

$$v_1^{(0)} = 0.25, \qquad v_2^{(0)} = 0.50, \qquad v_3^{(0)} = 0.75.$$

The residuals corresponding to the $v_j^{(0)}$ are:

$$R_1 = -0.25 + 0.40 \cdot 0.50 + 0.27 = 0.22$$

$$R_2 = 0.36 \cdot 0.25 - 0.50 + 0.36 \cdot 0.75 + 0.48 = 0.34$$

$$R_3 = 0.32 \cdot 0.50 - 0.75 + 1.07 = 0.48.$$

Table 1.10 gives the solution of the system by relaxation of the largest residual at each step.

Table 1.10

v_1	R_1	v_2	R_2	v_3	R_3
25	22	50	34	75	48
42	42	51	51	48	16
	6	15	15	21	21
9	9	8	8		3
1	1	3	3	4	4
		1	1		
77		128		148	

Table 1.11 shows how two additional figures in the v_j may be obtained by computing the residuals corresponding to the above values by means of the complete coefficients of Eqs. (c), and by relaxing them by means of the rounded coefficients of Eqs. (d). The largest residual is wiped out at every stage. Both residuals and unknowns are multiplied by 10^4 to avoid the decimal point.

Table 1.11

v_1	R_1	v_2	R_2	v_3	R_3
7700	~~52~~	12800	~~−36~~	14800	~~53~~
52			~~−11~~	53	
1	~~1~~	2	~~2~~	1	~~1~~
7753		12802		14854	

In the previous examples, relaxation was applied mechanically, always reducing to zero the largest residual, but the method becomes particularly advantageous if no such rule is used. In "block relaxation," for example, all (or a group of) the variables are changed by the same amount δ whenever convenient, changing the residual R_i by

$$\delta R_i = \left(-1 + \sum_{\substack{j=1 \\ j \neq i}}^{n} b_{ij}\right) \delta = B_i \delta, \qquad (1.10.3)$$

while in "under-relaxation" and "over-relaxation" the changes in the variables are taken small or large enough to obtain new residuals with a sign equal or opposite, respectively, to that of the previous residuals. In Table 1.12 the system of Eqs. (c), in which

$$B_1 = -1 + 0.40 = -0.60$$

$$B_2 = 0.36 - 1.00 + 0.36 = -0.28$$

$$B_3 = 0.32 - 1 = -0.68,$$

is first solved with an accuracy of 1 per cent by means of an initial "block" change of $+0.60$ and successive overrelaxation, while two more figures in the roots are then obtained by "simple relaxation." The last two lines contain the residuals computed by means of the complete coefficients of Eqs. (c) and the final values. The skill acquired by solving a number of systems and a certain amount of physical intuition related to the problem at hand will usually suggest changes which will lead to the correct roots in a few cycles. It is important to go through the process by choosing suitable values of δx rather than by trying to wipe out exactly the residuals. Beginners are inclined to decide on reducing a given R_i and to choose the δx_i that will produce this result. It is instead more

Table 1.12

v_1	R_1	v_2	R_2	v_3	R_3	Explanations
25	22	50	34	75	48	$v_j{}^{(0)}$ and $R_i{}^{(0)}$ of Eqs. (d)
60	−14	60	17	60	7	Block change $\delta = 60$
−7	6	20	8	15	13	Overrelaxation
	1		2	−2	2	
78			−1	148		Roots to 1 per cent
		130				
7800	31	13000	−200	14800	119	Residuals of Eqs. (c)
−49	−49	−200	20	55	55	Simple relaxation
1	1	2	2	1	1	
7752	1	12802	0	14856	1	Roots to 0.01 per cent and check of residuals
1				−1		Simple relaxation
7753		12802		14855		Final values of roots

expedient to choose the value of δx_i in round figures, and to compute the corresponding δR_i.

PROBLEMS

1.1 Evaluate the roots of the following equations by Newton's method and synthetic substitution to the number of figures specified.

(a) $x^3 + 1.2x^2 - 4x - 4.8 = 0$ (2 figures).
(b) $x^3 - 0.87x^2 - 15.651x + 23.701 = 0$ (3 figures).
(c) $x^3 + 6.6x^2 - 29.05x + 22.64 = 0$ (3 figures).

Ans. (a) $x_1 = 2$; $x_2 = -2$; $x_3 = -1.2$. (c) $x_1 = 2.10$; $x_2 = -9.80$; $x_3 = 1.10$.

1.2   Evaluate the roots of the following equations to three significant figures by Newton's method and synthetic substitution, and the quadratic formula, when necessary.

(a) $x^3 + 2.9x^2 + 14.89x + 6.85 = 0$.
(b) $x^3 - 2.4x^2 - 1.4x - 6.8 = 0$.
(c) $x^4 + 6.4x^3 + 24.04x^2 + 36.96x + 18.72 = 0$.
(d) $x^4 - 2x^3 + 1.99x^2 - 2x + 0.99 = 0$.
(e) $x^4 - x^3 - 0.44x^2 - 13.88x + 2.8 = 0$.

Ans.   (b) $x_1 = 3.40$; $x_{2,3} = -0.500 \pm 1.323i$.   (d) $x_1 = 1.100$; $x_2 = 0.900$; $x_{3,4} = \pm i$.

1.3   Evaluate to four significant figures the roots of the following equations.   Evaluate the largest root by backward synthetic substitution and linear interpolation.

(a) $x^3 - 4.65x^2 - 49.92x - 76.67 = 0$.
(b) $x^3 + 6.8x^2 - 62.49x + 63.468 = 0$.
(c) $x^3 - 13.6x^2 - 57.4x - 228.8 = 0$.
(d) $x^3 - 10.2x^2 - 51.8x - 71.00 = 0$.

Ans.   (a) $x_1 = 10.25$; $x_2 = -3.40$; $x_3 = -2.20$.   (c) $x_1 = 17.6$; $x_{2,3} = -2.00 \pm 3.00i$.

1.4   Evaluate to three significant figures the four roots of the following equation, two of which are near one another.

$$x^4 - 0.41x^3 + 1.632x^2 - 9.146x + 7.260 = 0.$$

Ans. $x_1 = 1.21$; $x_2 = 1.20$; $x_{3,4} = -1.00 \pm 2.00i$.

1.5   Evaluate the roots of the following equation to three significant figures by Friedmann's method.

$$x^4 - 14x^3 + 69.09x^2 + 182.56x + 109 = 0.$$

Ans. $x_{1,2} = -1.00 \pm 0.30i$; $x_{3,4} = 8.00 \pm 6.00i$.

1.6   Evaluate the roots of the following equation to three significant figures, using Friedmann's method to determine its complex roots.

$$x^5 - 20.2x^4 + 132.18x^3 - 60.592x^2 - 72.693x - 14.525 = 0.$$

1.7   Evaluate the real roots of the following equation to three significant figures by Newton's method.

$$\cos x = x^2.$$

Ans. $x_{1,2} = \pm 0.824$.

1.8   Evaluate the two smallest positive roots of the following equations to three significant figures by Newton's method.

(a) $\tan x = \tanh x$.   (b) $\cos x \cosh x + 1 = 0.$

(c) $\cos x \cosh x = 1$.   (d) $\tan x = x$.

(e) $\tan x = -x$.   (f) $\tan x = 2x$.

(g) $x \tan x = 1$.   (h) $x \tan x = 2$.

Ans.   (a) $x_1 = 3.93$; $x_2 = 7.07$.   (c) $x_1 = 4.73$; $x_2 = 7.85$.   (e) $x_1 = 2.03$; $x_2 = 4.91$.   (g) $x_1 = 0.860$; $x_2 = 3.43$.

1.9   Evaluate the lowest positive root of the following equation to three significant figures by expanding the function into a power series.

$$x \tan x = 1.$$

Ans. $x_1 = 0.860$.

1.10   Evaluate the positive root of the following equation to three significant figures by expanding the function into a power series.

$$\cos x = x^2.$$

1.11   Evaluate the first two zeros of the Bessel function of the first kind of order one to three significant figures by Newton's method.   *Hint:* Use a table of Bessel functions and remember that

$$J'_1(x) = -\frac{1}{x} J_1(x) + J_0(x).$$

Ans. $x_1 = 3.83$; $x_2 = 7.02$.

1.12   Evaluate to three significant figures the roots of the following systems of equations by Gauss's scheme.

(a)

x_1	x_2	x_3	c
3.5	2.8	6.2	9.87
2.7	8.0	3.0	−6.17
−4.0	−3.6	−2.8	5.65

(b)

x_1	x_2	x_3	c
2.1	−4.5	−2.0	19.07
3.0	2.5	4.3	3.21
−6.0	3.5	2.5	−18.25

(c)

x_1	x_2	x_3	x_4	c
2.0	-4	-3.25	1	4.84
3.0	-3	-4.30	8	8.89
1.0	-5	3.30	-20	-14.01
2.5	-4	2.00	-3	-20.29

(d)

x_1	x_2	x_3	x_4	x_5	c
3	-2	5.3	-2.1	1.0	28.3
1	4	-6.0	4.5	-6.0	-36.2
3	6	-7.3	-9.0	3.4	24.5
-2	-3	1.0	-4.0	6.0	16.2
1	-4	6.5	1.0	-3.0	4.3

Ans.　(b) $x_1 = 1.34$; $x_2 = -4.76$; $x_3 = 2.58$.　(d) $x_1 = 2.06$; $x_2 = 3.22$; $x_3 = 4.03$; $x_4 = -2.01$; $x_5 = 3.00$.

1.13　Obtain a first approximation of the roots of the following systems of equations by Gauss's scheme, using a slide rule.　Compute the corresponding errors longhand or on a calculator, and obtain additional significant figures by solving the error equations by slide rule.

(a)

x_1	x_2	x_3	c
3.5	2.8	6.2	9.8999
2.7	8.0	3.0	-6.1744
-4.0	-3.6	-2.8	5.6512

(b)

x_1	x_2	x_3	x_4	c
2.0	-4.0	-3.25	1.0	4.8392
3.0	-3.0	-4.30	8.0	8.8581
1.0	-5.0	3.30	-20.0	-13.9212
2.5	-4.0	2.00	-3.0	-20.2815

Ans.　(a) $x_1 = -3.0347$; $x_2 = -1.1904$; $x_3 = 3.8475$.

1.14 Perform the following matric operations.

(a) $\begin{bmatrix} 2 & 3 & 4 \\ 1 & 4 & 1 \\ 2 & 1 & 4 \end{bmatrix} + \begin{bmatrix} 1 & 2 & 0 \\ 3 & 7 & 2 \\ 1 & 8 & 5 \end{bmatrix}$
(b) $\begin{bmatrix} 2 & 1 \\ 3 & 3 \\ 4 & -1 \\ 5 & 2 \end{bmatrix} + \begin{bmatrix} 3 & 0 \\ 1 & 1 \\ 4 & 1 \\ 3 & 2 \end{bmatrix}$

(c) $\begin{bmatrix} 2 & 1 \\ 3 & 2 \\ 2 & 3 \end{bmatrix} \begin{bmatrix} 3 & 1 & 1 \\ 1 & 3 & 1 \end{bmatrix} + \begin{bmatrix} 6 & 1 & 2 \\ 2 & 4 & 3 \\ 3 & 0 & 1 \end{bmatrix}$

(d) $\begin{bmatrix} 3 & 2 & 2 \\ 4 & -3 & 0 \\ 5 & 0 & 5 \end{bmatrix} \begin{bmatrix} 1 & 3 & 0 \\ -1 & 0 & 1 \\ 2 & 5 & 2 \end{bmatrix}$
(e) $\begin{bmatrix} 2 & 0 & -3 \\ 4 & 1 & 1 \\ -2 & 0 & 4 \end{bmatrix} \begin{bmatrix} 1 & 1 & 2 \\ 0 & -1 & 3 \\ 4 & 0 & 0 \end{bmatrix}$

(f) $\begin{bmatrix} 1 & 2 & 0 & 3 \\ -1 & -1 & 5 & 4 \\ 2 & 0 & 2 & 1 \\ 0 & 1 & 2 & 1 \end{bmatrix} \begin{bmatrix} 1 & 2 & 3 & 0 \\ 1 & 0 & 3 & 2 \\ 2 & 3 & 0 & 1 \\ 5 & 1 & -1 & 0 \end{bmatrix}$
(g) $\begin{bmatrix} 2 & 1 \\ 3 & 2 \\ 1 & 2 \end{bmatrix} \begin{bmatrix} 3 & 1 & 1 \\ 1 & 3 & 1 \end{bmatrix}$

(h) $\begin{bmatrix} 2 & 1 \\ 1 & 3 \end{bmatrix} \begin{bmatrix} 2 & 1 & 1 \\ 1 & 2 & 1 \end{bmatrix}$
(i) $\begin{bmatrix} 0 & 2 & 3 \\ -2 & 1 & 1 \\ 3 & -4 & 6 \\ 1 & 0 & 0 \end{bmatrix} \begin{bmatrix} 3 & -1 \\ 2 & 4 \\ -1 & 0 \end{bmatrix}$

Ans. (a) $\begin{bmatrix} 3 & 5 & 4 \\ 4 & 11 & 3 \\ 3 & 9 & 9 \end{bmatrix}$
(d) $\begin{bmatrix} 5 & 19 & 6 \\ 7 & 12 & -3 \\ 15 & 40 & 10 \end{bmatrix}$

(f) $\begin{bmatrix} 18 & 5 & 6 & 4 \\ 28 & 17 & -10 & 3 \\ 11 & 11 & 5 & 2 \\ 10 & 7 & 2 & 4 \end{bmatrix}$
(h) $\begin{bmatrix} 5 & 4 & 3 \\ 5 & 7 & 4 \end{bmatrix}$

1.15 Evaluate to three significant figures the roots of the following system of equations by Cholesky's method.

	x_1	x_2	x_3	c
(a)	2.5	−3.0	4.6	− 1.05
	−3.5	2.6	1.5	−14.46
	−6.5	−3.5	7.3	−17.735

	x_1	x_2	x_3	c
(b)	-3.60	2.40	1.50	-1.359
	1.40	-1.30	2.65	-3.725
	4.26	-3.00	2.85	-3.623

(c) System of Problem 1.12(c).
(d) System of Problem 1.12(d).

	x_1	x_2	x_3	x_4	x_5	c
	2	-1	4	-3	1	11
(e)	-1	1	2	1	3	14
	4	2	3	3	-1	4
	-3	1	3	2	4	16
	1	3	-1	4	4	18

Ans. (a) $x_1 = 1.24$; $x_2 = -2.45$; $x_3 = -2.50$. (c) $x_1 = 2.34$; $x_2 = 4.51$; $x_3 = -6.00$; $x_4 = -1.30$. (e) $x_1 = 1.00$; $x_2 = 2.00$; $x_3 = 1.00$; $x_4 = -1.00$; $x_5 = 4.00$.

1.16 Evaluate to three significant figures the roots of the following system of equations by iteration.

	x_1	x_2	x_3	c
(a)	-6	1	1	-1133
	1	-6	1	-3200
	1	1	-6	-4200

	x_1	x_2	x_3	c
(b)	-1	0.4	0.5	-1.41
	0	-1	0.3	2.81
	0.2	0.3	-1	-4.48

(c)

x_1	x_2	x_3	x_4	c
10	8	6	0	16.4
0	10	8	4	-3.8
2	0	10	2	36.9
1	0	6	10	30.9

(d)

x_1	x_2	x_3	x_4	x_5	c
10	1	1	1	1	15
2	10	2	1	1	17
2	1	10	1	2	18
1	2	2	10	2	19
1	1	1	2	10	25

(e)

x_1	x_2	x_3	x_4	x_5	c
8.0	-2.4	-1.6	2.0	0	12.00
0	10.0	0	-4.0	-2.3	21.06
0	3.2	8.0	1.6	2.4	-23.28
-3.2	0	4.8	10.0	2.1	-14.06
-1.6	0	1.6	2.4	8.0	-22.32

(f)

x_1	x_2	x_3	x_4	x_5	c
4.00	0.80	0	1.20	0	5.60
0	8.00	1.60	1.60	2.40	-13.472
2.40	0.80	8.00	0	1.60	30.16
0	1.80	0	6.00	0.60	6.54
2.20	0	2.30	1.50	10.00	-15.631

Ans. (a) $x_1 = 467$; $x_2 = 762$; $x_3 = 905$. (c) $x_1 = 2.40$; $x_2 = -3.20$; $x_3 = 3.00$; $x_4 = 1.05$. (e) $x_1 = 1.20$; $x_2 = 2.00$; $x_3 = -3.25$; $x_4 = 1.00$; $x_5 = -2.20$.

1.17   Evaluate to three significant figures the roots of the following system of equations by relaxation.

(a) System of Problem 1.16(b).

(b)

	x_1	x_2	x_3	c
	-6	2	4	0
	1	1	-5	-350
	1	-6	2	-700

(c) System of Problem 1.16(c).
(d) System of Problem 1.16(e).
(e) System of Problem 1.16(f).

Ans. (b) $x_1 = 155$; $x_2 = 189$; $x_3 = 139$.   (e) $x_1 = 1.20$; $x_2 = -2.00$; $x_3 = 4.23$; $x_4 = 2.00$; $x_5 = -3.10$.

1.18   Solve by relaxation to three significant figures the following systems of equations.   Obtain first a rough approximation of the roots by means of coefficients and constants rounded off as indicated.

(a)

	x_1	x_2	x_3	c
	-1	0.875	0.121	1.132
	0.444	-1	0.222	-1.266
	0.092	0.545	-1	-2.256

(round off to one decimal figure)

(b)

	x_1	x_2	x_3	c
	10.22	1.25	3.12	21.047
	1.25	10.45	4.15	62.440
	3.12	4.15	10.62	109.726

(round off to two significant figures)

Ans.   (a) $x_1 = 2.10$; $x_2 = 3.12$; $x_3 = 4.15$.

CHAPTER II

Finite Differences and Their Applications

2.1 Introduction

Whenever a technical problem leads to a differential equation which cannot be integrated in closed form, approximate methods of solution must be employed. These may be based, for example, on series expansions, or may be purely numerical methods leading to the evaluation of the unknown integral at specified points of its interval of definition by simple arithmetical means. Initial value and boundary value problems, involving either ordinary or partial differential equations, may be solved by such methods. These numerical solutions do not usually allow the determination of general physical laws but do often indicate the dependence of the desired variables on the various parameters of the problem, particularly if the equations are written in nondimensional form.

Numerical methods for the solution of differential equations have become particularly popular in recent years because modern technical problems lead to complicated equations seldom solvable in finite terms, and because calculating machines have become available at moderate prices. The numerical approach also has the advantage of allowing the actual work to be carried out by operators without a knowledge of higher mathematics or of physics, with a resulting economy of effort on the part of highly trained personnel.

The numerical solution of differential equations consists essentially in obtaining the numerical values of the unknown integral at some *pivotal points*, spaced along the x-axis for ordinary differential equations, and in the x,y-plane for two-dimensional partial differential equations. To obtain the *pivotal values* of the integral f, the derivatives of f appearing in the differential equation are approximated either by the derivatives of nth degree parabolas passing through a certain number of pivotal points, or by Taylor expansions of the unknown function f, as shown in the following sections.

2.2 Interpolating Parabolas

The simplest method of obtaining approximate expressions for the derivatives of a function $y(x)$, which is known graphically or by means of a table at some pivotal points i, consists in substituting for the function y a parabola passing through a certain number of pivotal points, and in taking the derivatives of the parabola as approximate values of the derivatives of y.

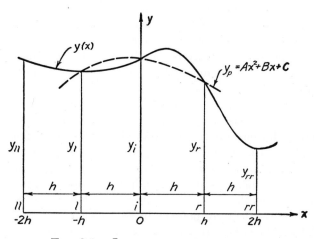

FIG. 2.1. INTERPOLATING PARABOLA.

For example, to evaluate the second derivative y'' of y, when y is known at three consecutive pivotal points l, i, r, evenly spaced by h on the x-axis, call the corresponding pivotal values y_l, y_i, y_r (Fig. 2.1)* and pass a quadratic parabola

$$y_p = Ax^2 + Bx + C \qquad (a)$$

through these points. Choosing, without loss of generality and for simplicity, the abscissa of the ith point as the origin, we obtain:

$$y(-h) = y_l = Ah^2 - Bh + C$$

$$y(0) = y_i = C$$

* The subscript i indicates the pivotal point at which we evaluate the derivative, while the subscripts l and r indicate the pivotal points to the left and right of i, respectively (Fig. 2.1).

$$y(h) = y_r = Ah^2 + Bh + C,$$

from which: $$y_l - 2y_i + y_r = 2Ah^2.$$

Since the second derivative of the parabola (a) equals $2A$, the second derivative y_i'' of y at i, is approximated by

$$y_i'' = \frac{1}{h^2}(y_l - 2y_i + y_r). \tag{2.2.1}$$

Analogous expressions for higher-order derivatives may be obtained by means of higher-degree interpolating parabolas, which may be made to pass through pivotal points symmetrically or unsymmetrically located with respect to the point i.   Thus passing a cubic parabola

$$y_p = Ax^3 + Bx^2 + Cx + D \tag{b}$$

through l, i, r, and the point rr to the right of r (Fig. 2.1) and choosing again i to be the origin, we obtain:

$$y(-h) = y_l = -Ah^3 + Bh^2 - Ch + D$$

$$y(0) = y_i = D$$

$$y(h) = y_r = Ah^3 + Bh^2 + Ch + D$$

$$y(2h) = y_{rr} = 8Ah^3 + 4Bh^2 + 2Ch + D.$$

Eliminating B, C, and D among these equations we obtain the value $6A$ of the third derivative of the parabola (b) and hence the following unsymmetrical approximation for y_i''':

$$y_i''' = \frac{1}{h^3}(-y_l + 3y_i - 3y_r + y_{rr}). \tag{2.2.2}$$

A list of such formulas for evenly spaced points is available, under the name of *Bickley's formulas*, in Southwell's *Relaxation Methods in Theoretical Physics*,* and will sometimes be referred to in the following sections.

Similar formulas can be obtained when the pivotal points are *not evenly spaced*.   For example, the second derivative at i of a

---

* R. V. Southwell, *Relaxation Methods in Theoretical Physics*, Oxford University Press, London, 1946.

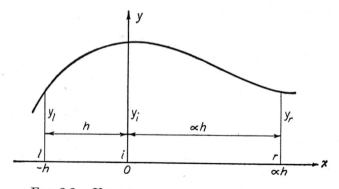

FIG. 2.2.   UNEQUAL SPACING OF PIVOTAL POINTS.

function known at 3 points spaced by h and αh, respectively (Fig. 2.2), is obtained by means of a quadratic parabola through these three points:

$$y(-h) = y_l = Ah^2 - Bh + C$$

$$y(0) = y_i = C$$

$$y(\alpha h) = y_r = \alpha^2 Ah^2 + \alpha Bh + C.$$

Eliminating the constants B and C, the derivative $2A$ of the parabola in terms of y_l, y_i, and y_r gives:

$$y_i'' = \frac{1}{h^2} \frac{2}{\alpha(\alpha + 1)} [\alpha y_l - (1 + \alpha)y_i + y_r], \qquad (2.2.3)$$

which is identical with Eq. (2.2.1) for $\alpha = 1$.

2.3   Taylor Series Expansions

It is obvious that, while a certain error is inherent in formulas of the type of Eqs. (2.2.1), (2.2.2), and (2.2.3), this error will vanish as the spacing h is made smaller and smaller.   In order to find out how the error depends on h, it is convenient to derive again these formulas by Taylor series expansions.

The Taylor series of $y(x + h)$ about x is given by*

* See, for example, *Engineering Problems*, pp. 167 ff.

$$y(x + h) = y(x) + hy'(x) + \frac{h^2}{2!} y''(x) + \frac{h^3}{3!} y'''(x) + \cdots$$

$$= \sum_{n=0}^{\infty} \frac{h^n}{n!} y^{(n)}(x), \tag{2.3.1}$$

where $y^{(n)}$ stands for $d^n y/dx^n$, $y^{(0)}(x) = y(x)$, and $0! = 1$.

Applying Eq. (2.3.1) with the symbols of Fig. 2.2, we obtain the expansions at $x + \alpha h$ and at $x - h$:

$$y_r = y_i + \alpha h y'_i + \frac{\alpha^2 h^2}{2} y_i'' + \frac{\alpha^3 h^3}{6} y_i''' + \frac{\alpha^4 h^4}{24} y_i^{IV} + \cdots$$

$$y_l = y_i - h y'_i + \frac{h^2}{2} y_i'' - \frac{h^3}{6} y_i''' + \frac{h^4}{24} y_i^{IV} - \cdots. \tag{2.3.2}$$

An approximate expression for y'_i is immediately obtained by subtraction:

$$y_r - y_l = (\alpha + 1)h y'_i + (\alpha^2 - 1) \frac{h^2}{2} y_i'' + (\alpha^3 + 1) \frac{h^3}{6} y_i''' + \cdots,$$

from which:

$$y'_i = \frac{1}{(\alpha + 1)h} (y_r - y_l) + (1 - \alpha) \frac{h}{2} y_i'' - \frac{1 + \alpha^3}{1 + \alpha} \frac{h^2}{6} y_i''' + \cdots.$$

This result indicates that the approximate expression for the first derivative:

$$y'_i = \frac{1}{(\alpha + 1)h} (y_r - y_l) \tag{2.3.3}$$

has an error

$$(1 - \alpha) \frac{h}{2} y_i'' - \frac{1 + \alpha^3}{1 + \alpha} \frac{h^2}{6} y_i''' + \cdots,$$

which approaches zero as fast as h if $\alpha \neq 1$, and as fast as h^2 if $\alpha = 1$, that is, if the pivotal points are evenly spaced.

Eliminating y_i'' between the two Eqs. (2.3.2), we obtain similarly an expression for y'_i:

$$y'_i = \frac{1}{\alpha(\alpha + 1)h} [y_r - (1 - \alpha^2)y_i - \alpha^2 y_l], \tag{2.3.4}$$

whose error approaches zero as fast as h^2 whatever α, and which becomes identical with Eq. (2.3.3) for $\alpha = 1$.

Eliminating y'_i between the two Eqs. (2.3.2), we obtain an expression for y_i'':

$$y_i'' = \frac{1}{h^2} \frac{2}{\alpha(\alpha+1)} [\alpha y_l - (1+\alpha)y_i + y_r]$$
$$+ (1-\alpha)\frac{h}{3} y_i''' - \frac{1+\alpha^3}{1+\alpha}\frac{h^2}{12} y_i^{IV} + \dots , \quad (2.3.5)$$

which shows that the expression (2.2.3) for y_i'' has an error approaching zero as fast as h for $\alpha \neq 1$ and as h^2 for $\alpha = 1$.

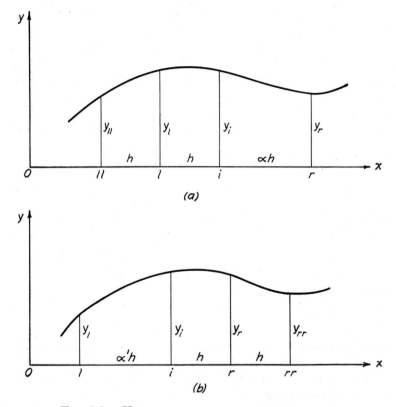

FIG. 2.3.   UNEQUAL SPACING OF PIVOTAL POINTS:

A variety of formulas may be obtained by this technique, and their error can be evaluated without difficulty. For example, the reader may want to prove that the approximate value of y_i'':

$$y_i'' = \frac{1}{\alpha(\alpha + 1)(\alpha + 2)h^2} [\alpha(\alpha^2 - 1)y_{ll} - 2(\alpha^3 - 4\alpha)y_l$$
$$+ (\alpha^3 - 7\alpha - 6)y_i + 6y_r], \quad (2.3.6)$$

obtained by equal spacing h between ll and l, and i and l, and spacing αh between i and r (Fig. 2.3a), has an error approaching zero as h^2. The corresponding formula for the points of Fig. 2.3b is given by:

$$y_i'' = \frac{1}{\alpha'(\alpha' + 1)(\alpha' + 2)h^2} [6y_l + (\alpha'^3 - 7\alpha' - 6)y_i$$
$$- 2(\alpha'^3 - 4\alpha')y_r + \alpha'(\alpha'^2 - 1)y_{rr}] \quad (2.3.7)$$

and has also an error approaching zero as h^2.

Whenever the pivotal points are *evenly spaced*, the Taylor series technique can be applied symbolically in conjunction with the concept of *difference*, which plays a most important role in all numerical computations. In this manner a large variety of practical approximations for the derivatives and the corresponding errors may be economically obtained, as shown in the following sections.

2.4 Backward Differences

Given the values

$$y_0, y_1, y_2, \ldots, y_{ll}, y_l, y_i, y_r, y_{rr}, \ldots, y_{n-2}, y_{n-1}, y_n$$

of a function $y(x)$ at the pivotal points of its interval of definition, evenly spaced by h, we call the *first backward difference of y at i* the difference

$$\nabla y_i \equiv y_i - y_l.^* \quad (2.4.1)$$

The *second backward difference* of y at i is defined as the difference of the first difference, and is therefore given by

$$\nabla(\nabla y_i) \equiv \nabla^2 y_i = (y_i - y_l) - (y_l - y_{ll})$$
$$= y_i - 2y_l + y_{ll}. \quad (2.4.2)$$

---

* The inverted capital Greek delta is used for backward differences, the normal capital delta for forward differences, and the lower-case delta for central differences.

Similarly, the nth backward difference is the difference of the $(n - 1)$th difference:

$$\nabla^n y_i \equiv \nabla(\nabla^{n-1} y_i).$$

It is easy to verify that the coefficients of the pivotal values in the nth difference are the coefficients of the binomial expansion of $(a - b)^n$. Thus, for example,

$$\nabla^3 y_i = y_i - 3y_{i-1} + 3y_{i-2} - y_{i-3} \qquad (2.4.3)$$

$$\nabla^4 y_i = y_i - 4y_{i-1} + 6y_{i-2} - 4y_{i-3} + y_{i-4}. \qquad (2.4.4)$$

The successive backward differences of a function are tabulated as shown in Table 2.1.

Table 2.1

Backward Differences

i	y_i	∇y_i	$\nabla^2 y_i$	$\nabla^3 y_i$	$\nabla^4 y_i$	$\nabla^5 y_i$
0	y_0					
1	y_1	∇y_1				
2	y_2	∇y_2	$\nabla^2 y_2$			
3	y_3	∇y_3	$\nabla^2 y_3$	$\nabla^3 y_3$		
4	y_4	∇y_4	$\nabla^2 y_4$	$\nabla^3 y_4$	$\nabla^4 y_4$	
5	y_5	∇y_5	$\nabla^2 y_5$	$\nabla^3 y_5$	$\nabla^4 y_5$	$\nabla^5 y_5$

The tabulation of successive differences is one of the simplest ways of checking a table of computed values of a function. For example, given the values of the function e^x and their first differences of Table 2.2, the sudden jump in ∇e^x between $x = 0.3$ and $x = 0.4$ and between $x = 0.4$ and $x = 0.5$ indicates that the value of e^x at $x = 0.4$ is doubtful. Evaluating $\nabla^2 e^x$ and assuming a linear variation of the second differences between the reliable values at $x = 0.3$ and $x = 0.7$, we obtain the values

$$\nabla^2 e^{0.4} = 0.01373; \quad \nabla^2 e^{0.5} = 0.01523; \quad \nabla^2 e^{0.6} = 0.01673;$$

from which we derive:

$$\nabla e^{0.4} = \nabla e^{0.3} + \nabla^2 e^{0.4} = 0.14219$$

$$\nabla e^{0.5} = \nabla e^{0.4} + \nabla^2 e^{0.5} = 0.15742.$$

The two values of $e^{0.4}$ obtained by means of these first differences are:

$$e^{0.4} = e^{0.3} + \nabla e^{0.4} = 1.49205; \quad e^{0.4} = e^{0.5} - \nabla e^{0.5} = 1.49130.$$

Their average is 1.49168, while the true value is 1.49182.

Table 2.2

x	0	0.1	0.2	0.3
e^x	1.00000	1.10517	1.22140	1.34986
∇e^x		0.10517	0.11623	0.12846
$\nabla^2 e^x$			0.01106	0.01223

x	0.4	0.5	0.6	0.7
e^x	1.57182	1.64872	1.82212	2.01375
∇e^x	0.22196	0.07690	0.17340	0.19163
$\nabla^2 e^x$				0.01823

It is well known[*] that the differential operator $D \equiv d/dx$ can be used symbolically as if it were a number, inasmuch as it satisfies formally the fundamental laws of algebra. The difference operator ∇ may also be used symbolically as a number (or variable) since it satisfies formally the laws of algebra, as shown by the following identities:

$$\nabla(y_i + y_j) = \nabla y_i + \nabla y_j = \nabla y_j + \nabla y_i$$

$$\nabla(cy_i) = c\nabla y_i$$

$$\nabla^m(\nabla^n y_i) = \nabla^{m+n} y_i.$$

[*] See any book on differential equations, or E. Stephens, *The Elementary Theory of Operational Mathematics*, McGraw-Hill Book Company, Inc., New York, 1937.

Making use of these properties, it is possible to express the differences of a function y in terms of its successive derivatives and, conversely, its derivatives in terms of its successive differences. The derivation of these expressions by symbolical methods is by far the most efficient.

Consider for this purpose the Taylor expansion of $y(x + h)$ about x,

$$y(x + h) = y(x) + \frac{h}{1!} y'(x) + \frac{h^2}{2!} y''(x) + \frac{h^3}{3!} y'''(x) + \ldots \quad \text{(a)}$$

which, using the powers of the symbol D to indicate the derivatives of y, becomes

$$y(x + h) = y(x) + \frac{h}{1!} Dy(x) + \frac{h^2}{2!} D^2y(x) + \frac{h^3}{3!} D^3y(x) + \ldots$$

$$= \left(1 + \frac{h}{1!} D + \frac{h^2}{2!} D^2 + \frac{h^3}{3!} D^3 + \ldots \right) y(x). \quad \text{(b)}$$

By means of the series expansion for e^x,

$$e^x = 1 + \frac{x}{1!} + \frac{x^2}{2!} + \frac{x^3}{3!} + \ldots ,$$

the differential operator on the right-hand side of Eq. (b) may be written symbolically as

$$1 + \frac{hD}{1!} + \frac{h^2D^2}{2!} + \frac{h^3D^3}{3!} + \ldots = e^{hD} \quad (2.4.5)$$

and hence $y(x + h)$ may also be written *symbolically* as

$$y(x + h) = e^{hD}y(x). \quad (2.4.6)$$

Setting $x = x_i$ and indicating as before $y(x_i + h)$ by y_r and $y(x_i)$ by y_i, Eq. (2.4.6) becomes

$$y_r = e^{hD}y_i. \quad (2.4.7)$$

Similarly, changing h into $-h$ in Eq. (2.4.6),

$$y(x - h) = e^{-hD}y(x) \quad (2.4.8)$$

and letting, as before, $y(x) = y_i$, and $y_l = y(x_i - h)$, we obtain:

$$y_l = e^{-hD}y_i. \tag{2.4.9}$$

The first backward difference ∇y_i [Eq. (2.4.1)] may now be written by means of Eq. (2.4.9) as

$$\nabla y_i = y_i - y_l = [1 - e^{-hD}]y_i \tag{2.4.10}$$

or, by Eq. (2.4.5) with h changed into $-h$, as

$$\nabla y_i = \left[\frac{hD}{1!} - \frac{h^2D^2}{2!} + \frac{h^3D^3}{3!} - \frac{h^4D^4}{4!} + \ldots \right] y_i$$

$$= \left[1 - \frac{hD}{2} + \frac{h^2D^2}{6} - \frac{h^3D^3}{24} + \ldots \right] hDy_i. \tag{2.4.11}$$

Equation (2.4.11) gives the expansion of ∇y_i into an infinite series of *all* the derivatives of y at i.

If Eq. (2.4.10) is written in purely operational form, by dropping y_i on both sides of the equation,

$$\nabla = (1 - e^{-hD}), \tag{2.4.12}$$

its "powers" may be used to evaluate the series expansions for the successive differences of a function. Thus, squaring Eq. (2.4.12), and making use of Eq. (2.4.5) with h changed into $-h$, we obtain the expansion for the second difference ∇^2 in the form:

$$\nabla^2 = (1 - e^{-hD})^2 = (1 + e^{-2hD} - 2e^{-hD})$$

$$= 1 + \left(1 - \frac{2hD}{1!} + \frac{4h^2D^2}{2!} - \frac{8h^3D^3}{3!} + \frac{16h^4D^4}{4!} - \ldots \right)$$

$$- 2\left(1 - \frac{hD}{1!} + \frac{h^2D^2}{2!} - \frac{h^3D^3}{3!} + \frac{h^4D^4}{4!} - \ldots \right)$$

or:

$$\nabla^2 = h^2D^2 - h^3D^3 + \tfrac{7}{12}h^4D^4 - \ldots \tag{2.4.13}$$

Similarly, cubing Eq. (2.4.12) or multiplying Eq. (2.4.12) by Eq. (2.4.13), we obtain:

$$\nabla^3 = h^3D^3 - \tfrac{3}{2}h^4D^4 + \tfrac{1}{4}h^5D^5 - \ldots , \tag{2.4.14}$$

while the higher powers of Eq. (2.4.12) will similarly give the expansion of $\nabla^n y_i$ in terms of the derivatives of y at i.

Conversely, to obtain expressions for the derivatives of y in terms of its differences, solve Eq. (2.4.12) for e^{-hD}:

$$e^{-hD} = 1 - \nabla, \tag{2.4.15}$$

and take the natural logarithms of both sides of this equation, obtaining:

$$\ln e^{-hD} = -hD = \ln (1 - \nabla) = -\left(\nabla + \frac{\nabla^2}{2} + \frac{\nabla^3}{3} + \frac{\nabla^4}{4} + \ldots\right).^*$$

Hence the expansion of the first derivative D into an infinite series of differences becomes:

$$hD = \nabla + \frac{\nabla^2}{2} + \frac{\nabla^3}{3} + \frac{\nabla^4}{4} + \ldots. \tag{2.4.16}$$

Taking successive powers of Eq. (2.4.16), we obtain the following expressions for the higher derivatives in terms of differences:

$$h^2D^2 = \nabla^2 + \nabla^3 + \tfrac{11}{12}\nabla^4 + \tfrac{5}{6}\nabla^5 + \ldots$$

$$h^3D^3 = \nabla^3 + \tfrac{3}{2}\nabla^4 + \tfrac{7}{4}\nabla^5 + \ldots$$

$$h^4D^4 = \nabla^4 + 2\nabla^5 + \tfrac{17}{6}\nabla^6 + \ldots \tag{2.4.17}$$

$$h^5D^5 = \nabla^5 + \tfrac{5}{2}\nabla^6 + \tfrac{25}{6}\nabla^7 + \ldots.$$

The difference expansions (2.4.11), (2.4.12), (2.4.13), (2.4.14), and (2.4.16), (2.4.17) allow the simple derivation of *unilateral differentiation formulas* and of their errors.

For example, solving Eqs. (2.4.11), (2.4.13) and (2.4.14) for D, D^2, and D^3, respectively, we obtain:

$$D = \frac{\nabla}{h} + \frac{hD^2}{2} - \frac{h^2D^3}{6} + \frac{h^3D^4}{24} - \ldots$$

$$D^2 = \frac{\nabla^2}{h^2} + hD^3 - \frac{7h^2D^4}{12} + \ldots \tag{2.4.18}$$

$$D^3 = \frac{\nabla^3}{h^3} + \frac{3hD^4}{2} - \frac{h^2D^5}{4} + \ldots,$$

from which, taking into account the first term of the series only,

---

* The series expansion of $\ln (1 \pm x)$ equals:

$$\ln (1 \pm x) = \pm x - x^2/2 \pm x^3/3 - x^4/4 \pm x^5/5 - \ldots.$$

$$Dy_i = \frac{1}{h}(y_i - y_l) + 0(h)$$

$$D^2y_i = \frac{1}{h^2}(y_i - 2y_l + y_u) + 0(h) \qquad (2.4.19)$$

$$D^3y_i = \frac{1}{h^3}(y_i - 3y_l + 3y_u - y_{uu}) + 0(h),$$

where the symbol $0(h)$ stands for an error "of the order of h" and is the sum of the terms neglected in Eqs. (2.4.18).

It can similarly be proved that the approximation of the nth derivative by the first term of its backward difference expansion has an error of the order of h.

To obtain formulas with errors of order h^2, the first two terms of the derivative expansions into differences must be taken into account.

Thus, eliminating h^2D^2 between Eqs. (2.4.11) and (2.4.13), we obtain:

$$\nabla + \frac{\nabla^2}{2} = hD + \tfrac{1}{3}h^3D^3 + \cdots$$

or, by Eqs. (2.4.1) and (2.4.2),

$$Dy_i = \frac{1}{2h}(3y_i - 4y_l + y_u) + 0(h^2). \qquad (2.4.20)$$

Similarly, adding Eqs. (2.4.13) and (2.4.14), we have

$$\nabla^2 + \nabla^3 = h^2D^2 - \tfrac{11}{12}h^4D^4 + \cdots$$

or, by Eqs. (2.4.2) and (2.4.3),

$$D^2y_i = \frac{1}{h^2}(2y_i - 5y_l + 4y_u - y_{uu}) + 0(h^2). \qquad (2.4.21)$$

In general, if the first m terms of the derivative expansions into backward differences are taken into account, the corresponding formulas have errors of order h^m.

The most commonly encountered derivative expressions in terms of backward differences are given in the "mathematical molecules" of Fig. 2.4 with the corresponding order of error in the derivatives.

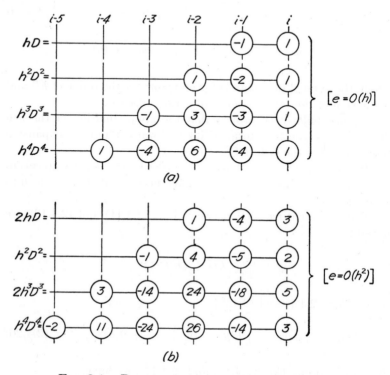

FIG. 2.4.   BACKWARD DIFFERENCE OPERATORS.

2.5   Forward Differences

Just as backward differences are defined by points all to the left of i, *forward differences* are defined by points all to the right of i.

The first forward difference of y at i is defined as:

$$\Delta y_i \equiv y_r - y_i \qquad (2.5.1)$$

and can be written symbolically by means of Eq. (2.4.7) as:

$$\Delta = e^{hD} - 1. \qquad (2.5.2)$$

The successive forward differences

$$\Delta^2 y_i = y_{rr} - 2y_r + y_i,$$
$$\Delta^3 y_i = y_{rrr} - 3y_{rr} + 3y_r - y_i,$$

$$\tag{2.5.3}$$

. . . .

have pivotal coefficients equal to the binomial coefficients of $(a - b)^n$ and are tabulated as in Table 2.3.

Table 2.3

Forward Differences

i	y_i	Δy_i	$\Delta^2 y_i$	$\Delta^3 y_i$	$\Delta^4 y_i$	$\Delta^5 y_i$
0	y_0	Δy_0	$\Delta^2 y_0$	$\Delta^3 y_0$	$\Delta^4 y_0$	$\Delta^5 y_0$
1	y_1	Δy_1	$\Delta^2 y_1$	$\Delta^3 y_1$	$\Delta^4 y_1$	
2	y_2	Δy_2	$\Delta^2 y_2$	$\Delta^3 y_2$		
3	y_3	Δy_3	$\Delta^2 y_3$			
4	y_4	Δy_4				
5	y_5					

In order to expand the derivatives of a function in terms of its forward differences, solve Eq. (2.5.2) for e^{hD} and take logs on both sides:*

$$hD = \ln(1 + \Delta) = \Delta - \frac{\Delta^2}{2} + \frac{\Delta^3}{3} - \frac{\Delta^4}{4} + \dots \tag{2.5.4}$$

Taking the powers of this equation, we obtain:

$$h^2 D^2 = \Delta^2 - \Delta^3 + \tfrac{11}{12}\Delta^4 - \tfrac{5}{6}\Delta^5 + \dots$$
$$h^3 D^3 = \Delta^3 - \tfrac{3}{2}\Delta^4 + \tfrac{7}{4}\Delta^5 - \dots$$
$$h^4 D^4 = \Delta^4 - 2\Delta^5 + \tfrac{17}{6}\Delta^6 - \dots$$
$$h^5 D^5 = \Delta^5 - \tfrac{5}{2}\Delta^6 + \tfrac{25}{6}\Delta^7 - \dots$$

$$\tag{2.5.5}$$

* See footnote on page 56.

Conversely, expanding Eq. (2.5.2), we obtain

$$\Delta = hD + \frac{h^2D^2}{2!} + \frac{h^3D^3}{3!} + \frac{h^4D^4}{4!} + \ldots , \qquad (2.5.6)$$

from which, taking powers of Δ,

$$\Delta^2 = h^2D^2 + h^3D^3 + \tfrac{7}{12}h^4D^4 + \ldots$$
$$\Delta^3 = h^3D^3 + \tfrac{3}{2}h^4D^4 + \tfrac{5}{4}h^5D^5 + \ldots \qquad (2.5.7)$$

. . . .

It may be proved that the error in the expansion of derivatives in terms of forward differences [Eqs. (2.5.4) and (2.5.5)] in which m terms are taken into account is of order h^m.

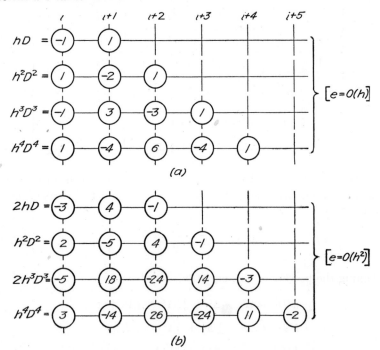

FIG. 2.5. FORWARD DIFFERENCE OPERATORS.

The "mathematical molecules" of Fig. 2.5 give the most commonly needed expressions for the derivatives in terms of forward differences and the corresponding errors in the derivatives.

2.6   Gregory-Newton Interpolation Formulas

Two important interpolation formulas, often used in engineering problems, are easily obtained by means of the forward and backward differences of a function.

Let us assume that the values of a Taylor-expandable function $y(x)$ be known at the pivotal points of its interval of definition, which are evenly spaced by h units, and let us call a the abscissa of one of these points.   Let the abscissa of the point at which we wish to evaluate the function be $a \pm xh$, where x is any real number. Expanding $y(a \pm xh)$ in a Taylor series about a, we obtain

$$y(a \pm xh) = y(a) \pm xhy'(a) + \frac{x^2h^2}{2} y'(a) \pm \frac{x^3h^3}{6} y'''(a) + \dots \quad \text{(a)}$$

The *Gregory-Newton forward interpolation formula* is obtained by substituting in the expansion of $y(a + xh)$ for the derivatives of y at a their expansions in terms of forward differences, given by Eqs. (2.5.4) and (2.5.5).   Substituting in the expansion of $y(a - xh)$ for the derivatives of y at a their expansions in terms of backward differences, given by Eqs. (2.4.16) and (2.4.17), we obtain the *Gregory-Newton backward interpolation formula*.   These substitutions, which the reader may want to check directly, are easily performed by symbolical methods.

Since, by Eq. (2.5.2),

$$e^{hD} = 1 + \Delta \qquad \text{(b)}$$

and, by Eq. (2.4.6) with a in place of x, and xh in place of h,

$$y(a + xh) = e^{xhD}y(a) = (e^{hD})^x y(a),$$

the expansion of Eq. (a) may be written symbolically:

$$y(a + xh) = (1 + \Delta)^x y(a).$$

The binomial expansion of $(1 + \Delta)^x$ in this equation gives the *forward interpolation formula:*

$$y(a + xh) = \left[1 + x\Delta + \frac{x(x-1)}{2!} \Delta^2 \right.$$
$$\left. + \frac{x(x-1)(x-2)}{3!} \Delta^3 + \dots \right] y(a). \quad \text{(2.6.1)}$$

Similarly, since by Eq. (2.4.12),

$$e^{-hD} = 1 - \nabla \qquad (c)$$

and, by Eq. (2.4.8) in which a is substituted for x, and xh for h,

$$y(a - xh) = e^{-xhD}y(a) = (e^{-hD})^x y(a),$$

the expansion of $y(a - xh)$ of Eq. (a) is written symbolically:

$$y(a - xh) = (1 - \nabla)^x y(a).$$

The binomial expansion of $(1 - \nabla)^x$ in this equation gives the *backward interpolation formula:*

$$y(a - xh) = \left[1 - x\nabla + \frac{x(x - 1)}{2!} \nabla^2 \right.$$
$$\left. - \frac{x(x - 1)(x - 2)}{3!} \nabla^3 + \ldots \right] y(a). \quad (2.6.2)$$

For example, given the values of $y = \sin x$ for $x = 10°(1°)13°,$*

Table 2.4

i	$x_i{}^\circ$	y_i	Δy_i	$\Delta^2 y_i$	$\Delta^3 y_i$
0	10	0.17365	0.01716	−0.00006	0
1	11	0.19081	0.01710	−0.00006	
2	12	0.20791	0.01704		
3	13	0.22495			

the value of $\sin x$ at $10°20'$ is obtained as shown in Table 2.4 by forward differences, with $a = 10°$ and $x(= 20') = \frac{1}{3}°$:

$$\sin 10°20' = 0.17365 + \frac{0.01716}{3} + \frac{(\frac{1}{3})(-\frac{2}{3})}{2} (-0.00006)$$
$$+ \frac{(\frac{1}{3})(-\frac{2}{3})(-\frac{5}{3})}{6} (0) = 0.17938.$$

The same value is obtained by backward differences with $a = 13°$ and $x(= 2°40') = \frac{8}{3}°$, as shown in Table 2.5:

* The symbol $x = a(h)b$ stands for "values of x from a to b in steps of h."

$$\sin 10°20' = 0.22495 - \frac{8(0.01704)}{3} + \frac{(\frac{8}{3})(\frac{5}{3})}{2}(-0.00006)$$

$$- \frac{(\frac{8}{3})(\frac{5}{3})(\frac{2}{3})}{6}(0) = 0.17938.$$

The true value of $\sin 10°20'$ is 0.17937.

Table 2.5

i	$x_i{}^0$	y_i	∇y_i	$\nabla^2 y_i$	$\nabla^3 y_i$
0	10	0.17365			
1	11	0.19081	0.01716		
2	12	0.20791	0.01710	−0.00006	
3	13	0.22495	0.01704	−0.00006	0

The Gregory-Newton formulas may also be used to *extrapolate* beyond the interval in which y is known. For example, by means of Table 2.4 the value of $\sin 13°30'$ is computed, letting in Eq. (2.6.1) $a = 10°$, $x = (3°30') = 3.5°$:

$$\sin 13°30' = 0.17365 + (3.5)(0.01716)$$

$$+ \frac{(3.5)(2.5)}{2}(-0.00006) = 0.23345.$$

This result is correct to the last figure computed.

2.7 Central Differences

Backward and forward differences were shown in Sects. 2.4 and 2.5 to lead to unilateral expressions for the derivatives of a function y, which in their simplest form have errors of order h.

Central differences, involving pivotal points symmetrically located with respect to i, are more accurate than backward or forward differences, and are particularly useful in the solution of boundary value problems.

Let the function $y(x)$ be known at the evenly spaced pivotal points i and, for the time being, at the middle points of the intervals

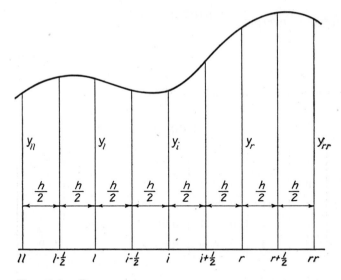

FIG. 2.6. PIVOTAL POINTS FOR CENTRAL DIFFERENCES.

defined by the pivotal points (Fig. 2.6). The *first central difference* of $y(x)$ at i is defined by

$$\delta y_i \equiv y\left(x_i + \frac{h}{2}\right) - y\left(x_i - \frac{h}{2}\right)$$

$$= y_{i+\frac{1}{2}} - y_{i-\frac{1}{2}}. \qquad (2.7.1)$$

The second central difference at i is the difference of the first difference:

$$\delta^2 y_i \equiv \delta(\delta y_i) = [y_{(i+\frac{1}{2})+\frac{1}{2}} - y_{(i-\frac{1}{2})+\frac{1}{2}}] - [y_{(i+\frac{1}{2})-\frac{1}{2}} - y_{(i-\frac{1}{2})-\frac{1}{2}}]$$

$$= y_r - 2y_i + y_l. \qquad (2.7.2)$$

The nth central difference is defined by

$$\delta^n y_i \equiv \delta(\delta^{n-1} y_i),$$

which leads to:

$$\delta^3 y_i = y_{r+\frac{1}{2}} - 3y_{i+\frac{1}{2}} + 3y_{i-\frac{1}{2}} - y_{l-\frac{1}{2}}, \qquad (2.7.3)$$

$$\delta^4 y_i = y_{rr} - 4y_r + 6y_i - 4y_l + y_{ll}. \qquad (2.7.4)$$

The coefficients of the pivotal values in the nth central difference are equal to the coefficients of the binomial expansion of $(a - b)^n$. Central differences are tabulated as shown in Table 2.6.

Table 2.6

Central Differences

i	y_i	δy_i	$\delta^2 y_i$	$\delta^3 y_i$	$\delta^4 y_i$	$\mu \delta y_i$	$\mu \delta^3 y_i$
0	y_0						
		$\delta y_{1/2}$					
1	y_1		$\delta^2 y_1$			$\mu \delta y_1$	
		$\delta y_{3/2}$		$\delta^3 y_{3/2}$			
2	y_2		$\delta^2 y_2$		$\delta^4 y_2$	$\mu \delta y_2$	$\mu \delta^3 y_2$
		$\delta y_{5/2}$		$\delta^3 y_{5/2}$			
3	y_3		$\delta^2 y_3$		$\delta^4 y_3$	$\mu \delta y_3$	$\mu \delta^3 y_3$
		$\delta y_{7/2}$		$\delta^3 y_{7/2}$			
4	y_4		$\delta^2 y_4$			$\mu \delta y_4$	
		$\delta y_{9/2}$					
5	y_5						

In order to eliminate the values of y at the intermediate points $\ldots, l - \frac{1}{2}, i \pm \frac{1}{2}, r + \frac{1}{2}, \ldots$ appearing in the expressions for the odd central differences, new averaged odd differences at i are defined as the average of the odd central differences at $i + \frac{1}{2}$ and $i - \frac{1}{2}$. Thus the *first averaged difference* at i is expressed by

$$\tfrac{1}{2}(\delta y_{i+1/2} + \delta y_{i-1/2}) = \tfrac{1}{2}[(y_r - y_i) + (y_i - y_l)] = \tfrac{1}{2}(y_r - y_l). \quad \text{(a)}$$

This averaging process is geometrically equivalent to taking as slope at i the slope of the chord P_rP_l rather than the slope of the chords P_iP_l or P_rP_i (Fig. 2.7). The averaging operation used in obtaining

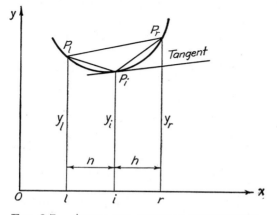

FIG. 2.7. AVERAGED CENTRAL DIFFERENCE.

Eq. (a) is usually symbolized by an operator μ, called the *averager* and defined by:

$$\mu y_i \equiv \tfrac{1}{2}(y_{i+\frac{1}{2}} + y_{i-\frac{1}{2}}). \tag{2.7.5}$$

By means of the averager the first averaged difference is written as:

$$\mu \delta y_i = \tfrac{1}{2}[\delta y_{i+\frac{1}{2}} + \delta y_{i-\frac{1}{2}}] = \tfrac{1}{2}(y_r - y_l). \tag{2.7.6}$$

The operators μ and δ are connected by a simple relation. In fact, squaring the μ operator:

$$\mu^2 y_i = \mu[\tfrac{1}{2}(y_{i+\frac{1}{2}} + y_{i-\frac{1}{2}})] = \tfrac{1}{2}[\tfrac{1}{2}(y_r + y_i) + \tfrac{1}{2}(y_i + y_l)]$$

$$= \tfrac{1}{4}(y_r + 2y_i + y_l),$$

and operating with $(1 + \delta^2/4)$ on y_i, we see, by Eq. (2.7.2), that:

$$\left(1 + \frac{\delta^2}{4}\right) y_i = y_i + \frac{1}{4}(y_r - 2y_i + y_l)$$

$$= \frac{1}{4}(y_r + 2y_i + y_l) = \mu^2 y_i.$$

Hence, we may write in symbolical form:

$$\mu^2 = 1 + \frac{\delta^2}{4}. \tag{2.7.7}$$

Equations (2.7.2), (2.7.6), and (2.7.7) allow the expansion of the derivatives of y in terms of its central differences, and the inverse expansions of differences in terms of derivatives, by symbolical methods.

By means of Eqs. (2.4.7) and (2.4.9), Eq. (2.7.6) becomes:

$$\mu \delta y_i = \frac{1}{2}(y_r - y_l) = \frac{1}{2} e^{hD} y_i - \frac{1}{2} e^{-hD} y_i$$

$$= \frac{e^{hD} - e^{-hD}}{2} y_i = \sinh(hD) y_i$$

or, in purely symbolical form,

$$\mu \delta = \sinh(hD). \tag{2.7.8}$$

Remembering the Taylor expansion of the hyperbolic sine:

$$\sinh x = x + \frac{x^3}{3!} + \frac{x^5}{5!} + \ldots,$$

the expansion of the first averaged central difference in terms of derivatives becomes:

$$\mu\delta = hD + \frac{h^3D^3}{6} + \frac{h^5D^5}{120} + \ldots \qquad (2.7.9)$$

Similarly by Eq. (2.7.2) and Eqs. (2.4.7), (2.4.9), the second central difference becomes:

$$\delta^2 y_i = e^{hD}y_i - 2y_i + e^{-hD}y_i = 2\left(\frac{e^{hD}+e^{-hD}}{2} - 1\right)y_i$$

$$= 2[\cosh(hD) - 1]y_i$$

and, remembering the Taylor expansion for $\cosh x$:

$$\cosh x = 1 + \frac{x^2}{2!} + \frac{x^4}{4!} + \ldots,$$

the second central difference may be written in symbolical form as

$$\delta^2 = h^2D^2 + \frac{h^4D^4}{12} + \frac{h^6D^6}{360} + \ldots \qquad (2.7.10)$$

The same result may be obtained by expanding into series the first *unaveraged* central difference [Eq. (2.7.1)]:

$$\delta y_i = y_{i+\frac{1}{2}} - y_{i-\frac{1}{2}} = (e^{hD/2} - e^{-hD/2})y_i$$

$$= 2\sinh\left(\frac{hD}{2}\right)y_i = \left(hD + \frac{h^3D^3}{2^2 \cdot 3!} + \frac{h^5D^5}{2^4 \cdot 5!} + \ldots\right),$$

from which, in general:

$$\delta^n = 2^n \sinh^n\left(\frac{hD}{2}\right) \qquad (2.7.11)$$

and in particular, for $n = 2$, we obtain Eq. (2.7.10).

The product of Eqs. (2.7.9) and (2.7.10) gives the third averaged difference expansion:

$$\mu\delta^3 = h^3D^3 + \frac{h^5D^5}{4} + \frac{8h^7D^7}{45} + \ldots, \qquad (2.7.12)$$

and the square of Eq. (2.7.10) the expansion of the fourth central difference:

$$\delta^4 = h^4D^4 + \frac{h^6D^6}{6} + \frac{27h^8D^8}{2160} + \ldots \qquad (2.7.13)$$

Conversely, to obtain the expansion of the first derivative in terms of central differences, we solve Eq. (2.7.8) for hD:

$$hD = \sinh^{-1}(\mu\delta).$$

Remembering the Taylor series for $\sinh^{-1} x$:

$$\sinh^{-1} x = x - \frac{x^3}{6} + \frac{3x^5}{40} - \cdots ,$$

we obtain:

$$hD = \mu\delta - \frac{\mu^3\delta^3}{6} + \frac{3\mu^5\delta^5}{40} - \cdots ,$$

and using Eq. (2.7.7) to eliminate even powers of μ, the expansion for hD finally becomes:

$$hD = \mu\left(\delta - \frac{\delta^3}{6} + \frac{\delta^5}{30} - \cdots\right). \tag{2.7.14}$$

Taking powers of hD and using again Eq. (2.7.7) to eliminate even powers of μ, we obtain similarly:

$$h^2D^2 = \delta^2 - \frac{\delta^4}{12} + \frac{\delta^6}{90} - \cdots$$

$$h^3D^3 = \mu\left(\delta^3 - \frac{\delta^5}{4} + \frac{7\delta^7}{120} - \cdots\right) \tag{2.7.15}$$

$$h^4D^4 = \delta^4 - \frac{\delta^6}{6} + \frac{7\delta^8}{240} - \cdots$$

Using the first term of these expansions, the derivatives of y may be approximated by the following central difference expansions, whose errors ϵ are given in terms of differences:

$$2hDy_i = (y_r - y_l) + \epsilon_1;$$

$$\left[\epsilon_1 = \mu\left(-\frac{\delta^3}{6} + \frac{\delta^5}{30} - \cdots\right)y_i\right]$$

$$h^2D^2y_i = y_r - 2y_i + y_l + \epsilon_2;$$

$$\left[\epsilon_2 = \left(-\frac{\delta^4}{12} + \frac{\delta^6}{90} - \cdots\right)y_i\right] \qquad [\epsilon = 0(h^2)]$$

$$2h^3D^3y_i = (y_{rr} - 2y_r + 2y_l - y_{ll}) + \epsilon_3; \tag{2.7.16}$$

$$\left[\epsilon_3 = \mu\left(-\frac{\delta^5}{4} + \frac{7\delta^7}{120} - \cdots\right)y_i\right]$$

$$h^4D^4y_i = y_{rr} - 4y_r + 6y_i - 4y_l + y_{ll} + \epsilon_4;$$

$$\left[\epsilon_4 = \left(-\frac{\delta^6}{6} + \frac{7\delta^8}{240} - \cdots\right)y_i\right].$$

A comparison of these equations with the expansions of Eqs. (2.7.9) to (2.7.13) proves that the error in the corresponding derivatives is of order h^2, and hence that averaged central difference expressions are more accurate than either forward of backward

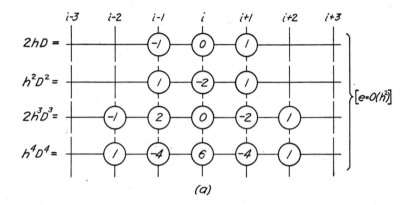

(a)

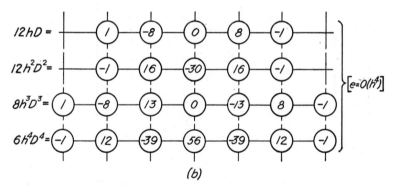

(b)

FIG. 2.8.   CENTRAL DIFFERENCE OPERATORS.

unilateral expressions.   It may similarly be proved that by taking into account the first two terms of the expansions (2.7.14) and (2.7.15) the error in the corresponding derivatives is of order h^4, and that considering m terms one obtains errors of order h^{2m}.

The "molecules" of Fig. 2.8 give the most commonly used central difference expressions for derivatives with errors of order h^2 and h^4.

2.8   Numerical Integration

Whenever a function cannot be integrated in finite terms, or the evaluation of its integral is too cumbersome, integration may be more conveniently performed by numerical methods.   Among the most widely used and most practical procedures for numerical integration are the *trapezoidal rule* and *Simpson's $\frac{1}{3}$ rule*, which will be derived and demonstrated in this section.

[a]   The Trapezoidal Rule

Consider the integral

$$A = \int_a^b f(x)dx, \qquad \text{(a)}$$

in which the function $f(x)$ is known at pivotal points of the interval

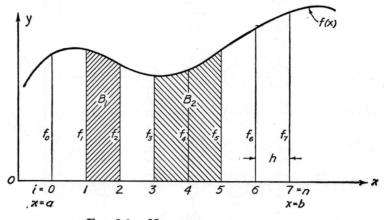

FIG. 2.9.   NUMERICAL INTEGRATION.

(a,b) evenly spaced by $h = (b - a)/n$ (Fig. 2.9).   The integral

$$B_1 = \int_x^{x+h} f(z)dz \qquad \text{(b)}$$

represents the area of a strip of width h limited by two adjoining pivotal ordinates at x and $x + h$.   Calling $y(x)$ the integral with upper variable limit

$$y(x) = \int_a^x f(z)dz, \qquad \text{(c)}$$

the integral B_1 is given in terms of y by:

$$B_1 = y(x + h) - y(x),$$

and the derivatives of y with respect to x are given in terms of $f(x)$ and its derivatives by:

$$y' = f(x); \quad y'' = f'(x); \quad \ldots ; \quad y^{(n)} = f^{(n-1)}(x); \quad \ldots .$$

Hence the Taylor series for y at $x + h$ [Eq. (a) of Sec. 2.4] becomes:

$$y(x + h) = y(x) + \frac{h}{1!} f(x) + \frac{h^2}{2!} f'(x) + \frac{h^3}{3!} f''(x) + \ldots \quad (d)$$

Substituting in this expansion for $hf'(x)$ its approximate value in terms of forward differences (Fig. 2.5), $f(x + h) - f(x)$, we obtain:

$$B_1 = y(x + h) - y(x) = hf(x) + \frac{h}{2} [f(x + h) - f(x)]$$

$$+ \frac{h^3}{6} f''(x) + \ldots$$

$$= \frac{h}{2} [f(x) + f(x + h)] + \frac{h^3}{6} f''(x) + \ldots . \quad (e)$$

The integral A is the sum of the n integrals B_1 corresponding to each of the n strips, and hence equals:

$$A = \int_a^b f(x)dx = h[\tfrac{1}{2}f_0 + f_1 + f_2 + \ldots$$

$$+ f_{n-1} + \tfrac{1}{2}f_n] + e_t, \quad (2.8.1)$$

where $f_i = f(ih)$, and the *error* e_t is:

$$e_t = \frac{h^3}{6} (f_0'' + f_1'' + f_2'' + \ldots + f''_{n-1}) + \ldots .$$

If in Eq. (e) we drop all the terms after the third, $(h^3/6)f''(x)$, the error e_t takes the form:

$$e_t \doteq \frac{h^3}{6} (f_0'' + f_1'' + \ldots + f''_{n-1}) = \frac{h^3}{6} nf''(\bar{x}_n),$$

where, by the theorem of the mean, $\bar{x}_n$ is a value of x between a and b. Hence with $nh = b - a$, the error in the trapezoidal rule becomes:

$$e_t = \frac{b - a}{6} f''(\bar{x}_n)h^2.$$

If $f''(\bar{x}_n)$ does not vary substantially with n, as is the case for functions with fairly smooth second derivative in (a,b), the error becomes practically of order h^2:

$$e_t = 0(h^2). \tag{2.8.2}$$

This property will be used in Section 2.9 to improve the accuracy of the trapezoidal rule.

The trapezoidal rule, which obviously approximates the curve

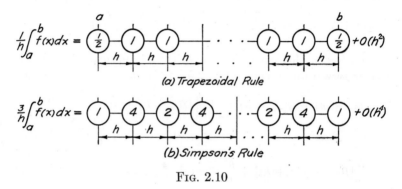

(a) Trapezoidal Rule

(b) Simpson's Rule

Fig. 2.10

to be integrated by straight-line segments, is conveniently represented by the molecule of Fig. 2.10a.

The value of the integral

$$A = \int_0^\pi \sin x \; dx = -\cos x \Big]_0^\pi = 2 \tag{f}$$

is computed by the trapezoidal rule with $n = 2$, 4, and 6 in Table 2.7. The corresponding errors are evaluated by means of the true value $A = 2$.

[b] Simpson's Rule

Using again Eq. (c), the area B_2 of *two strips* of width h adjoining at x (Fig. 2.9) may be written as:

$$B_2 = \int_{x-h}^{x+h} f(z)dz = y(x + h) - y(x - h). \tag{g}$$

Changing h into $-h$ in Eq. (d):

$$y(x - h) = y(x) - \frac{h}{1!} f(x) + \frac{h^2}{2!} f'(x) - \frac{h^3}{3!} f''(x) + \ldots, \tag{h}$$

Table 2.7

Numerical Integration by the Trapezoidal Rule

x	$\sin x$	$n = 2$ $h = \pi/2$ M		$n = 4$ $h = \pi/4$ M	
0	0	$\frac{1}{2}$	0	$\frac{1}{2}$	0
$\pi/4$	0.707			1	0.707
$\pi/2$	1.000	1	1.000	1	1.000
$3\pi/4$	0.707			1	0.707
π	0	$\frac{1}{2}$	0	$\frac{1}{2}$	0
		$\sum_2 =$	1.000	$\sum_4 =$	2.414

x	$\sin x$	$n = 6$ $h = \pi/6$ M	
0	0	$\frac{1}{2}$	0
$\pi/6$	0.500	1	0.500
$\pi/3$	0.866	1	0.866
$\pi/2$	1.000	1	1.000
$2\pi/3$	0.866	1	0.866
$5\pi/6$	0.500	1	0.500
π	0	$\frac{1}{2}$	0
		$\sum_6 =$	3.732

$$A_2 = \left(\frac{\pi}{2}\right) \cdot 1.000 = 1.571; \qquad e_2 = \frac{2 - 1.571}{2} \cdot 100 = 21 \text{ per cent.}$$

$$A_4 = \left(\frac{\pi}{4}\right) \cdot 2.414 = 1.896; \qquad e_4 = \frac{2 - 1.896}{2} \cdot 100 = 5.2 \text{ per cent.}$$

$$A_6 = \left(\frac{\pi}{6}\right) \cdot 3.732 = 1.954; \qquad e_6 = \frac{2 - 1.954}{2} \cdot 100 = 2.3 \text{ per cent.}$$

and subtracting Eq. (h) from Eq. (d), B_2 becomes:

$$B_2 = y(x + h) - y(x - h) = 2hf(x) + \frac{h^3}{3}f''(x) + \frac{h^5}{60}f^{IV}(x) + \ldots$$

If we now substitute in the last equation the approximate value of $h^2f''(x)$ in terms of central differences from Eq. (2.7.10):

$$h^2D^2f(x) = \left(\delta^2 - \frac{h^4D^4}{12} - \frac{h^6D^6}{360} - \ldots\right)f(x)$$

$$= f(x + h) - 2f(x) + f(x - h)$$

$$- \left(\frac{h^4D^4}{12} + \frac{h^6D^6}{360} + \ldots\right)f(x),$$

we obtain:

$$B_2 = 2hf(x) + \frac{h}{3}[f(x + h) - 2f(x) + f(x - h)]$$

$$- \frac{h^5f^{IV}}{36} + \frac{h^5f^{IV}}{60} - \ldots$$

$$= \frac{h}{3}[f(x + h) + 4f(x) + f(x - h)] - \frac{h^5f^{IV}(x)}{90} + \ldots$$

Dividing the area A into an *even* number n of strips of width h, A is approximately given by the sum of $n/2$ expressions like B_2 (*Simpson's ⅓ rule*):

$$A = \frac{h}{3}[f_0 + 4f_1 + 2f_2 + 4f_3 + \ldots$$

$$+ 2f_{n-2} + 4f_{n-1} + f_n] + e_s, \quad (2.8.3)$$

where the error e_s equals, by the theorem of the mean and with $nh = b - a$,

$$e_s = -\frac{h^5}{90}(f_1^{IV} + f_3^{IV} + \ldots + f^{IV}_{n-1}) + \ldots$$

$$\doteq -\frac{h^5}{90}\frac{n}{2}f^{IV}(\bar{x}_n) = -\left(\frac{b - a}{180}\right)f^{IV}(\bar{x}_n)h^4 + \ldots = 0(h^4). \quad (2.8.4)$$

Hence e_s is of order h^4. This property will be used in Sec. 2.9 to improve the accuracy of Simpson's rule.

Just as the trapezoidal rule approximates the area of one strip by the area under a straight line, it may be shown that Simpson's

$\frac{1}{3}$ rule approximates the area of two adjacent strips by the area under a quadratic parabola. Similar formulas may be obtained by means of higher-degree parabolas covering a larger number of strips, but the accuracy thus obtainable, in general, is not superior to the accuracy of the $\frac{1}{3}$ rule. Simpson's $\frac{1}{3}$ rule is conveniently represented by the molecule of Fig. 2.10b.

Table 2.8

Numerical Integration by Simpson's Rule

x	$\sin x$	$n = 2$ $h = \pi/2$ M		$n = 4$ $h = \pi/4$ M	
0	0	1	0	1	0
$\pi/4$	0.707			4	2.828
$\pi/2$	1.000	4	4	2	2.000
$3\pi/4$	0.707			4	2.828
π	0	1	0	1	0
		$\sum_{2} =$	4	$\sum_{4} =$	7.656

$$A_2 = \frac{\pi/2}{3} \cdot 4 = 2.094; \qquad e_2 = 4.7 \text{ per cent.}$$

$$A_4 = \frac{\pi/4}{3} \cdot 7.656 = 2.004; \qquad e_4 = 0.23 \text{ per cent.}$$

The evaluation of the integral (f) of this section by Simpson's rule with $n = 2$ and $n = 4$ is shown in Table 2.8.

When the number of strips is odd, $n = 2m + 1$, Simpson's rule may be applied to the first $2m$ strips, and the trapezoidal rule to the last. In order to obtain a more accurate result one may also obtain the value of the integrand at the middle of the last strip by interpolation (see Sec. 2.6) and use Simpson's rule with a spacing $h/2$ to cover the last strip.

## 2.9	Richardson's Extrapolations

It was shown in the previous sections that the error in the difference formulas for differentiation and integration depends on the spacing h of the pivotal points, and that it is of order h^2 or h^4 in the better approximated formulas.

Thus derivative values obtained by one term of their central difference expansions, and integrals obtained by the trapezoidal rule, have errors of order h^2, while derivatives obtained by two terms of their central difference expansions, and integrals obtained by Simpson's rule, have errors of order h^4.

The order of these errors is obtained by taking into account the higher terms of the expansions, but the reader will notice that in all the above cases the error in central difference expressions for the derivatives at a point x is represented by a series of the type:

$$e(x) = f_1(x)h^2 + f_2(x)h^4 + f_3(x)h^6 + \ldots \qquad (2.9.1)$$

Hence, for example, errors of order h^4 have expansions with $f_1(x) \equiv 0$.

When the expression evaluated by differences is independent of x, as is the case for definite integrals, the error series has constant coefficients and may be written as

$$e = c_1 h^2 + c_2 h^4 + c_3 h^6 + \ldots \qquad (2.9.2)$$

The same expression for the error is valid when the error is computed with various values of the spacing h *at the same point* x.

It will now be shown that the knowledge of the form of the error series allows the evaluation of better approximations of the derivatives and of the integrals with a minimum amount of added labor.

Let us assume, for example, that the value A of an integral has been computed numerically by using n_1 and n_2 strips in the trapezoidal rule, that is, by taking

$$h_1 = \frac{b - a}{n_1}, \qquad h_2 = \frac{b - a}{n_2},$$

and let us call A_{n_1} and A_{n_2} the corresponding approximations. If h_1 and h_2 are small enough to allow us to neglect all the terms except the first in Eq. (2.9.2), we may write:

$$e_1 \equiv A - A_{n_1} \doteq \frac{c_1(b - a)^2}{n_1{}^2}, \qquad e_2 \equiv A - A_{n_2} \doteq \frac{c_1(b - a)^2}{n_2{}^2},$$

where c_1 is unknown. Eliminating the unknown constant $c_1(b - a)^2$ between these two equations and solving for the true value A, we obtain the so-called *h^2-extrapolation formula:*

$$A_{n_1,n_2} = \frac{n_2^2}{n_2^2 - n_1^2} A_{n_2} - \frac{n_1^2}{n_2^2 - n_1^2} A_{n_1} = \alpha_1 A_{n_1} + \alpha_2 A_{n_2}, \quad (2.9.3)$$

which gives an excellent approximation of A whenever the higher terms of the error series are negligible.

Table 2.9

h^2—Extrapolation Coefficients

n_2/n_1	α_1	α_2
2/1	-0.3333333333	1.3333333333
3/2	-0.8	1.8
4/3	-1.2857142857	2.2857142857
5/4	-1.7777777778	2.7777777778
6/5	-2.2727272727	3.2727272727
7/6	-2.7692307692	3.7692307692
8/7	-3.2666666667	4.2666666667
3/1	-0.125	1.125
5/8	-0.5625	1.5625
7/5	-1.0416666667	2.0416666667

For example, taking $A_2 = 1.571$ and $A_4 = 1.896$ from Table 2.7, the value of the integral (f) of Sec. 2.8 given by Eq. (2.9.3) is

$$A_{2,4} = \frac{4^2}{4^2 - 2^2} 1.896 - \frac{2^2}{4^2 - 2^2} 1.571$$

$$= \tfrac{4}{3} \cdot 1.896 - \tfrac{1}{3} \cdot 1.571 = 2.004,$$

with an error of 0.4 per cent as against errors of 21 per cent and 5.2 per cent in A_2 and A_4, respectively.   Repeating the computation for $n = 4$, $n = 6$, we obtain similarly:

$$A_{4,6} = \frac{6^2}{6^2 - 4^2} 1.954 - \frac{4^2}{6^2 - 4^2} 1.896 = 2.0004,$$

with an error of 0.04 per cent.

Table 2.9 gives the coefficients

$$\alpha_1 = -\frac{n_1^2}{n_2^2 - n_1^2}, \qquad \alpha_2 = \frac{n_2^2}{n_2^2 - n_1^2} \qquad (2.9.4)$$

of the h^2-extrapolation formula [Eq. (2.9.3)] for the most commonly encountered ratios of the values of n_1 and n_2, since Eqs. (2.9.4) depend only on the ratio n_2/n_1.

When three approximations $A_{n_1}, A_{n_2}, A_{n_3}$ of A have been obtained by means of three spacings h_1, h_2, h_3 inversely proportional to n_1, n_2, n_3, we may take into account two terms of the error equation (2.9.2) and write:

$$e_1 \equiv A - A_{n_1} = \frac{c_1(b - a)^2}{n_1{}^2} + \frac{c_2(b - a)^4}{n_1{}^4}$$

$$e_2 \equiv A - A_{n_2} = \frac{c_1(b - a)^2}{n_2{}^2} + \frac{c_2(b - a)^4}{n_2{}^4}$$

$$e_3 \equiv A - A_{n_3} = \frac{c_1(b - a)^2}{n_3{}^2} + \frac{c_2(b - a)^4}{n_3{}^4}.$$

Eliminating the two unknown constants $c_1(b - a)^2$ and $c_2(b - a)^4$ between these equations and solving for the true value A, we obtain the (h^2, h^4)-*extrapolation formula*:

$$A_{n_1,n_2,n_3} = \frac{n_1{}^4}{(n_2{}^2 - n_1{}^2)(n_3{}^2 - n_1{}^2)} A_{n_1} - \frac{n_2{}^4}{(n_2{}^2 - n_1{}^2)(n_3{}^2 - n_2{}^2)} A_{n_2}$$
$$+ \frac{n_3{}^4}{(n_3{}^2 - n_1{}^2)(n_3{}^2 - n_2{}^2)} A_{n_3} = \beta_1 A_{n_1} + \beta_2 A_{n_2} + \beta_3 A_{n_3}, \quad (2.9.5)$$

whose coefficients are given in Table 2.10 for the most common ratios of $n_3/n_2/n_1$.

Table 2.10

(h^2, h^4)—Extrapolation Coefficients

$n_3/n_2/n_1$	β_1	β_2	β_3
3/2/1	0.0416666667	−1.0666666667	2.025
4/2/1	0.0222222222	−0.4444444444	1.4222222222
4/3/2	0.2666666667	−2.3142857143	3.0476190476
5/4/2	0.6349206349	−2.3703703704	3.3068783069
5/4/3	0.7232142857	−4.0634920635	4.3402777778
6/5/4	1.4222222222	−6.3131313131	5.8909090909
7/6/5	2.3674242424	−9.0629370629	7.6955128205
8/7/6	3.5604395604	−12.3128205128	9.7523809524
5/3/1	0.0052083333	−0.6328125	1.6276041667
7/5/3	0.1265625	−1.6276041667	2.5010416667

For example, using the three approximations A_2, A_4, A_6 of the integral (f) or Sec. 2.8 in Table 2.7 and the coefficients β corresponding to the ratios $6/4/2 = 3/2/1$ from Table 2.10, we obtain: $A_{2,4,6} = 0.04167 \cdot 1.571 - 1.06667 \cdot 1.896 + 2.025 \cdot 1.954 = 1.99991$, with an error of 0.005 per cent.

When the order of the error is h^4, then $c_1 = 0$ in Eq. (2.9.2), and the errors in two successive approximations with n_1 and n_2 subintervals take the form:

$$e_1 \equiv A - A_{n_1} = \frac{c_2(b - a)^4}{n_1^4} + \frac{c_3(b - a)^6}{n_1^6} + \cdots$$

$$e_2 \equiv A - A_{n_2} = \frac{c_2(b - a)^4}{n_2^4} + \frac{c_3(b - a)^6}{n_2^6} + \cdots .$$

Neglecting all but the first term of the error series and solving for A, we obtain the h^4-*extrapolation formula:*

$$A_{n_1,n_2} = \frac{n_2^4}{n_2^4 - n_1^4} A_{n_2} - \frac{n_1^4}{n_2^4 - n_1^4} A_{n_1} = \gamma_1 A_{n_1} + \gamma_2 A_{n_2}, \quad (2.9.6)$$

whose coefficients are given in Table 2.11.*

Table 2.11

h^4—Extrapolation Coefficients

n_2/n_1	γ_1	γ_2
2/1	−0.0666666667	1.0666666667
3/2	−0.2461538462	1.2461538462
4/3	−0.4628571429	1.4628571429
5/4	−0.6937669377	1.6937669377
6/5	−0.9314456036	1.9314456036
7/6	−1 1728506787	2.1728506787
8/7	−1 4165191740	2.4165191740
3/1	−0.0125	1.0125
5/3	−0.1488970588	1.1488970588
7/5	−0.3519144144	1.3519144144

* Tables 2.9, 2.10, and 2.11 have been computed by the Istituto Nazionale per le Applicazioni del Calcolo, the mathematical laboratory of the Italian National Research Council, directed by Prof. Mauro Picone. More complete tables of this type have been published by the author in *Proc.,* "First U.S. Congress of Applied Mechanics," *A.S.M.E.,* Chicago, 1952.

For example, using the values A_2 and A_4 of the integral (f) of Sec. 2.8 obtained in Table 2.8 by means of Simpson's rule, whose error is of order h^4, and the coefficients of Table 2.11 for $n_2/n_1 = 2/1$, we obtain the extrapolation:

$$A_{2,4} = -0.06667 \cdot 2.094 + 1.06667 \cdot 2.004 = 1.998,$$

with an error of 0.1 per cent.

Table 2.12

Approximations				h^2—Extrapolations		
h	n	$J'_{1/4}(0.5)$	$e(\%)$	n	$J'_{1/4}(0.5)$	$e(\%)$
0.4	1	0.30377	+38.6	2/1	0.20994	−4.2
0.2	2	0.23340	+6.5	4/2	0.21873	−1.6
0.1	4	0.22240	+1.5	8/4	0.21906	−0.013
0.05	8	. 0.21990	+0.37	......	......	......

(h^2,h^4)—Extrapolations		
n	$J'_{1/4}(0.5)$	$e(\%)$
4/2/1	0.21931	+0.10
8/4/2	0.21908	−0.004

As another example of extrapolation consider the approximate values of the first derivative of the Bessel function $J_{1/4}(x)$ at $x = 0.5$, which may be easily computed by the central difference operator [Eq. 2.7.16)]

$$J'_{1/4}(0.5) \doteq \frac{1}{2h} [J_{1/4}(0.5 + h) - J_{1/4}(0.5 - h)]$$

for $h = 0.4,\ 0.2,\ 0.1,\ 0.05$. These values appear in Table 2.12, column 3. Since the approximation of derivatives by central differences involves errors of the type of Eq. (2.9.1), h^2- and (h^2,h^4)-extrapolations may be evaluated in this case *at a given x* for $n_2/n_1 = 2/1$ and for $n_3/n_2/n_1 = 4/2/1$ by means of the coefficients of Tables 2.9 and 2.10. They appear in Table 2.12 together with the corresponding percentage of error evaluated from the true value of

$J'_{1/4} (0.5) = 0.21909$. The table proves again that a reduction in error may be obtained by extrapolation with very little additional labor.

The extrapolations of this section should not be used when the successive approximations do not approach the true value monotonically, since in this case the higher terms of the error series cannot be neglected.

PROBLEMS

2.1 Given three evenly spaced pivotal values y_0, y_1, y_2, determine by means of interpolating parabolas the first and second derivatives of y at: (a) 0; (b) 1; and (c) 2 in terms of the pivotal values at all three points.

Ans. (a) $y'_0 = \dfrac{1}{2h} (-3y_0 + 4y_1 - y_2)$. (b) $y'_1 = \dfrac{1}{2h} (-y_0 + y_2)$.

(c) $y'_2 = \dfrac{1}{2h} (y_0 - 4y_1 + 3y_2)$; $y''_{0,1,2} = \dfrac{y_0 - 2y_1 + y_2}{h^2}$.

2.2 Given four evenly spaced pivotal values y_0, y_1, y_2, y_3, determine by use of interpolating parabolas the following derivatives of y in terms of the pivotal values at all four points.

(a) y'_2. (b) y'_1. (c) y'_0. (d) y_0''. (e) y_2''. (f) y_3''.

Ans. (b) $y'_1 = (1/6h)(-2y_0 - 3y_1 + 6y_2 - y_3)$.
(d) $y_0'' = (1/h^2)(2y_0 - 5y_1 + 4y_2 - y_3)$.
(f) $y_3'' = (1/h^2)(-y_0 + 4y_1 - 5y_2 + 2y_3)$.

2.3 Determine an approximate expression for y'_i by means of an interpolating parabola passing through the points of Fig. 2.2.

Ans. $$y'_i = \frac{y_r - (1 - \alpha^2)y_i - \alpha^2 y_l}{h\alpha(1 + \alpha)}.$$

2.4 Determine an approximate expression for y_i''' by means of an interpolating parabola passing through the points of Fig. 2.3a.

2.5 Given evenly spaced pivotal values y_0, y_1, y_2, y_3, . . . , determine by means of Taylor series expansions the following derivatives, with errors of the indicated order. Determine the first term of the error series.

(a) y'_0; $e = 0(h^2)$.   (b) y'_1; $e = 0(h^2)$.
(c) y'_2; $e = 0(h^2)$.   (d) y_0''; $e = 0(h)$.
(e) y_1''; $e = 0(h^2)$.   (f) y'_2; $e = 0(h^3)$.
(g) y'_1; $e = 0(h^3)$.   (h) y'_0; $e = 0(h^3)$.
(i) y_0''; $e = 0(h^2)$.   (j) y_3''; $e = 0(h^2)$.

Ans. (a) $y'_0 = \dfrac{-3y_0 + 4y_1 - y_2}{2h}; e \doteq \dfrac{h^2 y_0'''}{3}.$

(c) $y'_2 = \dfrac{y_0 - 4y_1 + 3y_2}{2h}; e \doteq \dfrac{h^2 y_2'''}{3}.$

(e) $y_1'' = \dfrac{y_0 - 2y_1 + y_2}{h^2}; e \doteq -\dfrac{h^2 y_1^{IV}}{12}.$

(g) $y'_1 = \dfrac{-2y_0 - 3y_1 + 6y_2 - y_3}{6h}; e \doteq \dfrac{h^3 y_1^{IV}}{12}.$

(i) $y_0'' = \dfrac{2y_0 - 5y_1 + 4y_2 - y_3}{h^2}; e \doteq \dfrac{11h^2 y_0^{IV}}{12}.$

2.6 Given five evenly spaced values y_0, y_1, y_2, y_3, y_4, determine, by means of Taylor series expansions, the following derivatives of y in terms of all five pivotal values. Give the first term of the error in each case.

(a) y'_1; $e = 0(h^4)$.   (b) y_2''; $e = 0(h^4)$.

(c) y_0'''; $e = 0(h^2)$.   (d) y_0''; $e = 0(h^3)$.

(e) y_2'''; $e = 0(h^2)$.

Ans. (a) $y'_1 = \dfrac{1}{24h}(-6y_0 - 20y_1 + 36y_2 - 12y_3 + 2y_4);$

$\quad e \doteq -\tfrac{1}{20}h^4 y_1^{V}.$

(c) $y_0''' = \dfrac{1}{4h^3}(-10y_0 + 36y_1 - 48y_2 + 28y_3 - 6y_4);$

$\quad e \doteq \tfrac{21}{12}h^2 y_0^{V}.$

(e) $y_2''' = \dfrac{1}{4h^3}(-2y_0 + 4y_1 - 4y_3 + 2y_4);$

$\quad e \doteq -\tfrac{1}{4}h^2 y_2^{V}.$

2.7 Given six evenly spaced pivotal values $y_0, y_1, y_2, y_3, \ldots$, determine by means of Taylor series expansions the following derivatives in terms of all six pivotal values. Give the first term of the error series in each case.

(a) y_4''; $e = 0(h^4)$.

(b) y_3^{IV}; $e = 0(h^2)$.

(c) y'_2; $e = 0(h^5)$.

Ans. (a) $y_4'' = \dfrac{1}{60h^2}(5y_0 - 30y_1 + 70y_2 - 20y_3 - 75y_4 + 50y_5);$

$\quad e \doteq -\tfrac{13}{180}h^4 y_4^{IV}.$

(b) $y_3^{IV} = \dfrac{1}{5h^4}(5y_1 - 20y_2 + 30y_3 - 20y_4 + 5y_5); e \doteq -\tfrac{1}{6}h^2 y_3^{VI}.$

(c) $y'_2 = \dfrac{1}{120h}(6y_0 - 60y_1 - 40y_2 + 120y_3 - 30y_4 + 4y_5);$

$\quad e \doteq -\tfrac{1}{60}h^5 y_2^{VI}.$

2.8 Derive Eq. (2.3.6) of Sec. 2.3 by a Taylor series expansion and prove that the error is of order h^2.   Use the points of Fig. 2.3a.

2.9 Derive Eq. (2.3.7) of Sec. 2.3 by a Taylor series expansion and prove that the error is of order h^2.   Use the points of Fig. 2.3b.

2.10 Determine by Taylor series an approximate four-point formula for y_i''' and the first term of the corresponding error series by means of the points of Fig. 2.3a.

Ans. $y_i''' = \dfrac{6y_r + 6\alpha(2 + \alpha)y_l - 3\alpha(1 + \alpha)y_{ll} - 3(1 + \alpha)(2 + \alpha)y_i}{h^3\alpha(1 + \alpha)(2 + \alpha)}$.

$e \doteq \dfrac{7(1 + \alpha) - (1 + \alpha^3)}{4\alpha(1 + \alpha)(2 + \alpha)}\, hy_i^{IV}$.

2.11 Determine by Taylor series an approximate five-point formula for y_i''' and the first term of the corresponding error series by means of the points of Fig. 2.11.

Ans. $y_i''' = [36y_r + (\alpha^4 - 25\alpha^2 - 60\alpha - 36)y_i + (-3\alpha^4 + 57\alpha^2 + 90\alpha)y_l$

$+ (3\alpha^4 - 39\alpha^2 - 36\alpha)y_{ll} + (-\alpha^4 + 7\alpha^2 + 6\alpha)y_{lll}] \Big/ h^3(\alpha^4 + 18\alpha^3 + 11\alpha^2$

$- 6\alpha)$;

$e \doteq \dfrac{h^2(12\alpha^5 + 50\alpha^4 - 170\alpha^2 - 132\alpha)y_i^V}{40(\alpha^4 + 18\alpha^3 + 11\alpha^2 - 6\alpha)}$.

Fɪɢ. 2.11

2.12 Determine by Taylor series an approximate five-point formula for y_i^{IV} and the first term of the corresponding error series by means of the points of Fig. 2.11.

Ans. $y_i^{IV} = [24y_r - (12\alpha^3 + 24\alpha^2 + 36\alpha + 24)y_i + (36\alpha^3 + 60\alpha^2 + 48\alpha)y_l$

$- (36\alpha^3 + 48\alpha^2 + 12\alpha)y_{ll} + (12\alpha^3 + 12\alpha^2)y_{lll}] \Big/ h^4(\alpha^4 + 18\alpha^3 + 11\alpha^2 - 6\alpha)$;

$e \doteq \dfrac{h(-12\alpha^5 + 900\alpha^3 + 720\alpha^2 - 168\alpha)y_i^V}{6(\alpha^4 + 18\alpha^3 + 11\alpha^2 - 6\alpha)}$.

2.13 Given evenly spaced pivotal values $y_i, y_{i-1}, y_{i-2}, \ldots$, determine approximate expressions for: (a) y_i'''; (b) y_i^{IV}; (c) y_i^V with errors of order h by means of:

(1) Backward difference expansions.
(2) Interpolating parabolas passing through 4, 5, and 6 points, respectively, to the left of i.
(3) Taylor series expansions.

Obtain, where possible, the first term of the error series.

Ans. (a) $y_i''' = \dfrac{1}{h^3}(y_i - 3y_{i-1} + 3y_{i-2} - y_{i-3})$.

(b) $y_i^{IV} = \dfrac{1}{h^4}(y_i - 4y_{i-1} + 6y_{i-2} - 4y_{i-3} + y_{i-4})$.

(c) $y_i^{V} = \dfrac{1}{h^5}(y_i - 5y_{i-1} + 10y_{i-2} - 10y_{i-3} + 5y_{i-4} - y_{i-5})$.

2.14 Determine approximate expressions for the following derivatives using two terms of their backward difference expansions. Determine the first terms of the corresponding error series.

(a) y_i'. (b) y_i''. (c) y_i'''. (d) y_i^{IV}.

Ans. (b) $y_i'' = \dfrac{1}{h^2}(2y_i - 5y_{i-1} + 4y_{i-2} - y_{i-3})$; $e \doteq \frac{11}{12}h^2 y_i^{IV}$. (d) y_i^{IV}

$= \dfrac{1}{h^4}(3y_i - 14y_{i-1} + 26y_{i-2} - 24y_{i-3} + 11y_{i-4} - 2y_{i-5})$; $e \doteq \frac{34}{12}h^2 y_i^{VI}$.

2.15 Locate the error in the following table and correct it by linear interpolation of first backward differences.

x_i	1	2	3	4	5	6
y_i	0.01746	0.03492	0.05241	0.07154	0.08749	0.10510

7	8	9
0.12278	0.14054	0.15838

Ans. $y_4 = 0.06993$.

2.16 Locate the error in the following table using linear interpolation of second backward differences.

x_i	1	2	3	4	5	6	7	8
y_i	1.733	1.822	1.916	2.100	2.117	2.226	2.340	2.460

2.17 Given evenly spaced pivotal points y_i, y_{i+1}, y_{i+2}, . . . , determine approximate expressions for: .(a) y_i'''; (b) y_i^{IV}; (c) y_i^{V} with errors of order h, by means of:

(1) Forward difference expansions.
(2) Interpolating parabolas passing through 4, 5, and 6 points, respectively, to the right of i.
(3) Taylor series expansions.

Obtain, where possible, the first term of the error series.

Ans.   (a) $y_i''' = \dfrac{1}{h^3}(y_{i+3} - 3y_{i+2} + 3y_{i+1} - y_i)$.

(b) $y_i^{IV} = \dfrac{1}{h^4}(y_{i+4} - 4y_{i+3} + 6y_{i+2} - 4y_{i+1} + y_i)$.

(c) $y_i^{V} = \dfrac{1}{h^5}(y_{i+5} - 5y_{i+4} + 10y_{i+3} - 10y_{i+2} + 5y_{i+1} - y_i)$.

2.18   Determine approximate expressions for the following derivatives using two terms of their forward difference expansions. Determine the first term of the error series in each case.

(a) y'_i.   (b) y_i''.   (c) y_i'''.   (d) y_i^{IV}.

Ans.   (b) $y_i'' = \dfrac{1}{h^2}(2y_i - 5y_{i+1} + 4y_{i+2} - y_{i+3})$; $e \doteq \tfrac{11}{12}h^2 y_i^{IV}$.   (d) y_i^{IV}

$= \dfrac{1}{h^4}(3y_i - 14y_{i+1} + 26y_{i+2} - 24y_{i+3} + 11y_{i+4} - 2y_{i+5})$; $e \doteq \tfrac{34}{12}h^2 y_i^{VI}$.

2.19   Derive by direct substitution of difference expansions in the Taylor series (a) of Sec. 2.6, (a) the forward, and (b) the backward Gregory-Newton interpolation formulas.

2.20   Given $\tan x$ for $x = 23°(1°)28°$, evaluate by means of the Gregory-Newton forward and backward interpolation formulas, to five significant figures:

(a) $\tan 23°15'$.   (b) $\tan 27°13'$.

Ans.   (a) Forward, $\tan 23°15' = 0.42963$.   (b) Backward, $\tan 27°13' = 0.51433$.   *Note:* The symbol $x = a(h)b$ stands for the values of x from a to b in steps of h.

2.21   Evaluate from the following table:

(a) $f(3.8)$ to three significant figures, using the Gregory-Newton backward interpolation formula.

(b) $f(1.2)$ to three significant figures, using the Gregory-Newton forward interpolation formula.

(c) $f(5.12)$ to three significant figures, using the Gregory-Newton forward interpolation formula.

x_i	0	1	2	3	4
$f(x_i)$	1.00	1.50	2.20	3.10	4.60

Ans.   (b) 1.63.

2.22   Given $\sin x$ for $x = 5°(5°)30°$, evaluate to five significant figures by interpolation:

(a) $\sin 5°14'$.   (b) $\sin 25°25'$.   (c) $\sin 17°30'$.

Ans.   (b) 0.42917.

2.23   Given x^3 for $x = 1(1)5$, find by interpolation, the cubes of:

(a) 4.37.   (b) 1.35.   (c) 3.46.

Ans.   (a) $(4.37)^3 = 83.45$ (backward).   (c) $(3.46)^3 = 41.42$ (backward and forward).

2.24   Given evenly spaced pivotal values . . . , $y_{ll}, y_l, y_i, y_r, y_{rr},$ . . . , determine approximate expressions for: (a) y_i''; (b) y_i'''; (c) y_i^{IV}; (d) y_i^{V} with errors of order h^2, by means of:

(1) Central difference expansions, expressing derivatives in both averaged and unaveraged forms.

(2) Interpolating parabolas passing through pivotal points symmetrically located with respect to i.

(3) Taylor series expansions.

Obtain, where possible, the first term of the error series.

Ans.   See Fig. 2.8a.

2.25   Determine approximate expressions for the following derivatives using two terms of their central difference expansions:

(a) y'_i.   (b) y_i''.   (c) y_i'''.   (d) y_i^{IV}.

Ans.   See Fig. 2.8b.

2.26   Form tables of backward, forward, and central differences for the following functions:

(a) $\tan x$; $x = 1°(1°)6°$.   (b) $\cosh x$; $x = 0.1(0.1)0.7$.
(c) e^x; $x = 0(0.5)3.0$.   (d) $J_0(x)$; $x = 0(0.1)1.0$.
(e) $x^3 - 4x^2 + 5x + 3$; $x = 0(1)4$.   (f) $\log \sin x$; $x = 5°(5°)25°$.
(g) e^{-x}; $x = 0(0.5)3.0$.   (h) $\tanh x$; $x = 0.1(0.1)0.7$.

2.27   Obtain the following derivatives of the Bessel function $J_0(x)$ at the indicated points, with errors of the indicated order, using one term of their backward, central, or forward difference expansions.

x	0.0	0.1	0.2	0.3	0.4
$J_0(x)$	1.0000	0.9975	0.9900	0.9776	0.9604

(a) $\dfrac{dJ_0}{dx}\bigg]_{x=0.1}$; $e = 0(h^2)$.   (b) $\dfrac{d^2J_0}{dx^2}\bigg]_{x=0.1}$; $e = 0(h)$.

(c) $\dfrac{d^2J_0}{dx^2}\bigg]_{x=0.1}$; $e = 0(h^2)$.   (d) $\dfrac{d^4J_0}{dx^4}\bigg]_{x=0.2}$; $e = 0(h^2)$.

(e) $\dfrac{d^3J_0}{dx^3}\bigg]_{x=0}$; $e = 0(h)$.   (f) $\dfrac{d^2J_0}{dx^2}\bigg]_{x=0.4}$; $e = 0(h)$.

(g) $\dfrac{dJ_0}{dx}\bigg]_{x=0.4}$; $e = 0(h)$.

Ans.   (a) -0.0500.   (c) -0.5000.   (e) 0.1000.   (g) -0.1720.

2.28   Obtain the following derivatives of the Bessel function $Y_1(x)$ at the indicated points, with errors of the indicated order, using the first term of their backward, forward, or central difference expansions.

x	6.0	6.1	6.2	6.3	6.4
$Y_1(x)$	0.1750	-0.1998	-0.2223	-0.2422	-0.2596

(a) $\dfrac{d^4Y_1}{dx^4}\bigg]_{x=6.2}$; $e = 0(h^2)$.   (b) $\dfrac{dY_1}{dx}\bigg]_{x=6.0}$; $e = 0(h)$.

(c) $\dfrac{d^3Y_1}{dx^3}\bigg]_{x=6.3}$; $e = 0(h)$.   (d) $\dfrac{d^2Y_1}{dx^2}\bigg]_{x=6.3}$; $e = 0(h^2)$.

(e) $\dfrac{dY_1}{dx}\bigg]_{x=6.4}$; $e = 0(h)$.

Ans.   (b) -0.2480.   (d) 0.2500.

2.29   Locate the incorrect value of e^{-x} in the following table and correct it by linear interpolation of second differences.   Use:

(a) Forward differences.
(b) Backward differences.
(c) Central differences.

x	0	0.1	0.2	0.3	0.4	0.5	0.6	0.7
e^{-x}	1.000	0.905	0.819	0.741	0.640	0.607	0.549	0.497

Ans. $e^{-0.4} = 0.671$.

2.30   Given the following table, evaluate approximate expressions for the given derivatives at the indicated points.   Use formulas for unevenly spaced pivotal points.

x	0.0	1.2	2.4	3.9
y	3.41	2.68	1.37	-1.48

(a) $y'\big]_{x=2.4}$; $e = 0(h)$.   (b) $y'\big]_{x=2.4}$; $e = 0(h^2)$.

(c) $y'\big]_{x=1.2}$; $e = 0(h^2)$.   (d) $y''\big]_{x=2.4}$; $e = 0(h)$.

(e) $y''\big]_{x=2.4}$; $e = 0(h^2)$.

Ans. (b) -1.451.   (d) -0.5988.

2.31 Evaluate the given derivatives at the indicated points with errors of the indicated order. Use formulas for unevenly spaced pivotal points.

x	0.0	0.1	0.2	0.4
$J_0(x)$	1.0000	0.9975	0.9900	0.9604

(a) $\dfrac{dJ_0}{dx}\Big]_{x=0.2}$; $e = 0(h^2)$.   (b) $\dfrac{dJ_0}{dx}\Big]_{x=0.2}$; $e = 0(h)$.

(c) $\dfrac{d^2J_0}{dx^2}\Big]_{x=0.2}$; $e = 0(h^2)$.   (d) $\dfrac{d^2J_0}{dx^2}\Big]_{x=0.2}$; $e = 0(h)$.

(e) $\dfrac{d^2J_0}{dx^2}\Big]_{x=0.1}$; $e = 0(h^2)$.

Ans. (a) -0.0993.   (c) -0.4900.   (e) -0.5000.

2.32 Assuming that the error series of a formula of order h^4 may be stopped after the second term:

$$e \doteq c_2 h^4 + c_3 h^6,$$

derive the expressions for the coefficients of the so-called (h^4, h^6)-extrapolation formula, and compute the values of these coefficients for values of h inversely proportional to (a) 3, 2, 1; (b) 4, 3, 2; (c) 5, 4, 3.

Ans. $K_{ijk} = \dfrac{n_k{}^6(n_j{}^2 - n_i{}^2)k_k - n_j{}^6(n_k{}^2 - n_i{}^2)k_j + n_i{}^6(n_k{}^2 - n_j{}^2)k_i}{n_k{}^6(n_j{}^2 - n_i{}^2) - n_j{}^6(n_k{}^2 - n_i{}^2) + n_i{}^6(n_k{}^2 - n_j{}^2)}$.

(a) 1.301786; 0.304762; 0.002976.   (b) 1.681445; 0.718227; 0.036782.
(c) 2.170139; 1.300317; 0.130179.

2.33 Evaluate the second derivative of $J_0(x)$ at (a) $x = 0.2$, and (b) $x = 0.5$ by central differences with error of order h^2, using the table of Problem 2.26(d), with $h = 0.2$ and $h = 0.1$. Extrapolate and compare with the value obtained by the central difference formula with error of order h^4 and $h = 0.1$.

Ans.   (b) $h = 0.2$; $J_0''(0.5) = -0.4550$. $h = 0.1$; $J_0''(0.5) = -0.4600$.
$J_0''(0.5) \Big]_{0.1, 0.2} = -0.4617$.

2.34

(a) Evaluate the second derivative of $\sin x$ at $x = \pi/4$ by central difference expansions, with error of order: (1) h^2, and (2) h^4, taking $h = \pi/4$, $\pi/8$, and $\pi/16$. Extrapolate and compare with the true value.

(b) Evaluate the first derivative of $\sin x$ at $x = \pi/4$ using expressions with errors as above and $h = \pi/8$ and $\pi/16$.

Ans.   (a) $e = 0(h^2)$; $h = \pi/4$; $y'' = -0.67151$
$\qquad\qquad\qquad h = \pi/8$; $y'' = -0.69813$
$\qquad\qquad\qquad h = \pi/16$; $y'' = -0.70500$
$\qquad\quad e = 0(h^4)$; $h = \pi/8$; $y'' = -0.70702$
$\qquad\qquad\qquad h = \pi/16$; $y'' = -0.70729$.
$\qquad$ (b) $e = 0(h^2)$; $h = \pi/4$ $y' = 0.63662$
$\qquad\qquad\qquad h = \pi/8$ $y' = 0.68908$
$\qquad\qquad\qquad h = \pi/16$ $y' = 0.70257$
$\qquad\quad e = 0(h^4)$; $h = \pi/8$ $y' = 0.70656$
$\qquad\qquad\qquad h = \pi/16$ $y' = 0.70707$.

2.35   Evaluate the following integrals by the trapezoidal rule for the indicated values of n, and extrapolate.

(a) $\displaystyle\int_0^\pi \sin^3 x \, dx$ $\qquad$ $(n = 2,4,6)$.

(b) $\displaystyle\int_0^2 \sqrt{4x - x^2} \, dx$ $\qquad$ $(n = 2,4)$.

(c) $\displaystyle\int_0^2 e^{-x^2} \, dx$ $\qquad$ $(n = 2,4)$.

Ans.   (a) $n = 2$; 1.571. $n = 4$; 1.342. $n = 6$; 1.335. $n = 2, 4$; 1.266.
$n = 4, 6$; 1.330.   True $= 1.333$.   (c) $n = 2$; 0.877. $n = 4$; 0.881.
$n = 2, 4$; 0.8823.   True $= 0.8821$.

2.36   Evaluate the following integrals by Simpson's rule for the indicated values of n, and extrapolate.

(a) $\displaystyle\int_0^2 \sqrt{4x - x^2} \, dx$ $(n = 2,4)$.   (b) $\displaystyle\int_2^6 x\sqrt{3 + 4x} \, dx$ $(n = 2,4)$.

(c) $\displaystyle\int_0^4 \sqrt{16 - x^2} \, dx$ $(n = 2,4)$.   (d) $\displaystyle\int_1^3 x^2 \sinh x \, dx$ $(n = 2,4)$.

(e) $\displaystyle\int_1^5 \frac{dx}{x}$ $(n = 2,4,6)$.   (f) $\displaystyle\int_0^\pi \sin^3 x \, dx$ $(n = 2,4,6)$.

(g) $\displaystyle\int_0^4 \frac{dx}{\sqrt{25 + x^2}}$ $(n = 2,4)$.   (h) $\displaystyle\int_0^4 \frac{dx}{(25 - x^2)^{3/2}}$ $(n = 2,4)$.

Ans. (b) $A_2 = 71.702$
$A_4 = 71.691$
$A_{2,4} = 71.690$
$A = 71.693.$

(f) $A_2 = 2.094$
$A_4 = 1.268$
$A_6 = 1.330$
$A_{2,6} = 1.3205.*$
$A = 1.333.$

(d) $A_2 = 49.796$
$A_4 = 48.464$
$A_{2,4} = 48.375$
$A = 48.371.$

(h) $A_2 = 0.0577$
$A_4 = 0.0541$
$A_{2,4} = 0.0538.$
$A = 0.05333.$

2.37 Evaluate the following integrals, using the trapezoidal rule, for $n = 2$ and $n = 4$ subintervals and extrapolate.

(a) $\int_0^{\pi/2} \cos x \, dx.$

(b) $\int_3^7 x^2 \log x \, dx.$

(c) $\int_1^{11} \sqrt{1 + x^2} \, dx.$

(d) $\int_0^{0.8} \cosh x^2 \, dx.$

(e) $\int_3^7 \log x \, dx.$

(f) $\int_4^8 \frac{dx}{\sqrt{16x - x^2}}.$

(g) $\int_1^5 \frac{dx}{\sqrt{x}}.$

(h) $\int_0^4 \frac{dx}{\sqrt{25 - x^2}}.$

(i) $4 \int_0^1 \frac{dx}{1 + x^2}.$

Ans. (b) $A_2 = 185.7090; A_4 = 179.5385; A_{2,4} = 177.4819;$
$A = 177.4836.$
(d) $A_2 = 0.848; A_4 = 0.837; A_{2,4} = 0.834.$
(f) $A_2 = 0.5275; A_4 = 0.5244; A_{2,4} = 0.5234; A = 0.5236.$
(h) $A_2 = 0.9695; A_4 = 0.9389; A_{2,4} = 0.9286; A = 0.9267.$

2.38 Evaluate the integrals of Problem 2.37 by Simpson's rule and extrapolation for $n = 2$ and $n = 4$ subintervals.

Ans. (b) $A_2 = 177.454; A_4 = 177.481; A_{2,4} = 177.483.$
(d) $A_2 = 0.835; A_4 = 0.834; A_{2,4} = 0.834.$
(f) $A_2 = 0.5238; A_4 = 0.5234; A_{2,4} = 0.5234.$
(h) $A_2 = 0.9372; A_4 = 0.9286; A_{2,4} = 0.9280.$
(i) $A_2 = 3.1333; A_4 = 3.1413; A_{2,4} = 3.1419; A = \pi.$

*The h^2 and the h^4 extrapolations can be applied only to a monotonic sequence of values.

The Numerical Integration of Initial Value Problems

3.1 Introduction

Consider an nth order differential equation

$$y^{(n)}(x) = f(x,y,y', \ldots, y^{(n-1)}) \qquad (3.1.1)$$

with the n initial conditions

$$y(0) = y_0, \; y'(0) = y'_0, \; \ldots, \; y^{(n-1)}(0) = y_0^{(n-1)}. \qquad (3.1.2)$$

The numerical solution of this initial value problem consists in the evaluation of the integral $y(x)$ at pivotal points of its interval of definition, evenly spaced by h units. These values are obtained step by step, starting at the initial point, which is usually taken to be the origin, as indicated by Eq. (3.1.2).

The evaluation of y at the pivotal point $x_i = ih$ (i = integer) is performed by recurrence equations as soon as y is known at a certain number of preceding pivotal points $x_{i-1}, x_{i-2}, x_{i-3}, \ldots$ In order to apply these equations, it is therefore necessary to evaluate accurately $y(x)$ at the first few (1 to 4) pivotal points; this is usually done by a Taylor expansion of $y(x)$.

3.2 Starting the Solution of First-Order Equations

The starting of the solution of differential equations by Taylor series will be illustrated first by its application to a simple first-order *linear* equation with variable coefficients.

If we assume: (1) atmospheric pressure to be independent of temperature; (2) air to behave like an ideal gas; (3) gravitational attraction to follow Newton's inverse square law, it may be proved*

---

* See, for example, *Differential Equations*, Sec. 2.1.

that the atmospheric pressure p at a distance x from the center of the earth (Fig. 3.1), satisfies the differential equation

$$\frac{dp}{dx} + \frac{K}{x^2}\, p = 0,\qquad(3.2.1)$$

while its value on the surface of the earth may be taken to be

$$p(R) = p_0 = 2116 \text{ psf.}\qquad(3.2.2)$$

In these equations R is the radius of the earth in feet and $K = kM/cg$, (k = gravitational constant, M = mass of the earth,

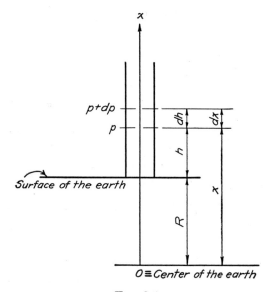

FIG. 3.1

c = thermodynamic constant, g = gravitational acceleration) is a constant having the dimensions of a length.

Whenever a differential equation is integrated numerically, it is convenient and useful to reduce it to *nondimensional form*. For this purpose, indicating the altitude by h, let:

$$z = \frac{h}{R};\qquad \therefore x = R + h = R(1+z);\quad dx = R\,dz$$

and

$$p(x) = p(R(1+z)) = p_0 y(z)\qquad(3.2.3)$$

and substitute in Eq. (3.2.1), obtaining:

$$\frac{dy}{dz} + \frac{K}{R} \frac{1}{(1+z)^2} y = 0.$$

Noting that $z \ll 1$, and therefore neglecting the square of z with respect to z, this equation reduces to

$$\frac{dy}{dz} = -\frac{K}{R} \frac{1}{1+2z} y.$$

By means of the values of k, M, c, and g in any consistent system of units, it is found that the value of the nondimensional ratio K/R equals 0.9, and hence that the equation in y becomes:

$$y' = -\frac{0.9}{1+2z} y, \tag{3.2.4}$$

while the initial condition reduces, by Eqs. (3.2.2) and (3.2.3) to:

$$y(0) = y_0 = 1. \tag{3.2.5}$$

To integrate the initial value problem (3.2.4), (3.2.5) by series, the values of the successive derivatives of $y(z)$ at the origin are obtained by differentiation from Eq. (3.2.4), using Eq. (3.2.5):

$$y'(0) = -0.9[(1+2z)^{-1}y]_{z=0} = -0.9,$$

$$y''(0) = -0.9[(1+2z)^{-1}y' - 2(1+2z)^{-2}y]_{z=0},$$

$$= -0.9(y'_0 - 2y_0) = +2.610,$$

$$y'''(0) = -0.9[(1+2z)^{-1}y'' - 4(1+2z)^{-2}y' + 8(1+2z)^{-3}y]_{z=0}$$

$$= -0.9(y_0'' - 4y'_0 + 8y_0) = -12.79.$$

$$y^{IV}(0) = -0.9[(1+2z)^{-1}y''' - 6(1+2z)^{-2}y'' + 24(1+2z)^{-3}y'$$
$$- 48(1+2z)^{-4}y]_{z=0}$$

$$= -0.9(y_0''' - 6y_0'' + 24y'_0 - 48y_0) = +88.24.$$

The first five terms of the Taylor expansion $y_T(z)$ of $y(z)$ about $z = 0$ thus become:

$$y_T(z) = y_0 + \frac{y'_0}{1!} z + \frac{y_0''}{2!} z^2 + \frac{y_0'''}{3!} z^3 + \frac{y_0^{IV}}{4!} z^4$$

$$= 1 - 0.9z + 1.305z^2 - 2.132z^3 + 3.677z^4.$$

Table 3.1 gives the values of $y_T(z)$ for $z = 0(0.02)0.10$ and for $z = 0.20$ and 0.30, together with the corresponding values of $y(z)$

Table 3.1

z	$y_T(z)$	$y(z)$
0	1.0000	1.0000
0.02	0.9825	0.9825
0.04	0.9660	0.9660
0.06	0.9503	0.9503
0.08	0.9354	0.9354
0.10	0.9213	0.9212
0.20	0.8610	0.8595
0.30	0.8197	0.8094

obtained by integrating Eq. (3.2.4) by separation of the variables:*

$$\frac{dy}{y} = -0.9 \frac{dz}{1 + 2z},$$

$$\int_{y_0}^{y} \frac{dy}{y} = \ln \frac{y}{y_0} = -0.9 \int_0^z \frac{dz}{1 + 2z} = -0.45 \ln (1 + 2z).$$

$$y(z) = (1 + 2z)^{-0.45}.$$

The value $y_T(0.3)$ is in error by -1.27 per cent.

To illustrate the integration by Taylor series of a *nonlinear* first-order equation, consider the electric circuit of Fig. 3.2.   The circuit

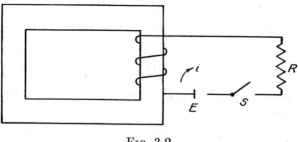

Fig. 3.2

* See, for example, *Differential Equations*, Sec. 4.2.

contains a coil with an iron core whose magnetization curve is given by

$$Ni = 0.6\varphi + 0.0033\varphi^3, \tag{a}$$

where φ is the flux in the core (in kilolines), N the number of turns of the coil, and i the current (in amperes) setting up the flux.

Kirchhoff's voltage law applied to the circuit gives:*

$$E = Ri + L\frac{di}{dt} = Ri + N\frac{d\varphi}{dt},$$

where φ is in webers (10^5 kilolines) and t is in seconds, or, by means of Eq. (a),

$$E = \frac{R}{N}(0.6\varphi + 0.0033\varphi^3) + N\frac{d\varphi}{dt} \cdot 10^{-5},$$

where φ is now expressed in kilolines. Hence with $E = 18$ volts, $N = 100$, $R = 3000$ ohms, and t in milliseconds, the flux is governed by the *nonlinear*, first-order equation:

$$\frac{d\varphi}{dt} + 1.8\varphi + 0.01\varphi^3 = 18. \tag{3.2.6}$$

If the switch S is closed at $t = 0$, the initial condition requires that

$$\varphi(0) = 0. \tag{3.2.7}$$

The flux φ approaches asymptotically its maximum value φ_m as t increases; hence φ_m is defined by the condition $d\varphi/dt = 0$ and, by Eq. (3.2.6), is a root of the cubic equation:

$$0.01\varphi^3 + 1.8\varphi - 18 = 0.$$

The only real root of this equation equals 7.5802; hence $\varphi_m = 7.5802$.

To reduce Eq. (3.2.6) to nondimensional form, we set in this equation,

$$\varphi(t) = \varphi_m y(t) \tag{3.2.8}$$

and obtain the equation for the nondimensional function $y(t)$:

$$\varphi_m \dot{y} = 18 - 1.8\varphi_m y - 0.01\varphi_m^3 y^3,$$

* See, for example, *Differential Equations*, Sec. 1.7.

where $\dot{y}$ stands for dy/dt. With $\varphi_m = 7.5802$ this equation becomes, finally,

$$\dot{y} = 2.3746 - 1.8y - 0.5746y^3, \qquad (3.2.9)$$

while the initial condition (3.2.7) requires that

$$y(0) = 0. \qquad (3.2.10)$$

To start the solution of the initial value problem (3.2.9), (3.2.10) by series, we differentiate Eq. (3.2.9) successively, obtaining:

$$\dot{y}_0 = 2.3746$$

$$\ddot{y}_0 = -1.8\dot{y}_0 - 0.5746 \cdot 3y_0^2\dot{y}_0 = -4.2743$$

$$\dddot{y}_0 = (-1.8 - 0.5746 \cdot 3y_0^2)\ddot{y}_0 - 0.5746 \cdot 6y_0\dot{y}_0^2 = 7.6937$$

$$y_0^{IV} = (-1.8 - 0.5746 \cdot 3y_0^2)\dddot{y}_0 - 0.5746 \cdot 6(3y_0\ddot{y}_0 + \dot{y}_0^2)\dot{y}_0$$
$$= -60.011$$

$$y_0^V = (-1.8 - 0.5746 \cdot 3y_0^2)y_0^{IV} - 0.5746 \cdot 6(4y_0\dot{y}_0\dddot{y}_0$$
$$+ 3y_0\ddot{y}_0^2 + 6\dot{y}_0^2\ddot{y}_0)$$

$$= 606.58.$$

With these values of the derivatives at zero the Taylor series for $y(t)$ becomes:

$$y(t) = 2.3746t - 2.1372t^2 + 1.2823t^3 - 2.5005t^4 + 5.0548t^5$$

and gives the values of Table 3.2 for $t = 0(0.05)0.20$ and $t = 0.30$. The third column of Table 3.2 contains the approximate values

Table 3.2

t	$y(t)$	$y_L(t)$
0	0	0
0.05	0.1135	0.1136
0.10	0.2172	0.2173
0.15	0.3116	0.3121
0.20	0.3973	0.3988
0.30	0.5476	0.5505

$y_L(t)$ of $y(t)$ obtained by linearizing Eq. (3.2.9), that is, by dropping the cubic term $-0.5746y^3$, in which case the solution reduces to:

$$y_L(t) = 1.3192(1 - e^{-1.8t}). \tag{b}$$

All problems involving a first-order differential equation with an initial condition, which is necessarily a condition on y, may be solved by the procedure illustrated in this section. The number of terms to be used in the Taylor series depends in each case on the type of problem and on the accuracy required.

3.3   Starting The Solution of Higher-Order Equations

The oscillations in a vacuum of a mathematical pendulum released from rest at $t = 0$ from an angle θ_0 satisfy the well-known nonlinear differential equation:*

$$\frac{d^2\theta}{dt^2} + \frac{g}{L} \sin \theta = 0 \tag{3.3.1}$$

and the initial conditions

$$\theta(0) = \theta_0, \qquad \dot{\theta}(0) = 0, \tag{3.3.2}$$

where θ is the angle between the pendulum and the vertical, t the time, g the acceleration of gravity, and L the length of the pendulum (Fig. 3.3).

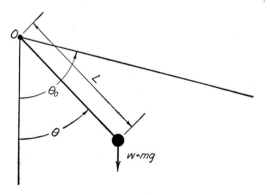

FIG. 3.3

* See, for example, *Differential Equations*, Sec. 2.7.

A rigorous solution of the initial value problem (3.3.1), (3.3.2), may be obtained in terms of nonelementary functions called *elliptic integrals** and shows that the period of oscillation of the pendulum is given by:

$$T = 4K \left(\frac{\theta_0}{2} \right) \sqrt{\frac{L}{g}}, \tag{a}$$

where K is the *complete elliptic integral of the first kind* and is tabulated, for example, in Peirce's *A Short Table of Integrals*. For $\theta_0 = 120°$, $K(\theta_0/2) = 2.1565$, and, with $g = 32.2$ ft/sec^2, $L = 3.22$ ft, the pendulum period equals $T = 2.7276$ sec.

To solve the same problem by numerical methods, the solution is started in nondimensional form, by setting

$$t = \frac{T}{4} \tau, \qquad \therefore \quad dt = \frac{T}{4} d\tau$$

$$(dt)^2 = \left(\frac{T}{4} \right)^2 (d\tau)^2 = (0.6819)^2 (d\tau)^2 = 0.46499 d\tau^2. \tag{b}$$

Equation (3.3.1), with $g/L = 10$ sec^{-2}, then becomes:

$$\frac{d^2\theta}{d\tau^2} \equiv \ddot{\theta} = -4.6499 \sin \theta, \tag{3.3.3}$$

while the initial conditions require that:

$$\theta(0) = \theta_0 = 120° = 2.0944 \text{ radians},$$
$$\dot{\theta}(0) = \dot{\theta}_0 = 0, \tag{3.3.4}$$

where dots indicate differentiation with respect to τ. From Eq. (3.3.3) and its derivatives, we obtain

$$\ddot{\theta}_0 = -4.6499 \sin \theta_0 = -4.0268$$

$$\dddot{\theta}_0 = -4.6499 \cos \theta_0 \cdot \dot{\theta}_0 = 0$$

$$\theta_0^{IV} = -4.6499 (\cos \theta_0 \cdot \ddot{\theta}_0 - \sin \theta_0 \cdot \dot{\theta}_0^2) = -9.3623,$$

and hence the Taylor series:

$$\theta(\tau) \doteq 2.0944 - 2.0134\tau^2 - 0.3901\tau^4. \tag{3.3.5}$$

* See, for example, *Differential Equations*, Secs. 9.3 and 9.4.

Table 3.3 gives the values of θ derived from this series for $\tau = 0(0.1)$ 0.4.

Table 3.3

$\tau = t/0.6819$	θ	θ_L
0	2.0944	2.0944
0.1	2.0742	2.0458
0.2	2.0132	1.9026
0.3	1.9100	1.6713
0.4	1.7623	1.3624

The linearized equation, valid for values of the angle θ small enough to have sine $\theta \doteq \theta$, is

$$\ddot\theta = -4.6499\theta$$

and yields the solution:

$$\theta_L = 2.0944 \cos 2.1564\tau. \tag{c}$$

The values of θ_L are given, for comparison, in the third column of Table 3.3.

The solution of the same problem when the pendulum oscillates in a viscous medium, which cannot be obtained by elliptic integrals, involves no increased difficulties when a Taylor series is used.

The differential equation of the pendulum in a viscous medium contains an additional damping term, $\mu\, d\theta/dt$, where μ is the frictional resistance per unit mass. With $\mu = 0.5875$ sec^{-1}, for example, and $g/L = 10$ sec^{-2} as before, Eq. (3.3.1) is transformed* into the equation:

$$\frac{d^2\theta}{dt^2} + 0.5875 \frac{d\theta}{dt} + 10 \sin \theta = 0. \tag{3.3.6}$$

If we again let $t = (T/4)\tau = 0.6819\tau$ (where T is the period of the undamped pendulum), this equation takes the form:

$$\ddot\theta + 0.4\dot\theta + 4.6499 \sin \theta = 0 \tag{3.3.7}$$

---

* See, for example, *Differential Equations*, Sec. 2.7.

(where dots indicate differentiation with respect to τ), while the initial conditions remain those of Eqs. (3.3.4). By means of Eq. (3.3.7) and its successive derivatives:

$$\ddot{\theta}_0 = -0.4\dot{\theta}_0 - 4.6499 \sin \theta_0 = -4.0268$$

$$\dddot{\theta}_0 = -0.4\ddot{\theta}_0 - 4.6499 \cos \theta_0 \cdot \dot{\theta}_0 = 1.6107$$

$$\theta_0^{IV} = -0.4\dddot{\theta}_0 - 4.6499 \cos \theta_0 \cdot \ddot{\theta}_0 + 4.6499 \sin \theta_0 \cdot \dot{\theta}_0^2$$
$$= -10.006,$$

we obtain, as before, the Taylor series solution:

$$\theta(\tau) = 2.0944 - 2.0134\tau^2 + 0.2685\tau^3 - 0.4169\tau^4, \quad (3.3.8)$$

which is tabulated in Table 3.4 for $\tau = 0(0.1)0.4$.

Table 3.4

τ	θ	θ_L	$\dot{\theta}$
0	2.0944	2.0944	0
0.1	2.0745	2.0465	−0.3963
0.2	2.0153	1.9076	−0.7865
0.3	1.9171	1.6875	−1.1806
0.4	1.7788	1.3994	−1.5886

The solution of the corresponding linearized equation

$$\ddot{\theta} + 0.4\dot{\theta} + 4.6499\theta = 0$$

(whose characteristic roots are $-0.2 \pm 2.1471i$) equals

$$\theta_L(\tau) = e^{-0.2\tau}(2.0944 \cos 2.1471\tau + 0.1951 \sin 2.1471\tau) \quad (d)$$

and is tabulated for comparison in the third column of Table 3.4.

The fourth column of this table contains the values of $\dot{\theta}$ evaluated by differentiating Eq. (3.3.8):

$$\dot{\theta} = -4.0268\tau + 0.8054\tau^2 - 1.6677\tau^3,$$

which will be used in a later section.

The methods used in this section on second-order differential equations can be extended to equations of any order, and are of

practical value in determining the solution in the neighborhood of
the origin (or initial point). As the distance from the origin
increases, the accuracy of the Taylor solution decreases, and a
larger number of terms of the series must be taken into account
for a given accuracy. Since this may become quite laborious, it is
more practical to prolong the solution by other methods, some of
which are illustrated in the following sections.

3.4 Adams's Method

Once the solution of a first-order differential equation

$$y' = f(x,y), \tag{3.4.1}$$

satisfying the initial condition

$$y(0) = y_0, \tag{3.4.2}$$

has been started by a Taylor series as shown in Sec. 3.2, the solution
may be extrapolated to other pivotal points by a formula due to
Adams, involving the backward differences of the function f in the
right-hand member of Eq. (3.4.1).

To obtain Adams's formula, consider the Taylor expansion
of $y(x + h)$ about x:

$$y(x + h) = y(x) + hy'(x) + \frac{h^2}{2} y''(x) + \frac{h^3}{6} y'''(x)$$

$$+ \frac{h^4}{24} y^{IV}(x) + \frac{h^5}{120} y^{V}(x) + \frac{h^6}{720} y^{VI}(x) + \cdots$$

and substitute in it for $y^{(n)}$ its value $\dfrac{d^{n-1}f}{dx^{n-1}} = f^{(n-1)}(x,y)$ given by

Eq. (3.4.1):

$$y(x + h) = y(x) + h\left[f(x,y) + \frac{h}{2} f'(x,y) + \frac{h^2}{6} f''(x,y) \right.$$

$$\left. + \frac{h^3}{24} f'''(x,y) + \frac{h^4}{120} f^{IV}(x,y) + \frac{h^5}{720} f^{V}(x,y) + \cdots \right].$$

Substituting in this equation for the successive total derivatives of
$f(x,y)$ with respect to x, the backward difference expansions of
Sec. 2.4 [Eqs. (2.4.16), (2.4.17)] and letting:

$$x = ih, \quad y(x) = y_i, \quad y(x + h) = y_{i+1}, \quad f(x_i,y_i) = f_i,$$

we obtain:

$$y_{i+1} = y_i + h[f_i + \tfrac{1}{2}(\nabla + \tfrac{1}{2}\nabla^2 + \tfrac{1}{3}\nabla^3 + \tfrac{1}{4}\nabla^4 + \tfrac{1}{5}\nabla^5 + \ldots)f_i$$
$$+ \tfrac{1}{6}(\nabla^2 + \nabla^3 + \tfrac{11}{12}\nabla^4 + \tfrac{5}{6}\nabla^5 + \ldots)f_i$$
$$+ \tfrac{1}{24}(\nabla^3 + \tfrac{3}{2}\nabla^4 + \tfrac{7}{4}\nabla^5 + \ldots)f_i + \tfrac{1}{120}(\nabla^4 + 2\nabla^5 + \ldots)f_i$$
$$+ \tfrac{1}{720}(\nabla^5 + \ldots)f_i + \ldots]$$

or *Adams's recurrence formula:*

$$y_{i+1} = y_i + h[1 + \tfrac{1}{2}\nabla + \tfrac{5}{12}\nabla^2 + \tfrac{3}{8}\nabla^3 + \tfrac{251}{720}\nabla^4$$
$$+ \tfrac{95}{288}\nabla^5 + \ldots]f_i. \quad (3.4.3)$$

The number of terms to be taken into account in the series of Eq. (3.4.3) depends on the number of pivotal values computed by the Taylor series and on the accuracy required in the solution.

Table 3.5

i	t	y_i	y_i^3	f_i	∇f_i	$\nabla^2 f_i$	$\nabla^3 f_i$	y_L
0	0	0	0	2.3746				0
1	0.1	0.2172	0.0103	1.9777	−0.3969			0.2173
2	0.2	0.3973	0.0627	1.6234	−0.3543	0.0426		0.3988
3	0.3	0.5476	0.1642	1.2946	−0.3288	0.0255	−0.0171	0.5505
4	0.4	0.6610	0.2888	1.0189	−0.2757	0.0531	0.0276	0.6770
5	0.5	0.7523	0.4258	0.7758	−0.2431	0.0326	−0.0205	0.7828
6	0.6	0.8183	0.5479	0.5868	−0.1890	0.0541	0.0215	0.8712
7	0.7	0.8706	0.6598	0.4284	−0.1584	0.0306	−0.0235	0.9449
8	0.8	0.9059	0.7435	0.3168	−0.1116	0.0468	0.0162	1.0067
9	0.9	0.9346	0.8164	0.2232	−0.0936	0.0180	−0.0288	1.0581
10	1.0	0.9519						1.1011
	∞	1.0000						1.3192

In Table 3.5 Adams's formula is used to prolong the solution of the nonlinear circuit problem of Sec. 3.2 [Eqs. (3.2.9), (3.2.10)]:

$$\dot{y} = f(y) = 2.3746 - 1.8y - 0.5746y^3. \qquad (a)$$
$$y(0) = 0.$$

The first four rows of Table 3.5 contain: (a) the values of y and y^3 at $t = 0, 0.1, 0.2, 0.3$ obtained from the series solution of Table 3.2; (b) the values of $\dot{y} = f(y)$* given by Eq. (a) at the same points; (c) the values of the first three backward differences of $f(y)$.

Adams's formula, cut after its fourth term and with $h = 0.1$, takes the form:

$$y_{i+1} = y_i + 0.1[f_i + \tfrac{1}{2}\nabla f_i + \tfrac{5}{12}\nabla^2 f_i + \tfrac{3}{8}\nabla^3 f_i], \qquad (b)$$

and allows the determination of y_4 at $t = 0.4$ in terms of y, f, and its differences at $t = 0.3$. Once y_4 is known, f_4 is evaluated by Eq. (a), and its differences are computed by means of Table 3.5. Equation (b) is then used to evaluate y_5, and so on. The pivotal values up to y_{10}, obtained step by step, are shown in Table 3.5.

The column y_L of Table 3.5 contains, for comparison, the values of the linearized solution of the same problem computed from Eq. (c) of Sec. 3.2.

The rigorous solution of Eqs. (a) of this section may be obtained by the method of the separation of the variables,† which gives t as a function of y in the form:

$$t = 0.2838\left[-\ln (1 - y) + \tfrac{1}{2}\ln \frac{y^2 + y + 4.1326}{4.1326} \right.$$
$$\left. + 0.7613\left(\tan^{-1}\frac{2y + 1}{3.9409} - \tan^{-1} 0.2537\right)\right]. \quad (c)$$

By means of this result, we find that for $y = 0.7523$, t equals 0.5040 rather than 0.5 as shown in Table 3.5, and that for $y = 0.9519$, t equals 0.9974 rather than 1.0000. Conversely, interpolating from the values of Table 3.5 by the forward Gregory-Newton interpolation formula [Eq. (2.6.1)], we obtain the results of Table 3.6, in which y_i are the interpolated values, y the true values, and ϵ the per cent errors.

These results not only prove the small discrepancies between the true and the extrapolated values of the solution after ten steps, but show that *in many cases it is actually economical to evaluate the solution of a differential equation by numerical methods even if a rigorous solution is available.* In the present problem, for example, it is

---

* Notice that in the present problem Eq. (3.4.1) takes the simplified form $y' = f(y)$, since the independent variable does not appear in f.

† See, for example, *Differential Equations*, Sec. 4.2b.

certainly simpler to proceed as in Table 3.5 than to derive first the rigorous solution (c) and then to evaluate it numerically; the

Table 3.6

t	0.5040	0.9974
y_i	0.7552	0.9513
y	0.7523	0.9519
$\epsilon(\%)$	0.38	0.06

evaluation of Eq. (c) is burdensome and, moreover, does not give the pivotal values of y.

3.5 The Runge-Fox Method for Linear Equations

A simple and efficient method of step-by-step integration, due to Fox and based upon a classical formula of Runge, allows the integration of first-order linear differential equations *without starting the solution by means of a Taylor expansion.*

Consider the Taylor expansion of $y(x + h)$ about $y(x)$,

$$y(x + h) = y(x) + hy'(x) + \frac{h^2}{2} y''(x) + \frac{h^3}{6} y'''(x)$$

$$+ \frac{h^4}{24} y^{\text{IV}}(x) + \frac{h^5}{120} y^{\text{V}}(x) + \ldots, \quad (3.5.1)$$

and the expansion of $y'(x + h)$ around $y'(x)$,

$$y'(x + h) = y'(x) + hy''(x) + \frac{h^2}{2} y'''(x)$$

$$+ \frac{h^3}{6} y^{\text{IV}}(x) + \frac{h^4}{24} y^{\text{V}}(x) + \ldots. \quad (3.5.2)$$

Multiplication of Eq. (3.5.2) by $\frac{1}{2}h$ and subtraction from Eq. (3.5.1) eliminate the term in $y''(x)$ between these two equations, giving:

$$y(x + h) = y(x) + \frac{h}{2} [y'(x) + y'(x + h)] - \frac{h^3}{12} y'''(x)$$

$$- \frac{h^4}{24} y^{\text{IV}}(x) - \frac{h^5}{80} y^{\text{V}}(x) - \ldots$$

or, with $x = ih$, $y(x) = y(ih) = y_i$, the *Runge-Kutta second-order formula:*

$$y_{i+1} = y_i + \frac{h}{2}[y'_i + y'_{i+1}] + \epsilon_{i+1}, \qquad (3.5.3)$$

where:

$$\epsilon_{i+1} = -\left(\tfrac{1}{12}h^3 y_i''' + \tfrac{1}{24}h^4 y_i^{IV} + \tfrac{1}{80}h^5 y_i^{V} + \ldots\right). \qquad (a)$$

The error ϵ_{i+1} of Eq. (a) may be expressed in terms of *unaveraged* central differences in the form*

* For this purpose, note that the unaveraged central difference of odd order $2n + 1$ at $i + \frac{1}{2}$ may also be written as the forward difference of the central difference of order $2n$ at i, since

$$\delta^{2n+1}y_{i+\frac{1}{2}} = \Delta(\delta^{2n}y_i). \qquad (b)$$

For example,

$$\delta^3 y_{i+\frac{1}{2}} = \delta(\delta^2 y_{i+\frac{1}{2}}) = \delta^2 y_{i+1} - \delta^2 y_i = \Delta(\delta^2 y_i).$$

By means of the symbolical expressions for the forward and central unaveraged differences [Eqs. (2.5.2) and (2.7.11)]:

$$\Delta = (e^{hD} - 1)$$

$$\delta^{2n} = 2^{2n} \sinh^{2n}\left(\frac{hD}{2}\right),$$

the left-hand member of Eq. (b) becomes:

$$\delta^{2n+1}y_{i+\frac{1}{2}} = 2^{2n}(e^{hD} - 1)\sinh^{2n}\left(\frac{hD}{2}\right)y_i.$$

Substitution of these expressions in Eq. (3.5.4) reduces this equation to Eq. (a). For example,

$$\delta^3 y_{i+\frac{1}{2}} = \left[2^2(e^{hD} - 1)\sinh^2\left(\frac{hD}{2}\right)\right]y_i$$

$$= 2^2\left[hD + \frac{h^2 D^2}{2!} + \frac{h^3 D^3}{3!} + \ldots\right]\left[\frac{h^2 D^2}{4} + \frac{h^4 D^4}{48} + \ldots\right]y_i$$

$$= \left[h^3 D^3 + \frac{h^4 D^4}{2} + \frac{h^5 D^5}{4} + \ldots\right]y_i,$$

$$\delta^5 y_{i+\frac{1}{2}} = \left[h^5 D^5 + \frac{h^6 D^6}{2} + \ldots\right]y_i,$$

by means of which Eq. (3.5.4) gives

$$\epsilon_{i+1} = -\left[\tfrac{1}{12}\left(h^3 D^3 + \frac{h^4 D^4}{2} + \frac{h^5 D^5}{4} + \ldots\right)\right.$$

$$\left. - \tfrac{1}{120}(h^5 D^5 + \ldots) + \ldots\right]y_i$$

$$= -\left(\tfrac{1}{12}h^3 D^3 + \tfrac{1}{24}h^4 D^4 + \tfrac{1}{80}h^5 D^5 + \ldots\right)y_i,$$

which is identical with Eq. (a).

$$\epsilon^{(n)}{}_{i+1} = -(\tfrac{1}{12}\delta^3 - \tfrac{1}{120}\delta^5 + \tfrac{1}{840}\delta^7 - \ldots)y^{(n)}{}_{i+\frac12}{}^* \quad (3.5.4)$$

and is *Fox's correction* to the *Runge-Kutta second-order formula* [Eq. (3.5.3)].

The Runge-Kutta formula with Fox's correction will now be used to obtain a recurrence formula for the solution of first-order linear differential equations.

Given a first-order *linear* differential equation:

$$y' = f(x)y + g(x) \quad (3.5.5)$$

and the initial condition:

$$y(0) = y_0, \quad (3.5.6)$$

let:

$$x = ih; \quad f(x) = f_i; \quad f(x + h) = f_{i+1};$$

$$g(x) = g_i; \quad g(x + h) = g_{i+1}.$$

Substituting Eq. (3.5.5) in Eq. (3.5.3):

$$y_{i+1} = y_i + \frac{h}{2}(f_i y_i + g_i + f_{i+1}y_{i+1} + g_{i+1}) + \epsilon_{i+1},$$

and solving this equation for y_{i+1}, we obtain the *Runge-Fox recurrence equation:*

$$y_{i+1}{}^{(n)} = \frac{1}{1 - \dfrac{h}{2}f_{i+1}}\left[\left(1 + \frac{h}{2}f_i\right)y_i{}^{(n)} + \frac{h}{2}(g_i + g_{i+1}) + \epsilon_{i+1}{}^{(n-1)}\right],$$

$$(3.5.7)$$

where the error $\epsilon_{i+1}{}^{(n-1)}$, given by Eq. (3.5.4), is of order h^3.

The Runge-Fox recurrence equation will now be applied to the solution of the atmospheric pressure problem of Sec. 3.2, which is governed by Eq. (3.2.4):

$$y' = -\frac{0.9}{1 + 2z}y, \quad (c)$$

and the condition [Eq. (3.2.5)]:

$$y(0) = 1. \quad (d)$$

---

* In this and the following sections the symbol $y_i{}^{(n)}$ will often be used to indicate the nth approximation of y at i.

In this case, with $h = 0.1$, $f(z) = -\dfrac{0.9}{1 + 2z}$, $g(z) = 0$, Eq. (3.5.7) becomes:

$$y_{i+1}^{(n)} = \frac{1}{1 - 0.05 f_{i+1}} [(1 + 0.05 f_i) y_i^{(n)} + \epsilon_{i+1}^{(n-1)}]. \qquad \text{(e)}$$

The values of $y_i^{(1)}$ in the third column of Table 3.7 were computed by means of Eq. (e) starting with $y_0 = 1$ and ignoring the correction ϵ_{i+1}. The value of $y(0.3)$ has an error of $+0.16$ per cent (evaluated from the true value in Table 3.1).

Table 3.7

z	f_i	$y_i^{(1)}$	$\delta y_{i+\frac{1}{2}}$	$\delta^2 y_i$	$\delta^3 y_{i+\frac{1}{2}}$	$\dfrac{\epsilon_{i+1}^{(1)}}{1 - 0.05 f_{i+1}}$	$y_i^{(2)}$
0	-0.9000	1.0000			(-0.0056)	$+0.0005$	1.0000
0.1	-0.7500	0.9205	-0.0795	0.0174	-0.0056	$+0.0005$	0.9210
0.2	-0.6428	0.8584	-0.0621	0.0118			0.8594
0.3	-0.5625	0.8081	-0.0503		(-0.0056)	$+0.0005$	0.8096

The successive columns of Table 3.7 contain the central unaveraged differences of $y_{i+\frac{1}{2}}$, the correction $\epsilon^{(1)}_{i+1}$, and the second approximation $y_i^{(2)}$ of y, evaluated by means of Eq. (e) with the correction. Since the value of $\delta^3 y_{i+\frac{1}{2}}$ can be computed only at the point $z = 0.15$, it was assumed that the third difference is constant and equal to -0.0056 at all points $i + \frac{1}{2}$. Hence:

$$\epsilon^{(1)}_{i+1} \doteq -\tfrac{1}{12} \delta^3 y_{i+\frac{1}{2}} = -\tfrac{1}{12} \cdot 0.0056 = 0.0005$$

whatever i, and

$$y^{(2)}_{i+1} = y^{(1)}_{i+1} + \frac{0.0005}{1 - 0.05 f_{i+1}}$$

The last value, $y^{(2)}(0.3)$, has an error of only 0.02 per cent.

When compared with the Taylor expansion, the Runge-Fox recurrence formula is found to allow the use of a larger h for the same accuracy, or to improve the accuracy of the results for the same value of h. The labor involved in its application is therefore considerably less than the labor required in similar step-by-step procedures.

3.6   The Solution of Simultaneous First-Order Equations

Adams's formula [Eq. (3.4.3)] may be conveniently used to solve systems of simultaneous first-order differential equations.   Consider the simple case of two simultaneous equations

$$y' = f(x,y,z), \qquad z' = \varphi(x,y,z), \qquad (3.6.1)$$

where y and z are functions of the same independent variable x, with the two initial conditions:

$$y(0) = y_0; \qquad z(0) = z_0. \qquad (3.6.2)$$

Applying Adams's formula to both equations, we obtain the recurrence equations:

$$y_{i+1} = y_i + h[1 + \tfrac{1}{2}\nabla + \tfrac{5}{12}\nabla^2 + \ldots]f_i$$
$$z_{i+1} = z_i + h[1 + \tfrac{1}{2}\nabla + \tfrac{5}{12}\nabla^2 + \ldots]\varphi_i, \qquad (3.6.3)$$

which can be used as soon as sufficient initial values for y and z have been obtained by Taylor series.

For example, the particularly simple set of simultaneous equations

$$y' = f(x,y,z) = z, \qquad z' = \varphi(x,y,z) = y \qquad (a)$$

with the conditions

$$y(0) = y_0 = 1, \qquad z(0) = z_0 = 2 \qquad (b)$$

give by differentiation:

$$y_0 = 1, \qquad\qquad z_0 = 2,$$
$$y'_0 = z_0 = 2, \qquad\quad z'_0 = y_0 = 1,$$
$$y_0'' = z'_0 = 1, \qquad\quad z_0'' = y'_0 = 2,$$

$$\cdots\cdots\cdots\qquad\cdots\cdots\cdots$$

and hence the Taylor series:

$$y = 1 + 2x + \frac{x^2}{2} + \ldots ; \qquad z = 2 + x + x^2 + \ldots .$$

From these series we obtain the values of y, z, ∇y, $\nabla^2 y$, $\nabla^2 z$ of the first three lines of Table 3.8 for $x = 0$, 0.1, 0.2.   The values of y

and z for $x = 0.3$ and 0.4 are then obtained by Eqs. (3.6.3) with $h = 0.1$, $f = z$, and $\varphi = y$. The true values of y and z at $x = 0.4$ are 1.903 and 2.573, respectively.

The procedure may obviously be extended to any number of simultaneous equations.

Table 3.8

x	y	∇f	$\nabla^2 f$	z	$\nabla \varphi$	$\nabla^2 \varphi$
0	1			2		
0.1	1.205	0.205		2.110	0.110	
0.2	1.420	0.215	0.010	2.240	0.130	0.020
0.3	1.651	0.231	0.016	2.393	0.153	0.023
0.4	1.899	0.248	0.017	2.570	0.177	0.024

The Runge-Fox method may also be extended to solve simultaneous linear equations. The reader may derive the recurrence equations for systems of two or more equations following the pattern of these sections (see Problem 3.17).

3.7 The Adams-Störmer Method for Second-Order Equations

[a] Complete equation

The solution of a second-order equation

$$y'' = f(x,y,y') \tag{3.7.1}$$

with initial conditions

$$y(0) = y_0, \qquad y'(0) = y'_0 \tag{3.7.2}$$

is reduced to the integration of two simultaneous first-order equations by setting

$$y' = z(x,y), \tag{3.7.3}$$

so that Eq. (3.7.1) becomes:

$$y'' = z' = f(x,y,z). \tag{3.7.4}$$

Applying Adams's formula [Eq. (3.4.3)] to the two first-order equations (3.7.3) and (3.7.4), we obtain the recurrence formulas:

$$z_{i+1} = z_i + h[1 + \tfrac{1}{2}\nabla + \tfrac{5}{12}\nabla^2 + \ . \ . \ .]f_i$$
$$y_{i+1} = y_i + h[1 + \tfrac{1}{2}\nabla + \tfrac{5}{12}\nabla^2 + \ . \ . \ .]z_i.$$

(3.7.5)

The solution is started, as usual, by a Taylor series, and the integration is then continued as indicated in Table 3.9 in which the

Table 3.9

i	x	y	z	∇z	$\nabla^2 z$	. . .	f	∇f	$\nabla^2 f$	. . .
$i-2$	x_{i-2}	y_{i-2}	z_{i-2}				f_{i-2}			
$i-1$	x_{i-1}	y_{i-1}	z_{i-1}	∇z_{i-1}			f_{i-1}	∇f_{i-1}		
i	x_i	y_i	z_i	∇z_i	$\nabla^2 z_i$	. . .	f_i	∇f_i	$\nabla^2 f_i$	. . .
$i+1$	x_{i+1}	y_{i+1}	z_{i+1}	∇z_{i+1}	$\nabla^2 z_{i+1}$	. . .	f_{i+1}	∇f_{i+1}	$\nabla^2 f_{i+1}$	. . .
$i+2$	x_{i+2}	y_{i+2}	z_{i+2}	∇z_{i+2}	$\nabla^2 z_{i+2}$	. . .	f_{i+2}	∇f_{i+2}	$\nabla^2 f_{i+2}$	. . .

values above the double line are known from the Taylor series, and the values below the double line are obtained by means of Eqs. (3.7.5) moving from left to right.

A certain simplification of the procedure may be obtained when the derivative y' is not needed, by eliminating z between the two Eqs. (3.7.5) and hence by saving the labor of differencing z. For this purpose, applying the second of Eqs. (3.7.5) at y_{i+1} and y_i,

$$y_{i+1} - y_i = h[1 + \tfrac{1}{2}\nabla + \tfrac{5}{12}\nabla^2 + \ . \ . \ .]z_i$$
$$y_i - y_{i-1} = h[1 + \tfrac{1}{2}\nabla + \tfrac{5}{12}\nabla^2 + \ . \ . \ .]z_{i-1},$$

and subtracting the second from the first equation, we obtain:

$$y_{i+1} - 2y_i + y_{i-1} = h[1 + \tfrac{1}{2}\nabla + \tfrac{5}{12}\nabla^2 + \ . \ . \ .](z_i - z_{i-1})$$
$$= h[1 + \tfrac{1}{2}\nabla + \tfrac{5}{12}\nabla^2 + \ . \ . \ .]\nabla z_i.$$

(3.7.6)

But, by Eqs. (2.4.11) and (3.7.4),

$$\nabla z_i = [1 - \tfrac{1}{2}hD + \tfrac{1}{8}h^2D^2 + \ . \ . \ .]hDz_i$$
$$= [1 - \tfrac{1}{2}hD + \tfrac{1}{6}h^2D^2 + \ . \ . \ .]hf_i,$$

and substituting in the bracket for the powers of hD the difference expansions of Eqs. (2.4.16) to (2.4.17),

$$\nabla z_i = [1 - \tfrac{1}{2}\nabla - \tfrac{1}{12}\nabla^2 - \ldots]hf_i.$$

Hence, substituting this value of ∇z_i in Eq. (3.7.6), we obtain the *Adams-Störmer recurrence formula:*

$$y_{i+1} = -y_{i-1} + 2y_i + h^2[1 + \tfrac{1}{12}\nabla^2 + \tfrac{1}{12}\nabla^3 + \tfrac{19}{240}\nabla^4 + \tfrac{3}{40}\nabla^5 + \ldots]f_i. \quad (3.7.7)$$

[b] Incomplete equation

Whenever the right-hand member of Eq. (3.7.1) does not depend on y', the integration of the equation can be performed by means of Eq. (3.7.7) alone; however, when y'' is a function of y', Eq. (3.7.7) must be used together with the first of Eqs. (3.7.5).

Equation (3.7.7) will now be applied to the extrapolation of the solution of the frictionless pendulum problem, governed by Eq. (3.3.3)

$$\ddot{\theta} = -4.6499 \sin \theta, \qquad\qquad\qquad \text{(a)}$$

with the initial conditions

$$\theta_0 = 2.0944, \qquad \dot{\theta}_0 = 0, \qquad\qquad \text{(b)}$$

Table 3.10

τ	θ_i	f_i	∇f_i	$\nabla^2 f_i$
0	2.0944	−4.0268		
0.1	2.0742	−4.0728	−0.0460	
0.2	2.0132	−4.2021	−0.1293	−0.0833
0.3	1.9101	−4.3849	−0.1828	−0.0535
0.4	1.7631	−4.5643	−0.1794	+0.0034
0.5	1.5705	−4.6499	−0.0856	0.0938
0.6	1.3313	−4.5174	+0.1325	0.2181
0.7	1.0467	−4.0259	0.4915	0.3590
0.8	0.7215	−3.0713	0.9546	0.4631
0.9	0.3652	−1.6605	1.4108	0.4562
1.0	−0.0081			

which was started in Sec. 3.3 (Table 3.3). In this case

$$\ddot{\theta} = f(\theta) = -4.6499 \sin \theta$$

does not depend on either τ or $\dot{\theta}$, and only Eq. (3.7.7) is needed for the solution. Table 3.10 gives the results of the extrapolation started with three values of y for $h = 0.1$, taking into account second differences of f.

Table 3.11

τ	θ_i	$\dot{\theta}_i$	f_i	∇f_i	$\nabla^2 f_i$
0	2.0944	0	−4.0268		
0.1	2.0745	−0.3963	−3.9139	0.1129	
0.2	2.0153	−0.7865	−3.8833	+0.0306	−0.0823
0.3	1.9172	−1.1767	−3.9030	−0.0197	−0.0503
0.4	1.7800	−1.5701	−3.9205	−0.0175	+0.0022
0.5	1.6036	−1.9629	−3.8624	+0.0581	0.0756
0.6	1.3886	−2.3431	−3.6355	0.2269	0.1688
0.7	1.1374	−2.6883	−3.1445	0.4910	0.2641
0.8	0.8550	−2.9672	−2.3219	0.8226	0.3316
0.9	0.5497	−3.1444	−1.1713	1.1506	0.3280
1.0	0.2330	−3.1903	+1.0452	2.2165	1.0659
1.1	−0.0724	−2.9305			

Interpolating linearly from Table 3.10, we obtain $\theta = 0$ at $\tau = 0.9978$ with an error of 0.2 per cent in the period of the oscillations obtained rigorously by an elliptic integral solution (see Sec. 3.3).

The simultaneous use of the first of Eqs. (3.7.5) and of Eq. (3.7.7) is illustrated in Table 3.11, which gives the solution of the friction pendulum problem of Sec. 3.3, governed by Eq. (3.3.7),

$$\ddot{\theta} + 0.4\dot{\theta} + 4.6499 \sin \theta = 0, \qquad (c)$$

and conditions (b) of this section, using $h = 0.1$ and three initial values from the Taylor solution of Table 3.4. In this case,

$$\ddot{\theta} = f(\theta,\dot{\theta}) = -0.4\dot{\theta} - 4.6499 \sin \theta$$

and the recurrence equations become

$$\dot{\theta}_{i+1} = \dot{\theta}_i + 0.1[1 + 0.5\nabla + 0.4167\nabla^2]f_i$$
$$\theta_{i+1} = -\theta_{i-1} + 2\theta_i + 0.01[1 + 0.0833\nabla^2]f_i. \tag{d}$$

A linear interpolation between $\tau = 1.0$ and $\tau = 1.1$ gives $\tau = 1.0763$ for the passage of the pendulum through the vertical position, an increase of 7.63 per cent over the time for the undamped pendulum.

3.8 Fox's Methods for Second-Order Linear Equations

[a] Complete equation

A simple formula for the step-by-step integration of the second-order *linear* differential equation

$$y'' + f(x)y' + g(x)y = F(x) \tag{3.8.1}$$

with the initial conditions

$$y(0) = y_0, \qquad y'(0) = y'_0 \tag{3.8.2}$$

may be obtained as suggested by Fox. The equation is multiplied by h^2:

$$h^2y'' + hf(x)(hy') + h^2g(x)y = h^2F(x)$$

and the terms h^2y'' and hy' are expressed by means of their *central* difference expansions of Eqs. (2.7.16), letting $x = ih$ and calling y_i, f_i, g_i, F_i the values of y, f, g, and F at x:

$$y_{i+1} - 2y_i + y_{i-1} + \frac{h}{2}f_i(y_{i+1} - y_{i-1}) + h^2g_iy_i$$

$$= h^2F_i + \left(\frac{\delta^4}{12} - \frac{\delta^6}{90} + \ldots\right)y_i + hf_i\mu\left(\frac{\delta^3}{6} - \frac{\delta^5}{30} + \ldots\right)y_i.$$

Solving this equation for y_{i+1}, we obtain *Fox's formula for second-order linear equations:*

$$y_{i+1}^{(n)} = \frac{1}{1 + \frac{h}{2}f_i}\left[-\left(1 - \frac{h}{2}f_i\right)y_{i-1}^{(n)} + (2 - h^2g_i)y_i^{(n)}\right.$$

$$\left. + h^2F_i + \epsilon_{i+1}^{(n-1)}\right], \tag{3.8.3}$$

where the correction $\epsilon_{i+1}{}^{(n-1)}$ equals

$$\epsilon_{i+1}{}^{(n-1)} = \left(\frac{\delta^4}{12} - \frac{\delta^6}{90} + \ldots \right) y_i{}^{(n-1)}$$

$$+ hf_{i\mu} \left(\frac{\delta^3}{6} - \frac{\delta^5}{30} + \ldots \right) y_i{}^{(n-1)} \quad (3.8.4)$$

and is of order h^3.

The solution y is started by means of a Taylor series* in order to obtain y_1, and is then extrapolated by means of Eq. (3.8.3), neglecting the correction. The differences of the first approximation $y^{(1)}$ thus obtained are then used to evaluate $\epsilon^{(1)}$, and Eq.

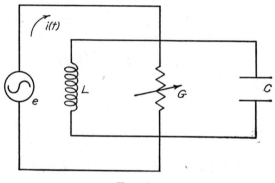

FIG. 3.4

(3.8.3) is used again with these $\epsilon^{(1)}$ to obtain a second approximation $y^{(2)}$ of y. The procedure is repeated until the corrections have identical values in two successive approximations.

To illustrate this procedure, consider the electric circuit of Fig. 3.4 in which the inductance L, the variable conductance $G(t)$, and the capacitance C are connected in parallel. If $G(t)$ varies according to the law:

$$G(t) = G_0(1 + a \sin 10^3 t), \quad (a)$$

Kirchhoff's second law† yields for the voltage e the equation:

$$C \frac{de}{dt} + G(t)e + \frac{1}{L} \int e \, dt = i$$

---

* See also Problem 3.36 for a solution without Taylor's expansion.
† See, for example, *Differential Equations*, Sec. 1.7.

or, after differentiation with respect to t and division by C,

$$\frac{d^2e}{dt^2} + \frac{G(t)}{C}\frac{de}{dt} + \left(\frac{1}{LC} + \frac{1}{C}\frac{dG(t)}{dt}\right)e = \frac{1}{C}\frac{di}{dt}.$$

With $C = 1$ microfarad $(10^{-6}$ farad$)$, $L = 0.02778$ henry, $G_0 = 0.007$ mho, $a = 0.5$, $i = \dfrac{10^{-9}}{6}$ sin $6 \cdot 10^3t$, and neglecting the time-varying part, $\dfrac{1}{C}\dfrac{dG}{dt} = 3.5 \cdot 10^6$ cos 10^3t, in comparison with the constant term $1/LC = 36 \cdot 10^6$,* the equation for the voltage becomes:

$$\frac{d^2e}{dt^2} + 7000(1 + 0.5 \sin 10^3t)\frac{de}{dt} + 36 \cdot 10^6e = \cos 6 \cdot 10^3t.$$

A change in the time unit from t seconds to τ milliseconds $(\tau = 10^3t)$ changes the equation to:

$$\ddot{e} + 7(1 + 0.5 \sin \tau)\dot{e} + 36e = \cos 6\tau, \qquad (b)$$

where a dot denotes differentiation with respect to τ. Initial rest conditions require that

$$e(0) = e_0 = 0, \qquad \dot{e}(0) = \dot{e}_0 = 0. \qquad (c)$$

To start the solution we write

$$\ddot{e} = -7(1 + 0.5 \sin \tau)\dot{e} - 36e + \cos 6\tau; \qquad \ddot{e}_0 = 1$$

and find by differentiation

$$\dddot{e} = -7(1 + 0.5 \sin \tau)\ddot{e} - (3.5 \cos \tau + 36)\dot{e} - 6 \sin 6\tau;$$
$$\dddot{e}_0 = -7$$

$$e^{IV} = -7(1 + 0.5 \sin \tau)\dddot{e} - (7 \cos \tau + 36)\ddot{e} + (3.5 \sin \tau)\dot{e}$$
$$- 36 \cos 6\tau; \qquad e_0^{IV} = -30.$$

---

* In order to solve the complete equation without neglecting the term involving dG/dt, set $e = dv/dt$ and write the circuit equation in terms of v:

$$\frac{d^2v}{dt^2} + \frac{G(t)}{C}\frac{dv}{dt} + \frac{1}{L}v = i.$$

Once this equation has been solved for v, $e(t)$ is obtained by differentiation.

We thus obtain the series expansion for $e(\tau)$ in the neighborhood of the origin:

$$e(\tau) = \tfrac{1}{2}\tau^2 - \tfrac{7}{6}\tau^3 - \tfrac{30}{24}\tau^4 = 0.5\tau^2 - 1.1667\tau^3 - 1.25\tau^4,$$

from which

$$e(0.05) = 0.00110, \qquad e(0.10) = 0.00371.$$

The application of Eq. (3.8.3) to the initial value problem of Eqs. (b), (c), with

$$h = 0.1, \quad f(\tau) = 7(1 + 0.5 \sin \tau), \quad g(\tau) = 36, \quad F(\tau) = \cos 6\tau,$$

gives the recurrence equation for the first approximation $e^{(1)}$ of e:

$$e_{i+1}^{(1)} = \frac{1}{1 + 0.05f_i} [-(1 - 0.05f_i)e_{i-1}^{(1)} + 1.64e_i^{(1)} + 0.01F_i], \quad (d)$$

Table 3.12

τ	f_i	$1 + 0.05f_i$	$1 - 0.05f_i$	$0.01F_i$	$e_i^{(1)}$
0	7.00000				0
0.1	7.34944	1.36747	0.63253	0.00825	0.00371
0.2	7.69534	1.38477	0.61523	+0.00362	0.01048
0.3	8.03432	1.40172	0.59828	−0.00227	0.01337
0.4	8.36297	1.41815	0.58185	−0.00737	0.00955
0.5	8.67801	1.43390	0.56610	−0.00990	+0.00036
0.6	8.97624	1.44881	0.55119	−0.00897	−0.01026
0.7	9.25477	1.46274	0.53726	−0.00490	−0.01794
0.8	9.51076	1.47554	0.52446	+0.00087	−0.01969
0.9	9.74166	1.48708	0.51292	0.00635	−0.01491
1.0	9.94514	1.49726	0.50274	0.00960	−0.00538
1.1	10.11924	1.50596	0.49404		+0.00552

in which ϵ is neglected. Starting with $e_0^{(1)} = 0$ and $e_1^{(1)} = 0.00371$, we obtain the results of Table 3.12.

To evaluate a second approximation by Fox's correction ϵ, we difference $e^{(1)}$ and compute the correction by means of its first two terms:

$$\epsilon_{i+1}{}^{(1)} = \left(\frac{\delta^4}{12} + hf_i\frac{\mu\delta^3}{6}\right)e_i{}^{(1)} = (0.08333\delta^4 + 0.01667f_i\mu\delta^3)e_i{}^{(1)}. \quad \text{(e)}$$

The results of this computation appear in Table 3.13.

The values (in parentheses) of $\mu\delta^3$ and δ^4 for $\tau = 0.1$, 1.0, and 1.1 are obtained by extrapolation at sight. The values (in parentheses) of $\mu\delta^3$ for $\tau = 0.2$ to $\tau = 0.9$ are the averages of the adjoining values of δ^3.

Table 3.13

τ	$e_i{}^{(1)}$	$10^5\delta e_{i+\frac{1}{2}}^{(1)}$	$10^5\delta^2 e_i{}^{(1)}$	$10^5\delta^3 e_i{}^{(1)}$ and $10^5\mu\delta^3 e_i{}^{(1)}$	$10^5\delta^4 e_i{}^{(1)}$	ϵ_{i+1}	$e_i{}^{(2)}$	$e_i{}^{(3)}$
0	0						0	0
0.1	0.00371	371	+306	(−250)	(250)	−0.00010	0.00371	0.00371
0.2	0.01048	677	−388	−694 (−488)	411	−0.00028	0.01040	0.01040
0.3	0.01337	+289	−671	−283 (−75)	417	+0.00025	0.01308	0.01305
0.4	0.00955	−382	−537	+134 (264)	260	0.00058	0.00942	0.00938
0.5	+0.00036	−919	−143	394 (415)	+43	0.00064	+0.00073	+0.00096
0.6	−0.01026	−1062	+294	437 (368)	−138	0.00044	−0.00934	−0.00909
0.7	−0.01794	−768	593	299 (180)	−239	+0.00008	−0.01673	−0.01656
0.8	−0.01969	−175	653	+60 (−59)	−238	−0.00029	−0.01862	−0.01851
0.9	−0.01491	+478	475	−178 (−258)	−160	−0.00055	−0.01435	−0.01468
1.0	−0.00538	953	137	−338 (−400)	(0)	−0.00066	−0.00550	−0.00588
1.1	+0.00552	1090		(−250)	(200)	−0.00026	+0.00476	+0.00445

The values of $e_i{}^{(2)}$ are obtained by means of the recurrence equation:

$$e_{i+1}{}^{(2)} = \frac{1}{1 + 0.05f_i}[-(1 - 0.05f_i)e_{i-1}{}^{(2)} + 1.64e_i{}^{(2)}$$
$$+ 0.01F_i + \epsilon_{i+1}{}^{(1)}], \quad \text{(f)}$$

where $\epsilon_{i+1}{}^{(1)}$ is taken from Table 3.13. Differencing the values $e_i{}^{(2)}$, one computes the new corrections and hence the values of $e_i{}^{(3)}$ which are given in the last column of Table 3.13. The differencing of $e^{(3)}$

shows that the corrections of $e^{(3)}$ are identical with the corrections of $e^{(2)}$, and the process is therefore stopped at this point.

[b] Incomplete equation (Noumerov's method)

When a second-order *linear* differential equation lacks the first derivative term and hence is of the form

$$y'' + f(x)y = F(x), \tag{3.8.5}$$

its integration may be performed by another very powerful procedure, due to Noumerov and Fox.   Multiplying Eq. (3.8.5) by h^2 and substituting for the second derivative its expansion in terms of central differences [Eq. (2.7.15)], Eq. (3.8.5) becomes:

$$\left(\delta^2 - \frac{\delta^4}{12} + \frac{\delta^6}{90} + \ldots\right) y_i + h^2 f_i y_i = h^2 F_i.$$

Operating on both sides of this equation with $\left(1 + \frac{\delta^2}{12}\right)$, the term in δ^4 is eliminated and the equation takes the form:

$$\left(\delta^2 + \frac{\delta^6}{240} - \frac{13\delta^8}{15120} + \ldots\right) y_i + h^2 f_i y_i + \frac{h^2\delta^2}{12}(f_i y_i) = h^2 F_i + \frac{h^2\delta^2}{12} F_i$$

or: $y_{i+1} - 2y_i + y_{i-1} + h^2 f_i y_i + \frac{h^2}{12}(f_{i+1}y_{i+1} - 2f_i y_i + f_{i-1}y_{i-1})$

$$= h^2 F_i + \frac{h^2}{12}(F_{i+1} - 2F_i + F_{i-1}) - \left(\frac{\delta^6}{240} - \frac{13\delta^8}{15120} + \ldots\right) y_i.$$

Solving this equation for y_{i+1}, we obtain the *Noumerov-Fox recurrence formula:*

$$y_{i+1}^{(n)} = \frac{1}{1 + \frac{h^2}{12}f_{i+1}} \left[-\left(1 + \frac{h^2}{12}f_{i-1}\right) y_{i-1}^{(n)} + \left(2 - \frac{5h^2}{6}f_i\right) y_i^{(n)}\right.$$

$$\left. + \frac{h^2}{12}(F_{i-1} + 10F_i + F_{i+1}) + \epsilon_{i+1}^{(n-1)}\right], \tag{3.8.6}$$

where: $\epsilon_{i+1}^{(n-1)} = -\left(\frac{\delta^6}{240} - \frac{13\delta^8}{15120} + \ldots\right) y_i^{(n-1)}. \tag{3.8.7}$

Only y_0 and y_1 are needed to start the solution, and the correction, being of the order of h^6, is often negligible even for fairly large values of h.

To illustrate the use of Eqs. (3.8.6) and (3.8.7), consider the electric circuit of Fig. 3.5 with an inductance and a capacitance in series, in which the capacitance varies according to the law:

$$\frac{1}{C} = \frac{1}{C_0} (1 + a \cos 10^3 t). \qquad \text{(g)}$$

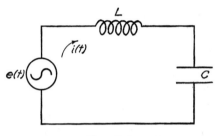

FIG. 3.5

The charge $q(t)$ on the capacitor satisfies the equation:*

$$\frac{d^2q}{dt^2} + \frac{1}{LC} q = \frac{1}{L} e(t).$$

If, as in the previous example, $1/(LC_0) = 36 \cdot 10^6$ in practical units, the equation becomes:

$$\frac{d^2q}{dt^2} + 36 \cdot 10^6(1 + 0.4 \cos 10^3 t)q = \cos 6 \cdot 10^3 t$$

or, with $\tau = 1000t$,

$$\ddot{q} + 36(1 + 0.4 \cos \tau)q = \cos 6\tau, \qquad \text{(h)}$$

where a dot denotes differentiation with respect to τ. Initial rest conditions require that:

$$q(0) = q_0 = 0, \qquad \dot{q}(0) = \dot{q}_0 = i(0) = 0. \qquad \text{(i)}$$

To start the solution, we write, by differentiation,

$$\ddot{q} = -36(1 + 0.4 \cos \tau)q + \cos 6\tau; \qquad \ddot{q}_0 = 1$$

$$\dddot{q} = -36(1 + 0.4 \cos \tau)\dot{q} + 14.4 (\sin \tau)q - 6 \sin 6\tau; \qquad \dddot{q}_0 = 0$$

$$q^{IV} = -36(1 + 0.4 \cos \tau)\ddot{q} + 28.8 (\sin \tau)\dot{q} + 14.4 (\cos \tau)q$$
$$- 36 \cos 6\tau; \; q_0^{IV} = -86.4,$$

---

* See, for example, *Differential Equations*, Sec. 2.8.

and obtain the series expansion valid in the neighborhood of zero:

$$q(t) = \frac{\tau^2}{2} - \frac{86.4\tau^4}{24} = 0.5\tau^2 - 3.6\tau^4,$$

by means of which $q(0.1) = q_1 = 0.00464$.* The application of Eq. (3.8.6) without correction to the initial value problem of Eqs. (h), (i), with

$$h = 0.1, \qquad f(\tau) = 36(1 + 0.4 \cos \tau), \qquad F(\tau) = \cos 6\tau,$$

gives the recurrence equation:

$$q_{i+1}^{(1)} = \frac{1}{1 + \frac{0.01}{12} f_{i+1}} \left[- \left(1 + \frac{0.01}{12} f_{i-1}\right) q_{i-1}^{(1)} \right.$$

$$\left. + \left(2 - \frac{5}{6} 0.01\right) q_i^{(1)} + \frac{0.01}{12} (F_{i-1} + 10F_i + F_{i+1}) \right]. \quad \text{(j)}$$

Starting with $q_0 = 0$, $q_1 = 0.00464$, Eq. (j) gives the results of

Table 3.14

τ	f_i	$1 + \frac{0.01}{12} f_i$	$2 - \frac{5}{6} 0.01 f_i$	$\frac{0.01}{12}(F_{i-1} + 10F_i + F_{i+1})$	q	q_c
0	50.4	1.04200	1.58002		0	0
0.1	50.328	1.04194	1.58062		0.00464	0.00471
0.2	50.11308	1.04176	1.58241	0.00801	0.01475	0.01553
0.3	49.75704	1.04146	1.58537	+0.00352	0.02115	0.02435
0.4	49.26312	1.04105	1.58949	−0.00221	+0.01532	0.02252
0.5	48.63708	1.04053	1.59471	−0.00716	−0.00465	+0.00588
0.6	47.88504	1.03990	1.60097	−0.00961	−0.03171	−0.00221
0.7	47.01384	1.03918	1.60823	−0.00871	−0.05258	−0.05084
0.8	46.03248	1.03836	1.61641	−0.00476	−0.05426	+0.06641
0.9	44.95104	1.03746	1.62542	+0.00085	−0.03105	−0.05796
1.0	43.78032	1.03648	1.63518	0.00616	+0.01161	−0.00233
1.1	42.53184	1.03544		0.00932	0.05845	+0.02856

Table 3.14, which also contains the solution of the equation with constant coefficients corresponding to Eq. (h):

$$\ddot{q} + 36q = \cos 6\tau,$$

* See Problem 3.36 for solution without Taylor's series expansion.

satisfying the conditions (i), that is,

$$q_c = \frac{\tau}{12} \sin 6\tau. \tag{k}$$

The corrections ϵ evaluated by means of Eq. (3.8.7) change by one or two units the last figure of q and hence are negligible.

3.9 Accumulation of Error in Step-by-Step Integration

The corrections ϵ evaluated in the preceding sections indicate the discrepancy between the true and the approximate values of the solution y, due to one step of the numerical integration process, and are also called *truncation errors*.   It is natural to expect the truncation errors to accumulate and the results obtained after a large number of steps to be more inaccurate than those near the origin. Both the truncation errors and the accumulated errors depend essentially upon the spacing h.   To give an idea of how the results of step-by-step integration may diverge from the true solutions, the finite difference equation corresponding to a simple differential equation will be rigorously solved in this section.

Consider the initial value problem:

$$\ddot{y} + \omega^2 y = 0 \tag{3.9.1}$$

$$y_0 = 1 \qquad \dot{y}_0 = 0,$$

whose rigorous solution is given by

$$y = \cos \omega t, \tag{3.9.2}$$

and apply to Eq. (3.9.1) the Noumerov-Fox procedure [Eqs. (3.8.6), (3.8.7)].

Multiplying Eq. (3.9.1) by h^2, substituting $(\delta^2 - \delta^4/12)y_n$ for $h^2\ddot{y}^*$ and operating on the whole equation with $(1 + \delta^2/12)$, we obtain the finite difference equation:

$$\delta^2 y_n + \frac{\omega^2 h^2}{12} (12 + \delta^2)y_n = 0$$

or, with:

$$\delta^2 y_n = y_{n+1} - 2y_n + y_{n-1}$$

$$2c = \frac{\frac{5}{6}\omega^2 h^2 - 2}{1 + \frac{1}{12}\omega^2 h^2}, \tag{a}$$

* The subscript i has been changed to n to avoid confusion with the imaginary unit $i = \sqrt{-1}$.

the equation:

$$y_{n+1} + 2cy_n + y_{n-1} = 0. \tag{3.9.3}$$

A rigorous solution of this difference equation may be obtained by letting in Eq. (3.9.3)

$$y_n = Ax^n, \tag{3.9.4}$$

where x is an undetermined number:

$$Ax^{n-1}(x^2 + 2cx + 1) = 0. \tag{b}$$

If Eq. (3.9.4) is to be a solution of Eq. (3.9.3), Eq. (b) must be satisfied for all values of n.   Hence x must be a root of the quadratic equation:

$$x^2 + 2cx + 1 = 0.$$

We thus find two values for x:

$$x_{1,2} = c \pm \sqrt{c^2 - 1}. \tag{3.9.5}$$

Let us now consider separately the four cases: $c > 1$; $c = 1$; $c = 0$; $c = -1$.

For $c > 1$, the roots $x_{1,2}$ are both real and negative; x_1 is less than 1 in absolute value, and x_2 is larger than 1 in absolute value. Hence, with r_1 and r_2 positive, x_1 and x_2 may be written as:

$$x_1 = (-1)e^{-r_1}; \qquad x_2 = (-1)e^{+r_2},$$

and by Eq. (3.9.4) the general solution of Eq. (3.9.3) takes the form:

$$y_n = C_1(-1)^n e^{-r_1 n} + C_2(-1)^n e^{r_2 n}. \tag{3.9.6}$$

To satisfy the initial conditions we must have:

$$C_1 + C_2 = 1; \qquad -r_1 C_1 + r_2 C_2 = 0,$$

from which:

$$C_1 = \frac{r_2}{r_1 + r_2}; \qquad C_2 = \frac{r_1}{r_1 + r_2}$$

and finally:

$$y_n = \frac{(-1)^n}{r_1 + r_2} (r_2 e^{-r_1 n} + r_1 e^{r_2 n}). \tag{3.9.7}$$

Equation (3.9.7) proves that when $c > 1$, that is, when, by Eq. (a),

$$\frac{\frac{5}{6}\omega^2 h^2 - 2}{1 + \frac{1}{12}\omega^2 h^2} > 2$$

and hence

$$\omega^2 h^2 > 6,$$

the numerical solution of the Noumerov-Fox's method grows indefinitely with n (due to the positive exponential e^{rzn}) and after a few steps cannot represent to any degree of accuracy the oscillating solution (3.9.2).

For $c = 1$, $x_1 = x_2 = -1 = e^{\pi i} = \cos \pi + i \sin \pi$ and, by Eq. (3.9.4), taking the part of the solution which satisfies the initial conditions,

$$y_n = \cos \pi n.$$

The numerical solution is now oscillating and of unit amplitude as the true solution. Its frequency may be computed by letting $t = nh$, and hence:

$$y_n = \cos \frac{\pi}{h} t = \cos \left(\frac{\pi}{\omega h} \right) \omega t.$$

With $c = 1$, Eq. (a) gives $\omega^2 h^2 = 6$, and hence the frequency of the numerical solution is

$$\frac{\pi}{\sqrt{6}} \omega = 1.28 \, \omega.$$

For $c = 0$, $x_{1,2} = \pm i = \cos \frac{\pi}{2} \pm i \sin \frac{\pi}{2}$. Hence:

$$y_n = \cos \frac{\pi}{2} n = \cos \frac{\pi}{2} \frac{t}{h} = \cos \left(\frac{\pi}{2\omega h} \right) \omega t,$$

and the corresponding frequency is $\frac{\pi}{2\omega h} \omega$. But for $c = 0$, Eq. (a) gives $\omega^2 h^2 = \frac{12}{5}$; hence the numerical solution has a frequency

$$\frac{\pi}{2 \sqrt{12/5}} \omega = \sqrt{5/3} \frac{\pi}{4} \omega = 1.01\omega.$$

For $c = -1$, Eq. (a) gives $h = 0$, and hence the numerical solution approaches in the limit the correct solution of Eq. (3.9.2).

It is thus seen that the Noumerov-Fox method will not converge at all, in this simple problem, for $\omega^2 h^2 > 6$, that is, for a time interval

$$h > \frac{\sqrt{6}}{\omega} = \frac{\sqrt{6}}{2\pi} T = \frac{T}{2.56},$$

where T is the period of the solution. The method will converge for $h < T/2.56$ and will give good results for

$$\omega^2 h^2 < \tfrac{12}{5} \quad \therefore \quad h < 2\sqrt[3]{\tfrac{3}{5}}\frac{1}{\omega} = \sqrt[3]{\tfrac{3}{5}}\frac{T}{\pi} = \frac{T}{4.05}.$$

The Noumerov-Fox method gives, therefore, good results for a time interval less than one-quarter of the period.

Since in the solution of complex vibrational problems this method is often applied to the first few modes of vibration of a system, it is well to remember that the time interval must be smaller than one-quarter of the shortest period to be considered.

Similar results can be obtained for more complicated differential problems.

PROBLEMS

3.1 Evaluate, by means of a Taylor series expansion, the integral of the following problem at:

(a) $x = 0.1(0.1)0.3$ to three significant figures.
(b) $x = 1.0, 1.1$ to four significant figures.

$$y' - 2y = 3e^x; \quad y(0) = 0.$$

Ans. (a) $y(0.1) = 0.348; \ y(0.2) = 0.811; \ y(0.3) = 1.415.$ (b) $y(1) = 13.91; y(1.1) = 17.87.$

3.2 Evaluate to four significant figures the integral of the following problem at $x = 2.1$ and 2.2 by means of a Taylor series expansion about $x = 2$:

$$y' + \frac{1}{x}y^2 = 0; \quad y(2) = 1.442.$$

3.3 Evaluate the integral of the following problems to four significant figures at $x = 0.1(0.1)0.3$, by Taylor series:

(a) $y'' = -xy; y(0) = 1; y'(0) = 0.5.$
(b) $y'' + yy' = x^2; y(0) = 1; y'(0) = 1.$

Ans. (a) $y(0.1) = 1.050$; $y(0.2) = 1.099$; $y(0.3) = 1.145$. (b) $y(0.1) = 1.095$; $y(0.2) = 1.180$; $y(0.3) = 1.257$.

3.4 Evaluate to three significant figures the integral of the following problem at $x = 0.2$ and 0.4, by means of a Taylor series expansion:

$$y''y^2 + 1 = 0; \quad y(0) = -1; \quad y'(0) = 1.$$

3.5 Evaluate the integral of the following problem to four significant figures at $x = 1.1(0.1)1.3$, using a Taylor series expansion:

$$y'' + y^2 y' = x^3; \quad y(1) = 1; \quad y'(1) = 1.$$

Ans. $y(1.1) = 1.100$; $y(1.2) = 1.201$; $y(1.3) = 1.306$.

3.6 A mathematical pendulum of length L (Fig. 3.3) is released from rest from an angle $\theta = 160°$, and oscillates in a viscous medium of coefficient $\mu = 1.2$ sec^{-1} per unit mass. Determine θ in the interval $t = 0(0.1)0.2$ by Taylor series.

3.7 Evaluate to three significant figures the integral of Problem 3.1 at $x = 0.4(0.1)0.6$, using Adams's formula with differences up to the third order. Use the starting values determined in Problem 3.1.

Ans. $y(0.4) = 2.20$; $y(0.5) = 3.20$; $y(0.6) = 4.49$.

3.8 Evaluate to three significant figures the integral of the following problem at $x = 1.0(0.1)1.6$, using Adams's method with differences up to the third order, after starting the solution by Taylor series:

$$y' + \frac{1}{x} y = \frac{1}{x^2}; \quad y(1) = 1.$$

3.9 Evaluate to three significant figures the integral of Problem 3.2 using Adams's method with differences up to the third order.

Ans. $y(2.4) = 1.14; y(2.5) = 1.09; y(2.6) = 1.04; y(2.7) = 1.00; y(2.8) = 0.97$.

3.10 Evaluate to four significant figures the integral of the following problem at $x = 0(0.1)0.6$, using Adams's method with differences up to the third order, after starting the solution by Taylor series:

$$y' + y^2 = e^x; \quad y(0) = 1.$$

3.11 A body of compact shape has a terminal velocity of 500 fps when falling freely through air. Determine its velocity v as a function of time in the interval $t = 0(1)6$ sec by Adams's method with second-order differences, if $v_0 = 200$ fps and air resistance is assumed proportional to v^2. (*Note:* The equation of motion is $m\ddot{x} + \mu \dot{x}^2 = mg$, where m is the mass.)

The terminal velocity is reached when $\dot{x} = $ constant:

$$(\dot{x})_t = \sqrt{\frac{mg}{\mu}}.$$

Ans.

t	0	1	2	3	4	5	6
v	200	226	251	274	296	316	334

3.12 A body is dropped from a plane with the help of a parachute. Its terminal velocity is 30 fps. Determine the velocity v in the interval $t = 0(0.1)0.5$, assuming $v_0 = 20$ fps and air resistance proportional to $v^{3/2}$. Use Adams's method with differences of the first order.

3.13 The shunt field of a dc motor has an inductance of $L = 200$ h, and is connected in series with a resistance R. The resistance increases slightly with current and may be expressed as $R = R_0 + ri$, where i is the current (amperes) flowing through R, and $R_0 = 100$ ohms, $r = 10$ ohms per ampere. A steady voltage $E = 120$ v is applied to the circuit by closing a switch. Find by Adams's method the current $i(t)$ in the interval $t = 0(0.5)2.5$ sec, and compare the result with the current in a linear circuit with $R = 106$ ohms, if $i(0) = 1.2$ a.

Ans.

t	1.5	2.0	2.5
i	1.129	1.117	1.108

3.14 Evaluate to three significant figures the first approximation of the integral of the following problem at $x = 1.1(0.1)1.3$, using the Runge-Fox method.

$$y' + \frac{1}{x}y = \frac{1}{x^2}; \quad y(1) = 1.$$

Ans. $y(1.1) = 0.996; y(1.2) = 0.986; y(1.3) = 0.971.$

3.15 Evaluate to three significant figures the first and second approximations of the integral of the following problem at $x = 0.1(0.1)0.4$, using the Runge-Fox method with error corrections.

$$y' - 2y = 3e^x; \quad y(0) = 0.$$

3.16 Evaluate to three significant figures the first and second approximations of the integral of the following problem at $x = 1.1(0.1)1.3$, using the Runge-Fox method with error corrections.

$$y' - x^3y = x^2; \quad y(1) = 1.$$

Ans. $y(1.1) = 1.24; y(1.2) = 1.58; y(1.3) = 2.10.$

3.17 Determine recurrence equations of the Runge-Fox type (see Secs. 3.5, 3.6) for the solution of the simultaneous equations:

$$y' = y + z \qquad z' = z - y$$

$$y_0 = 0.1 \qquad z_0 = 0.2$$

and apply them to the evaluation of $y(x)$ and $z(x)$ in the interval $x = 0(0.1)0.3$, ignoring the corrections.

Ans. $y_1 = 0.1326$; $y_2 = 0.1696$, $y_3 = 0.2112$; $z_1 = 0.2088$, $z_2 = 0.2149$, $z_3 = 0.2176$.

3.18 Evaluate to three significant figures by Adams's method in the interval $x = 0(0.1)0.4$ the functions $y(x)$ and $z(x)$, satisfying the following equations and conditions. Start the solution by a Taylor series and use differences up to the second order.

(a) $y' = 2z^2 - y$, $y(0) = 1$; $z' = zy$, $z(0) = 1$.
(b) $y' = z - y^2$, $y(0) = 1$; $z' = zy$, $z(0) = 1$.

Ans. (a) $y(0.3) = 1.492$, $y(0.4) = 1.803$; $z(0.3) = 1.434$, $z(0.4) = 1.683$.
(b) $y(0.3) = 1.041$, $y(0.4) = 1.072$; $z(0.3) = 1.355$, $z(0.4) = 1.506$.

3.19 Evaluate to four significant figures the integral of the following problem at $x = 1.0(0.1)1.5$, using the Adams-Störmer method with differences up to the second order. Start the solution by a Taylor series.

$$y'' + 3xy' + x^2y = e^x \qquad y(0) = 1, \quad y'(0) = 1.$$

3.20 Evaluate to three significant figures the integral of the following problem at $x = 0(0.2)1.0$, using the Adams-Störmer method with differences up to the second order, after starting the solution by a Taylor series.

$$xy'' + y' + xy = 0; \qquad y(0) = 1; \quad y'(0) = 0.$$

Ans. $y(0.6) = 0.912$; $y(0.8) = 0.847$; $y(1.0) = 0.766$.

3.21 Evaluate to four significant figures the integral of the following problem at $x = 0(0.1)0.6$, using the Adams-Störmer method with differences up to the second order. Start the solution by a Taylor series.

$$y'' + yy' = x^2; \quad y(0) = 1; \quad y'(0) = 1.$$

3.22 Evaluate to four significant figures the integral of the following problem at $x = 1.0(0.1)1.5$, using the Adams-Störmer method with differences up to the second order. Start the solution by a Taylor series.

$$y'' + y^2y' = x^3; \quad y(1) = 1; \quad y'(1) = 1.$$

Ans. $y(1.3) = 1.3053$; $y(1.4) = 1.4132$; $y(1.5) = 1.5266.$

3.23 Evaluate to four significant figures the integral of the following problem at $x = 0(0.1)0.5$, after starting the solution by a Taylor series:

$$y'' + 2xy = 3x^3 + 1; \quad y(0) = 1; \quad y'(0) = 1.$$

(a) Use the general Adams-Störmer method with differences of the second order.

(b) Use the Adams-Störmer recurrence equation valid when y' is absent.

3.24 Evaluate to four significant figures the integral of the following problem at $x = 0(0.1)0.5$:

$$y'' + x^2 y = 3e^x; \quad y(0) = 1; \quad y'(0) = 1.$$

(a) Use the general Adams-Störmer method with differences up to the second order.

(b) Use the Adams-Störmer recurrence equation valid when y' is absent. Start the solutions by a Taylor series.

Ans. (a) $y(0.3) = 1.1488$; $y(0.4) = 1.2730$; $y(0.5) = 1.4400$. (b) 1.1489; 1.2731; 1.4400.

3.25 An elastic sphere of mass 1 is pressed slightly against a rigid flat body and then released from rest at $t = 0$. Express the displacement of a point of the sphere away from the point of contact (the so-called *approach* α) in terms of the time t by means of a Taylor series. The differential equation of motion of the sphere is given by: $m\ddot{\alpha} + k\alpha^{3/2} = 0$, where k is the elastic constant of the sphere,* and the initial conditions state that

$$\alpha(0) = \alpha_0; \quad \dot{\alpha}(0) = 0.$$

Evaluate α at $t = 0.1$ and $t = 0.2$ by a Taylor series expansion, and prolong the solution to $t = 0.5$ by the Adams-Störmer formula, assuming $k = 10$ and $\alpha_0 = 1$.

3.26 A rocket of mass M is launched vertically from the earth's surface $(x = R)$ with an initial speed V_0. Determine by the Adams-Störmer method, using first-order differences, the value of x for $t = 0(1)6$, assuming air resistance proportional to the velocity, and the earth's attraction inversely proportional to x^2, if in a consistent set of units:

$$R = 10; \quad V_0 = 5; \quad \mu = 0.1; \quad k = 1,$$

where μ is the coefficient of air resistance per unit of mass, and k is the

---

* See, for example, S. Timoshenko, *Theory of Elasticity*, McGraw-Hill Book Company, Inc., New York, 1934, pp. 339 ff.

gravitational constant. (*Note:* The equation governing the displacement is: $M\ddot{x} + \mu M\dot{x} + Mk/x^2 = 0.*$)

Ans.

t	0	1	2	3	4	5	6
x	10.00	14.75	19.03	22.90	26.41	29.58	32.45

3.27 Prolong the solution of Problem 3.6 to the interval 0.2(0.1)0.5 by the Adams-Störmer method using second-order differences.

3.28 A body of mass M oscillates freely on a horizontal frictionless slide under the action of a nonlinear spring, whose spring rate equals $k_0 + rx^2$. The body goes through the origin $x = 0$ with a velocity v_0. Determine the value of x for $t = 0(0.5)3$ by the Adams-Störmer method using second order differences, for the following values of the constants in a consistent system of units:

$$M = 1, \quad k_0 = 1, \quad r = \tfrac{1}{2}, \quad v_0 = 1.$$

(*Note:* The equation governing the motion is: $M\ddot{x} + (k_0 + rx^2)x = 0.†$)

Ans.

t	0	0.5	1.0	1.5	2.0	2.5	3.0
x	0	0.478	0.823	0.892	0.658	0.236	−0.244

3.29 The body of Problem 3.28 oscillates under the action of a spring of spring rate $k_0 - rx^2$, where $k_0 = 1$, $r = \tfrac{1}{2}$, and starts at $x = 1$ with zero speed. Determine the value of x in the interval $t = 0(1)4$ by the Adams-Störmer method, using second-order differences.

3.30 The equation of motion for an electron placed in an electrostatic field due to an infinite positively charged wire is‡

$$m\ddot{x} + \frac{k}{x} = 0,$$

where x is the distance of the electron from the wire. If $k/m = 2$, and the electron starts from rest at a distance of 8 units from the wire at $t = 0$, determine x for $t = 0(2)10$ by the Adams-Störmer recurrence formula, using second-order differences. *Note:* Assume that the electron can cross the wire through an infinitesimal gap.

* See, for example, *Differential Equations*, Sec. 9.2.
† See, for example, *Differential Equations*, Sec. 9.8.
‡ See, for example, *Differential Equations*, Sec. 7.5.

Ans.

t	0	2	4	6	8	10
x	8.000	7.496	5.943	3.026	-2.620	-4.630

3.31   Evaluate to three significant figures the first and second approximations of the integral of the following problem at $x = 0(0.2)1.0$, using Fox's method and the first two terms of the error expansion:

$$xy'' + y' + xy = 0; \quad y(0) = 1; \quad y'(0) = 0.$$

Ans. $y(0.4) = 0.960; y(0.6) = 0.912; y(0.8) = 0.847; y(1.0) = 0.766.$

3.32   Evaluate to four significant figures, the integral of the following problem at $x = 0(0.2)1.0$, using Fox's method:

$$y'' + 3xy' + x^2y = e^x; \quad y(0) = 1; \quad y'(0) = 1.$$

3.33   Evaluate to three significant figures, the first and second approximations of the integral of the following problem at $x = 0(0.4)2.0$, using Fox's method and the first two terms of the error expansion:

$$xy'' + y' + xy = 0; \quad y(0) = 1; \quad y'(0) = 0.$$

Ans. $y(0.8) = 0.846; y(1.2) = 0.671; y(1.6) = 0.456; y(2.0) = 0.224.$

3.34   Evaluate to three significant figures the integral of the following problem at $x = 0(0.1)0.5$ by the Noumerov-Fox recurrence formula:

$$y'' + x^2y = 3e^x; \quad y(0) = 1; \quad y'(0) = 1.$$

Evaluate $y(0.1)$ by Taylor series.

3.35   Evaluate to four significant figures the integral of the following problem at $x = 0(0.1)0.5$ by the Noumerov-Fox recurrence formula:

$$y'' + 2xy = 3x^3 + 1; \quad y(0) = 1; \quad y'(0) = 1.$$

Ans.   Taylor series: $y(0) = 1; y(0.1) = 1.105.$ $y(0.2) = 1.217; y(0.3) = 1.335; y(0.4) = 1.456; y(0.5) = 1.577.$

3.36   A mathematical pendulum of length L (Fig. 3.3) moves through the origin $\theta = 0$ at $t = 0$ with an angular velocity $\dot{\theta} = 1$ radian per sec. Assuming small deflections, determine the values of θ in the interval $0(0.1)0.5$, by the Noumerov-Fox recurrence formula, assuming $g/L = 20$ sec^{-2}.

(a) Obtain θ at $t = 0.1$ and $t = 0.2$ by approximating θ_0 by $\mu \left(\delta - \dfrac{\delta^3}{6} \right) \theta_0$ and by applying the difference equation at $t = -0.1$ $t = 0$, and $t = 0.1$.

(b) Obtain θ at $t = 0.1$ by means of a Taylor series.

3.37 The pendulum of Problem 3.36 oscillates in a viscous medium of $\mu = 1.2$ per unit mass. Determine the values of θ in the interval $0(0.1)0.5$ by the Fox method. *Note:* Obtain θ at $t = 0.1$ by Taylor series.

t	0.1	0.2	0.3	0.4	0.5	0.6
θ	0.091	0.155	0.182	0.171	0.130	0.068

Ans.

3.38 The series R-L-C circuit of Fig. 3.6 contains an inductance L of 0.1 henry, a capacitance C of 0.05 μf ($0.05 \cdot 10^{-6}$ farad) and a resistance R

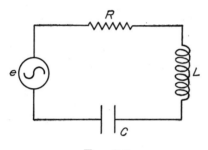

FIG. 3.6

of 5000 ohms. The circuit elements are connected in series with a 22.5-v battery and switch. There is no initial charge q on the capacitor, and no current i flows in the circuit at time $t = 0$.

(a) Find the charge q after the switch is closed by the Fox method in the interval $t = 0(0.01)0.04$ sec.

(b) Determine the charge q in the same circuit if $R = 0$.

(c) Determine the charge in the same circuit if $R = 2000$ ohms and a current of 5 ma flows initially in the same direction in which the battery voltage is applied. *Note:* The differential equation of the circuit is given by:

$$L\ddot{q} + R\dot{q} + (1/C)q = e,$$

where e is the battery voltage. The current i is the time derivative of the charge q.

Ans. (b) True values of q:

$10^2 t$	1	2	3	4
q	0.0112	0.0439	0.0998	0.1753

3.39 Prove that the step-by-step integration of the problem:

$$y'' + \omega^2 y = 0; \quad y(0) = 1; \quad y'(0) = 0,$$

obtained by substituting $\delta^2 y$ for $h^2 y''$, leads to an oscillating solution with a frequency equal to 1.11ω when the time interval $h = T/4.44$, where $T = 2\pi/\omega$ is the period of the true solution; and that the solution diverges for $h > T/4.44$.

The Numerical Integration of Ordinary
Boundary Value Problems

4.1 Boundary Value Problems

The solution of ordinary boundary value problems by finite differences reduces the integration of a differential equation to the evaluation of the roots of a system of simultaneous algebraic equations. These roots are the values of the required solution at the pivotal points of its interval of definition, which is one-dimensional for ordinary differential equations.

Problems involving first-order, ordinary differential equations are necessarily of the initial value type. Boundary value problems lead, instead, to second- and higher-order equations; of these the odd-order equations, with different numbers of conditions at the two ends of the interval, are sometimes hard to handle numerically and are usually transformed into even-order equations by either integration or differentiation.

Whenever possible, the derivatives appearing in the differential equation are expanded in terms of central differences, since the accuracy of these expansions is greater than the accuracy obtainable by lateral differences.

The derivatives involved in the boundary conditions of the problem may be expressed in terms of lateral or of central differences. For example, the following boundary conditions at the origin are translated by means of Eqs. (2.7.16) into the corresponding central difference conditions by using the first term of their expansions:

$$
\begin{aligned}
y(0) &= 0 & y_0 &= 0 \\
y'(0) &= 0 & y_1 - y_{-1} &= 0 \\
y''(0) &= 0 & y_1 - 2y_0 + y_{-1} &= 0
\end{aligned}
\tag{4.1.1}
$$

$$y'''(0) = 0 \qquad y_2 - 2y_1 + 2y_{-1} - y_{-2} = 0$$
$$y^{IV}(0) = 0 \qquad y_2 - 4y_1 + 6y_0 - 4y_{-1} + y_{-2} = 0. \tag{4.1.1}$$

These equations are actually used to define the values y_{-1} and y_{-2}, which lie beyond the interval of definition of y, in terms of y_0, y_1, y_2, and have errors of order h^2.

When central differences of order h^2 are used in the equations, and either forward or backward differences are used in the boundary conditions, these last should also have errors of order h^2 whenever possible. Hence, for example, the conditions of Eqs. (4.1.1) should be expressed in terms of the difference operators of Fig. 2.5b:

$$y(0) = 0, \qquad y_0 = 0$$
$$y'(0) = 0, \qquad -y_2 + 4y_1 - 3y_0 = 0$$
$$y''(0) = 0, \qquad -y_3 + 4y_2 - 5y_1 + 2y_0 = 0 \tag{4.1.2}$$
$$y'''(0) = 0, \qquad -3y_4 + 14y_3 - 24y_2 + 18y_1 - 5y_0 = 0$$
$$y^{IV}(0) = 0, \qquad -2y_5 + 11y_4 - 24y_3 + 26y_2 - 14y_1 + 3y_0 = 0.$$

4.2   Step-by-Step Integration of Boundary Value Problems

Ordinary boundary value problems of the second order can be solved by the methods of Chapter III, that is, by step-by-step forward integration formulas, in conjunction with trial and error and/or interpolation procedures.

Consider, for example, the simple problem:

$$y'' - y = 0; \qquad y(0) = 0, \quad y(1) = 1 \tag{a}$$

and start its solution by a Taylor series, *assuming* the value y'_0 to be equal to 1:

$$y_0 = 0, \quad y'_0 = 1, \quad y_0'' = 0, \quad y_0''' = 1, \quad \dots$$
$$y = x + \frac{x^3}{3!} + \frac{x^5}{5!} + \dots = \sinh x.$$

The value of y at 1 equals in this case:

$$y(1) = 1 + \frac{1}{3!} + \frac{1}{5!} + \dots = \sinh 1 = 1.175,$$

and has an error of $+0.175$.   For $y'_0 = 0$, the Taylor solution would

give $y(x) \equiv 0$ and hence $y(1) = 0$ with an error of -1.0.   Interpolating linearly between the two assumed values of y'_0 [Eq. (1.2.6)],
we obtain:

$$y'_0 = \frac{1 \cdot (-1) - 0 \cdot (0.175)}{-1 - 0.175} = 0.851,$$

and with this value of y'_0 a Taylor series gives the new approximation:

$$y_0 = 0, \quad y'_0 = 0.851, \quad y_0'' = 0, \quad y_0''' = 0.851, \quad \ldots$$

$$y = 0.851 \left(x + \frac{x^3}{3!} + \frac{x^5}{5!} + \ldots \right) = 0.851 \sinh x, \qquad \text{(b)}$$

whose value at $x = 1$ equals

$$y(1) = 0.851 \sinh 1 = 1.000.$$

The value of y given by Eq. (b) is therefore the solution of the
boundary problem (a).

In general, the interpolation process will have to be applied
more than once before the solution is obtained.   Any other method
of step-by-step integration can, of course, be used in the same way
to solve second-order boundary value problems.

The forward integration method of this section is particularly
useful in solving nonlinear equations, since the methods of the
following sections can be applied only to linear equations in the
general case.

4.3   Solution of Second Order Problems by Central Differences

In order to illustrate the general method of solution of ordinary
boundary value problems by central differences, we shall consider
the heat-flow problem of determining the temperature u in a
circular wire of length L and radius R, connecting two bodies kept
at constant temperatures u_0 and u_n, respectively, and losing heat
to the surrounding medium kept at a temperature $U(x)$ (Fig. 4.1).

Equating the heat entering an element of length dx of the wire to
the heat leaving its surface, it may be found* that the boundary

* See, for example, *Differential Equations*, Sec. 2.13.

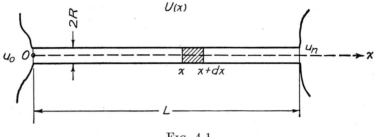

Fɪɢ. 4.1

value problem in question reduces to:

$$u'' - \frac{2k_1}{kR} u = - \frac{2k_1}{kR} U$$

$$u(0) = u_0 \qquad u(L) = u_n,$$

(4.3.1)

where: k = the thermal conductivity of the wire,

k_1 = boundary conductance of the wire,

x = axis of wire with origin at left end.

To reduce the problem to nondimensional form, let

$$z = \frac{x}{L}; \quad v(z) = \frac{u(x)}{u_n}; \quad F(z) = \frac{U(x)}{U(0)},$$

obtaining:

$$v'' - \frac{2k_1 L^2}{kR} v = - \frac{2k_1 L^2}{kR} \frac{U(0)}{u_n} F(z)$$

$$v(0) = \frac{u_0}{u_n} \qquad v(1) = 1,$$

(4.3.2)

where primes indicate differentiation with respect to z.

In a particular case it will be assumed that:

$$L = 100 \text{ cm}, R = 1 \text{ cm},$$

$$k = 1 \text{ cal/sec } °C \text{ cm}^2/\text{cm},$$

$$k_1 = 6 \cdot 10^{-4}(\tfrac{3}{2}z + \tfrac{1}{3}) \text{ cal/sec } °C \text{ cm}^2,*$$

$$u_0 = 0, \quad U(0)/u_n = 1,$$

$$F(z) = e^z,$$

---

* The boundary conductance k_1 is known to vary linearly between 0°C and 500°C to a first approximation.

so that the boundary value problem of Eqs. (4.3.2) reduces to

$$v'' - 2(9z + 2)v = -2(9z + 2)e^z,$$
$$v(0) = 0, \qquad v(1) = 1. \tag{4.3.3}$$

To transform Eqs. (4.3.3) into the corresponding difference problem, the interval of definition $(0,1)$ of the variable z is divided into n equal parts of width $h = 1/n$, the differential equation is multiplied by h^2, and $(\delta^2 v + \epsilon_2)$ is substituted for $h^2 v''$, according to Eq. (2.7.16). The equation thus becomes:

$$v_l - 2v_i + v_r + \epsilon_{2i} - 2h^2(9z_i + 2)v_i = -2h^2(9z_i + 2)e^{z_i}$$

or:

$$v_l - c_{hi}v_i + v_r = -(c_{hi} - 2)e^{z_i} - \epsilon_{2i} \qquad (i = 1,2, \ldots, n-1),$$

(4.3.4)

where

$$c_{hi} = 2[1 + h^2(9z_i + 2)]. \tag{4.3.5}$$

The boundary conditions are in this case

$$v_0 = 0, \qquad v_n = 1. \tag{4.3.6}$$

Equation (4.3.4) holds, and is applied at the $n - 1$ internal pivotal points, $i = 1, 2, \ldots, n - 1$, and leads to a set of $n - 1$ linear algebraic equations in the $n - 1$ unknown pivotal values v_i. Once this system is solved, v is known, as required, at the $n + 1$ pivotal points $v_i(i = 0,1, \ldots, n)$. By increasing the number of subintervals n, the accuracy of the solution can be indefinitely improved, at least theoretically.

The problem represented by Eqs. (4.3.4), (4.3.6) will now be solved for $n = 2,3,4$, successively, that is for decreasing values of h. The correction ϵ_{2i} will be neglected at first.

Approximation $n = 2$. Eq. (4.3.4) applied at $z_1 = \frac{1}{2}$ (Fig. 4.2a), with

$$v_l = v_0 = 0, \qquad v_r = v_2 = 1,$$
$$h = \tfrac{1}{2}, \qquad c_{h1} = 2[1 + 0.25(9 \cdot 0.5 + 2)] = 5.25,$$

gives

$$0 - 5.25v_1 + 1 = -3.25e^{0.5} = -5.359 \tag{4.3.7}$$

$$v(\tfrac{1}{2}) = v_1^{(1)} = 1.211.$$

Approximation $n = 3$.   Eq. (4.3.4) applied at $z_1 = \frac{1}{3}$, $z_2 = \frac{2}{3}$ (Fig. 4.2b), with

$$v_0 = 0, \quad v_n = v_3 = 1$$

$$h = \tfrac{1}{3}, \quad c_{hi} = 2[1 + \tfrac{1}{9}(9z_i + 2)],$$

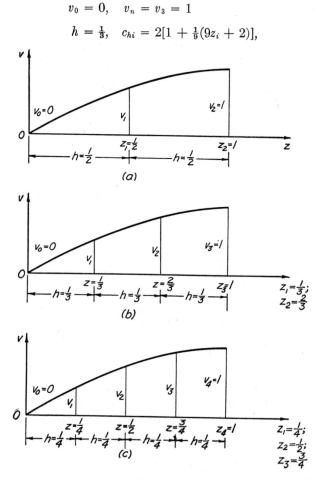

(a)

(b)

(c)

Fig. 4.2

gives:

at $z_1 = \frac{1}{3}$ $0 - 3.1111v_1 + v_2 = -1.1111e^{1/3} = -1.5507,$

at $z_2 = \frac{2}{3}$ $v_1 - 3.7778v_2 + 1 = -1.7778e^{2/3} = -3.4628,$

$$v(\tfrac{1}{3}) = v_1^{(1)} = 0.9599, \quad v(\tfrac{2}{3}) = v_2^{(1)} = 1.4354.$$

Approximation $n = 4$. Eq. (4.3.4) applied at $z_1 = \frac{1}{4}$, $z_2 = \frac{1}{2}$, $z_3 = \frac{3}{4}$ (Fig. 4.2c), with

$$v_0 = 0, \quad v_n = v_4 = 1,$$

$$h = \tfrac{1}{4}, \quad c_{hi} = 2[1 + \tfrac{1}{16}(9z_i + 2)]$$

gives:

at $z_1 = \frac{1}{4}$ $-2.5312\, v_1 + v_2 = -0.6821,$

at $z_2 = \frac{1}{2}$ $v_1 - 2.8125\, v_2 + v_3 = -1.3396,$ (4.3.8)

at $z_3 = \frac{3}{4}$ $v_2 - 3.0938\, v_3 = -3.3156.$

Equations (4.3.8) can be solved by any of the methods given in Chapter I. For example, the solution *by relaxation* of this system was given in Table 1.12 as:

$$v_1^{(1)} = 0.7753; \quad v_2^{(1)} = 1.2802; \quad v_3^{(1)} = 1.4855, \quad (4.3.9)$$

and is labeled $v_i^{(1)}$ to indicate that it is a first approximation in which the corrections ϵ have been neglected.

Table 4.1

n	1	2	3	4
v_1	0.6646	0.6915	0.7539	0.7699
v_2	1.0682	1.2260	1.2664	1.2767
v_3	1.4169	1.4680	1.4810	1.4843
n	5	6	7	8
v_1	0.7739	0.7750	0.7752	0.7753
v_2	1.2793	1.2800	1.2802	1.2802
v_3	1.4852	1.4854	1.4855	1.4855

The same solution is obtained *by iteration* in Table 4.1, with starting values $v_2^{(0)} = 1$, $v_3^{(0)} = 1$.

Table 4.2 gives the solution of the system (4.3.8), once again, by Cholesky's method.

By increasing the number of pivotal points the graph of $v(z)$ can be obtained to any degree of accuracy at the cost of increased labor.

Table 4.2

	v_1	v_2	v_3	c	1	2	3	v_1	v_2	v_3	k
1	2.5312	-1	0	0.6821	2.5312	0	0	1	-0.3951	0	0.2695
2	-1	2.8125	-1	1.3396	-1	2.4174	0	0	1	-0.4137	0.6656
3	0	-1	3.0938	3.3156	0	-1	2.6801	0	0	1	1.4855

$$v_3 = 1.4855$$
$$v_2 = 0.6656 + 0.4137 \cdot 1.4845 = 1.2802$$
$$v_1 = 0.2695 + 0.3951 \cdot 1.2802 = 0.7753$$

The accuracy of $v(z)$ may also be increased with small additional labor by the use of Fox's corrections or by extrapolation, as shown in the following sections.

4.4   Improvement of Solution by Corrections

[a]   Gauss's scheme

The system of Eqs. (4.3.8) appears solved by Gauss's scheme in the first five columns of Table 4.3.   Its roots $v_i^{(1)}$ appear on the first row of the lower part of the table and check (within one unit in the last significant figure) the roots computed by relaxation, iteration, or Cholesky's scheme.

The roots $v_i^{(1)}$ are obtained neglecting the corrections ϵ.   To evaluate the corrections, the successive central differences of the $v_i^{(1)}$ are evaluated in Table 4.4.   For lack of better values, the fourth difference $\delta^4 v$ is assumed constant and equal to $\delta^4 v_2 = -0.3618$, the assumed values of $\delta^4 v_i$ appearing enclosed in parentheses.   By means of $\delta^4 v$ and the first term in the expansion of ϵ_2 [Eq. (2.7.16)], an approximate value of the correction ϵ_2 is given by:

$$\epsilon_2^{(1)} \doteq -\frac{\delta^4 v}{12} = 0.0301,$$

Table 4.3

Rows	v_1	v_2	v_3	c	$c + \epsilon'_2$	$c + \epsilon''_2$	Explanation
1	-2.5312	1	0	-0.6821	-0.7122	-0.7130	I
2	1	-2.8125	1	-1.3396	-1.3697	-1.3705	II
3	0	1	-3.0938	-3.3156	-3.3457	-3.3465	III
4	2.5312	-7.1190	2.5312	-3.3908	-3.4670	-3.4690	$2.5312 \times (2)$
5		-6.1190	2.5312	-4.0729	-4.1792	-4.1820	$(1) + (4)$
6		6.1190	-18.9310	-20.2882	-20.4723	-20.4772	$6.1190 \times (3)$
7			-16.3998	-24.3611	-24.6515	-24.6592	$(5) + (6)$

Approx.	v_1 from row 1	v_2 from row 3	v_3 from row 7	for
1	0.7752	1.2801	1.4854	c
2	0.7968	1.3048	1.5032	$c + \epsilon'_2$
3	0.7974	1.3054	1.5036	$c + \epsilon''_2$

which, substituted in Eqs. (4.3.8), gives:

at $z = \frac{1}{4}$ $-2.5312v_1 + v_2 = -0.6821 - 0.0301 = -0.7122,$

at $z = \frac{1}{2}$ $v_1 - 2.8125v_2 + v_3 = -1.3396 - 0.0301 = -1.3697,$

at $z = \frac{3}{4}$ $v_2 - 3.0938v_3 = -3.3156 - 0.0301 = -3.3457.$

$$(4.4.1)$$

The system (4.4.1) has the same coefficients as system (4.3.8), but different constants. It may therefore be conveniently solved by adding a new column of constants to the Gauss's scheme of

Table 4.4

i	v_i	$\delta v_{i+\frac{1}{2}}$	$\delta^2 v_i$	$\delta^3 v_{i+\frac{1}{2}}$	$\delta^4 v_i$	ϵ_2
0	0					
		0.7752				
1	0.7752		-0.2703		(-0.3618)	(0.0301)
		0.5049		-0.0293		
2	1.2801		-0.2996		-0.3618	0.0301
		$+0.2053$		-0.3911		
3	1.4854		-0.6907		(-0.3618)	(0.0301)
		-0.4855				
4	1.0000					

Table 4.3. Its roots $v_i^{(2)}$ appear in the second row of the lower part of Table 4.3.

Differencing the $v_i^{(2)}$ we obtain, similarly, an improved value of the correction ϵ_2 and a new set of values for the constants in the right-hand members of Table 4.3. Solving these equations, we obtain the approximations $v_i^{(3)}$ of v, and the process is continued until the corrections become stable. In the present problem this takes place in the third approximation and leads to the final values appearing in the third row of the lower part of Table 4.3.

Fox's corrections may also be used in connection with the approximation $n = 2$ of the same problem (page 137), by expressing the correction in terms of v^{IV} [Eq. (2.7.10)]:

$$\epsilon_2 \doteq -\frac{h^4 v^{IV}}{12}. \qquad (a)$$

v^{IV} is obtained by two differentiations of Eq. (4.3.3):

$$v^{IV} = 2(9z + 2)v'' + 36v' - 2(9z + 20)e^z,$$

and using again Eq. (4.3.3):

$$v^{IV} = 2(9z + 2)[2(9z + 2)v - 2(9z + 2)e^z] + 36v' - 2(9z + 20)e^z.$$

In this expression the derivative v' is replaced by the corresponding averaged central difference

$$v'_1 \doteq \mu\delta v_1 = \frac{v_2 - v_0}{2} = 0.5.$$

Applying Eq. (a) at $z = \frac{1}{2}$ with $v' = 0.5$, we obtain

$$\epsilon_2^{(1)} = - \frac{h^4 v^{IV}}{12} = 0.619$$

and hence a corrected equation (4.3.7)

$$-5.25v_1 + 1 = -5.359 - 0.619 = -5.978,$$

from which $v_1^{(2)} = 1.329$. Repeating the process we find, successively:

$$\epsilon_2^{(2)} = 0.515, \qquad v_1^{(3)} = 1.309,$$

$$\epsilon_2^{(3)} = 0.533, \qquad v_1^{(4)} = 1.313,$$

$$\epsilon_2^{(4)} = 0.529, \qquad v_1^{(5)} = 1.312.$$

The same method of approximating the correction by derivatives could have been used in the solution for $n = 4$.

[b]   Relaxation

Relaxation becomes particularly efficient when Fox's corrections are used to improve the results obtained by rough finite difference formulas. For instance, it was found above that a first correction $\epsilon_2^{(1)} = 0.0301$ had to be added to all constants of the system (4.3.8) to obtain the corrected system (4.4.1). Hence the constants k of the corrected system ˙(4.4.1), *ready for iteration*, equal the constants $k^{(1)}$ of the uncorrected system (4.3.8) ready for iteration [system (c), Sec. 1.10] increased by $\delta k_i^{(1)} = \epsilon_2^{(1)}/a_{ii}$:

$$\delta k_1^{(1)} = 0.0301/2.5312 = 0.0119$$

$$\delta k_2^{(1)} = 0.0301/2.8125 = 0.0107$$

$$\delta k_3^{(1)} = 0.0301/3.0938 = 0.0097.$$

Therefore, if the roots of the uncorrected system from Table 1.12 are used as starting values, the residuals R_i equal the δk_i, and the corrected roots may be computed by relaxation of these residuals. As shown in Table 4.5, block relaxation may be used in the first

Table 4.5

	7753	~~119~~	12802	~~107~~	14855	~~87~~
	200	~~1~~	200	~~51~~	200	~~−39~~
	19	~~19~~	50	~~1~~	−23	~~−28~~
		−1		−2	~~−9~~	−1
					~~−2~~	
$v_i{}^{(2)}$	7972	−1	13050	1	15032	0

step with rounded-off coefficients [system (d), Sec. 1.10] and with $\delta = 200$, and the final residuals are computed with the complete coefficients of system (c), Sec. 1.10.

The second corrections $\epsilon_i{}^{(2)}$, obtained by means of the values $v_i{}^{(2)}$, lead to new increments $\delta k_i = \epsilon_i{}^{(2)}/a_{ii}$:

$$\delta k_1{}^{(2)} = 0.0122, \quad \delta k_2{}^{(2)} = 0.0110, \quad \delta k_3{}^{(2)} = 0.0100,$$

which differ by 3 units in the last place from the previous $\delta k_i{}^{(1)}$. Hence, using as initial values the $v_i{}^{(2)}$ of Table 4.5 and these differences of 0.0003 as residuals, we obtain the third approximations $v_i{}^{(3)}$ with a small amount of additional labor, as shown in Table 4.6.

Table 4.6

	7972	~~8~~	13050	~~8~~	15032	~~8~~
	4	~~4~~	3	~~1~~	4	~~4~~
		1	3	~~3~~	~~8~~	1
$v_i{}^{(3)}$	7976	0	13056	0	15036	1

A more accurate graph of the temperature function $v(z)$ may be obtained by subdividing its interval of definition $(0,1)$ into 6 subintervals of width $h = \frac{1}{6}$. The set of linear equations for the pivotal values v_i becomes in this case, by Eq. (4.3.4), the system of

Table 4.7. This system is relaxed in Table 4.8 with initial values obtained by linear interpolation from the roots corresponding to $h = \frac{1}{4}$. The residuals are checked after obtaining 3, 4, and 5 figures of the roots; the corrections are evaluated by differences.*

Table 4.7

v_1	v_2	v_3	v_4	v_5	k	Block Coefficients
-1	0.4557				0.1047	-0.5443
0.4390	-1	0.4390			0.1702	-0.1220
	0.4235	-1	0.4235		0.2521	-0.1530
		0.4091	-1	0.4091	0.3541	-0.1818
			0.3596	-1	0.8760	-0.6404

The second approximations of the roots are then computed and differenced again to obtain the corrections to the corrections and hence the third approximation of the roots.

4.5 Improvement of Solution by Extrapolation

In the previous sections the temperature function $v(z)$ in the boundary value problem (4.3.3) was obtained by means of central differences. In particular, h^2v'' was approximated by δ^2v, and this entails an error of order h^2 in v. Hence the h^2- and (h^2, h^4)-extrapolations [Sec. 2.9], can be used to improve, for example, the value of $v(\frac{1}{2})$.

Table 4.9 gives the first approximation values of $v(\frac{1}{2})$ obtained by means of $n = 2, 4,$ and 6 subintervals; the values of the h^2-extrapolation for $n_2/n_1 = 4/2$ and $n_2/n_1 = 6/4$, and the values of the (h^2, h^4)-extrapolation for $n_3/n_2/n_1 = 6/4/2$. The extrapolation coefficients were taken from Table 2.9 and Table 2.10, respectively.

For example, the h^2-extrapolation

$$v(\tfrac{1}{2}) \Big]_{2,4} = 1.3333 \cdot 1.2802 - 0.3333 \cdot 1.2110 = 1.3033$$

is only 0.16 per cent off the value $v_2^{(3)} = 1.3054$ obtained by 4 subintervals and 2 corrections (Table 4.3). Similarly, the value

$$v(\tfrac{1}{2}) \Big]_{4,6} = 1.8 \cdot 1.2957 - 0.8 \cdot 1.2802 = 1.3081$$

* The sixth difference was assumed constant in this example.

Table 4.8

	v_1	v_2	v_3	v_4	v_5		Explanations
	0.56	0 1.00	−1 1.31	−8 1.43	8 1.33	11	Initial values and residuals.
				6	8 12	−1	
					−1		
	0.560	0 1.000	−9 1.310	−8 1.490	−7 1.450	15	Roots to one unit in the second decimal place.
	−5	−4 −9	−8 −7	−7 −3	0 16	−1	
		8 −3	−2	−1	−3	−2	
				−2			
	0.5550	−1 0.9880	−21 1.3030	−27 1.4870	−1 1.4660	−17	Roots to one unit in the third decimal place.
	−24	−19 −40	−28 −40	13 −30	−17 −30	−29	
	−7	−23 −8	2 −20	−8 −10	13 −3	1	
		1 −12	−7 −8	−18 −3	1	−8	
		−8 −4	1 −5	1	−7	−1	
		1	−16	−2	−16		
		−1	2	7	−2		
			−1	1	−8		
			−4	−8			
			−2	−8			
				−1			
	0.5519	1 0.9816	−8 1.2957	0 1.4827	−1 1.4627	−1	Check of residuals.
		−3		−4			
$v_i^{(1)}$	0.5519	5 0.9813	7 1.2957	24 1.4827	58 1.4627	95	First approximations to one unit in the fourth decimal place and first corrections.
	40	37 70	60 120	92 160	114 150	−58	
	3	−8 10	−16 8	−28 6	−46 10	8	
		2 3	8 2	2 4	3	10	
		8	−2	8	8	2	
			2	−2	4		
			8	1	1		
			1	2			
				1			
		0	0	0	0	−1	Check of residuals
$v_i^{(2)}$	0.5562	1 0.9896	1 1.3087	1 1.4997	2 1.4787	3	Second approximations and corrections to the corrections.
	2	2 2	2 3	8 4	4 4	−1	
		1	1	1	1	1	
$v_i^{(3)}$	0.5564	0.9899	1.3090	1.5001	1.4791		Third approximations.

is only 0.07 per cent off the value $v_3{}^{(3)} = 1.3090$ obtained by 6 sub-intervals with 2 corrections (Table 4.8), presumably the best value obtainable without extrapolation.

Table 4.9 contains also the values of $v(\tfrac{1}{2})$, obtained by 2, 4, and 6 subintervals, improved by means of Fox's corrections. Since the inclusion of a correction $-\delta^4 v/12$ is equivalent to taking into account the first *two* terms in the difference expansion for $h^2 D^2$ [Eq. (2.7.15)], the error in the second derivative of the *corrected*

Table 4.9

n	Uncor-rected $v(\tfrac{1}{2})$	n	h^2-extr.	n	(h^2,h^4)-extr.	Cor-rected $v(\tfrac{1}{2})$	n	h^4-extr.
2	1.2110	2,4	1.3033	2,4,6	1.3088	1.3120	2,4	1.3050
4	1.2802	4,6	1.3081			1.3054	4,6	1.3099
6	1.2957					1.3090		

solution is of order h^4, and h^4-extrapolations may be applied to the corrected values of $v(\tfrac{1}{2})$. The results of the h^4-extrapolation applied to the corrected values appear in Table 4.9 for $n_2/n_1 = 4/2$ and $n_2/n_1 = 6/4$. Thus, with the coefficients of Table 2.11, we have:

$$v(\tfrac{1}{2})\Big]_{2,4} = 1.0667 \cdot 1.3054 - 0.0667 \cdot 1.3120 = 1.3050,$$

$$v(\tfrac{1}{2})\Big]_{4,6} = 1.2462 \cdot 1.3090 - 0.2462 \cdot 1.3054 = 1.3099.$$

It is seen from this example that h^2-type extrapolations can be used to good advantage to save the labor of differencing that is involved in computing the corrections.

In connection with the finite difference solution of boundary value problems, it is well to note that better approximations for the derivatives of a function may be obtained either by increasing the number of terms in the finite difference expansions or by decreasing the spacing h. The first procedure involves more complicated formulas and a smaller number of pivotal points, the second a larger number of pivotal points and simpler formulas. The choice between these two methods rests essentially with the type of problem to be handled and with the mental make-up of the computer, but only a decrease in h can guarantee an approach to the correct solution.

4.6 Solution of Higher-Order Problems by Central Differences

As an example of solution by central differences of a boundary value problem involving higher-order derivatives, consider the deflections of a beam on an elastic foundation under a uniform

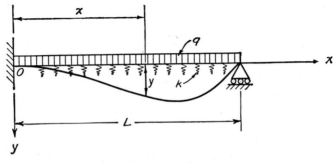

FIG. 4.3

load q.   The beam has a flexural rigidity EI, is built in at the left end $(x = 0)$ and simply supported at the right end $(x = L)$ (Fig. 4.3).

The boundary value problem governing the beam deflections y is given by*

$$y^{\mathrm{IV}} + \frac{k}{EI}\, y = \frac{q}{EI};$$

$$y(0) = y'(0) = y(L) = y''(L) = 0,$$

(4.6.1)

where k is the *foundation modulus* (force per unit deflection per unit length of beam).

To solve the problem by central differences of order h^2, the equation is first transformed to nondimensional form by the change of variable:

* See, for example, *Differential Equations*, Sec. 10.8.

$$z = \frac{x}{L}; \qquad \frac{d}{dx} = \frac{1}{L}\frac{d}{dz}; \qquad x = 0, \quad z = 0; \qquad x = L, \quad z = 1,$$

and becomes:
$$\frac{d^4y}{dz^4} + \frac{kL^4}{EI}\,y = \frac{qL^4}{EI}$$

The interval of definition $(0,1)$ of z is then divided into n equal parts of length $h = 1/n$, and the equation is multiplied through by $h^4 = 1/n^4$:

$$\frac{h^4\,d^4y}{dz^4} + \frac{kL^4}{n^4EI}\,y = \frac{qL^4}{n^4EI}.$$

Approximating $h^4\,d^4y/dz^4$ by δ^4y_i, we obtain:

$$\delta^4y_i + \frac{kL^4}{n^4EI}\,y_i = \frac{qL^4}{n^4EI}$$

or, by means of Eqs. (2.7.16):

$$y_u - 4y_l + 6y_i - 4y_r + y_{rr} + \frac{kL^4}{n^4EI}\,y_i = \frac{qL^4}{n^4EI}.$$

Letting finally:
$$\frac{kL^4}{EI} = K, \qquad\qquad (4.6.2)$$

the difference equation representing Eq. (4.6.1) takes the form

$$y_u - 4y_l + \left[\frac{K}{n^4} + 6\right]y_i - 4y_r + y_{rr} = \frac{qL^4}{n^4EI}. \qquad (4.6.3)$$

For $k = 375$ psi, $E = 30 \cdot 10^6$ psi, $I = 3 \cdot 10^3 \text{in.}^4$, $L = 120$ in., $q = 6240$ lbs/in., the constant K takes the value 6, the quantity $qL^4/EI = 10$, and Eq. (4.6.3) becomes:

$$y_u - 4y_l + 6\left(\frac{n^4 + 1}{n^4}\right)y_i - 4y_r + y_{rr} = \frac{100}{n^4}. \qquad (a)$$

The boundary conditions of Eq. (4.6.1) are transformed into central difference conditions by Eqs. (4.1.1):

$$y_0 = 0; \quad y_{-1} = y_1; \quad y_n = 0; \quad y_{n+1} = -y_{n-1}. \qquad (b)$$

The difference problem of Eqs. (a) and (b) can now be solved starting with large values of h, that is, small values of n, and the accuracy of y may be increased to any degree of accuracy by increasing n in steps of one.

Approximation n = 2. With $n = 2$ (Fig. 4.4a) Eq. (a) applied at $z = \frac{1}{2}$ gives:

$$y_1 - 4 \cdot 0 + 6 \frac{2^4 + 1}{2^4} y_1 - 4 \cdot 0 - y_1 = \frac{100}{2^4},$$

from which: $y(\frac{1}{2}) = y_1 = 0.98.$

Approximation n = 3. With $n = 3$, Eq. (a) gives:

at $z = \frac{1}{3}$ $y_1 + 6 \frac{3^4 + 1}{3^4} y_1 - 4y_2 = \frac{100}{3^4},$

at $z = \frac{2}{3}$ $-4y_1 + 6 \frac{3^4 + 1}{3^4} y_2 - y_2 = \frac{100}{3^4},$

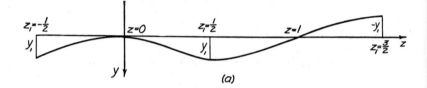

(a)

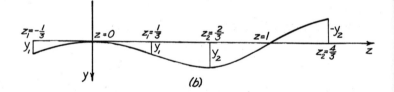

(b)

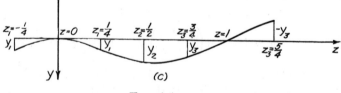

(c)

FIG. 4.4

from which: $y(\frac{1}{3}) = y_1 = 0.56;$ $y(\frac{2}{3}) = y_2 = 0.69.$

Approximation n = 4. With $n = 4$, Eq. (a) gives:

at $z = \frac{1}{4}$ $y_1 + 6 \frac{4^4 + 1}{4^4} y_1 - 4y_2 + y_3 = \frac{100}{4^4},$

at $z = \frac{1}{2}$ $-4y_1 + 6\,\dfrac{4^4 + 1}{4^4}\,y_2 - 4y_3 = \dfrac{100}{4^4}$,

at $z = \frac{3}{4}$ $y_1 - 4y_2 + 6\,\dfrac{4^4 + 1}{4^4}\,y_3 - y_3 = \dfrac{100}{4^4}$,

from which:

$$y(\tfrac{1}{4}) = y_1 = 0.34; \quad y(\tfrac{1}{2}) = y_2 = 0.64; \quad y(\tfrac{3}{4}) = y_3 = 0.51.$$

The value of y at $z = \frac{1}{2}$ may be improved by h^2-extrapolation using the $n = 2$ and $n = 4$ solutions:

$$y(\tfrac{1}{2})\,\Big]_{2,4} = 1.333 \cdot 0.64 - 0.333 \cdot 0.98 = 0.53,$$

and has an error of 4.5 per cent when compared with the value obtained by a rigorous solution of the same problem.

4.7   Solution of Characteristic Value Problems

The numerical solution of characteristic value problems is one of the important branches of modern numerical analysis. It is essential in the fields of vibrations and elastic stability.

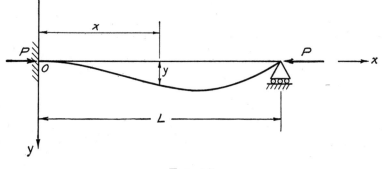

FIG. 4.5

Only one method of solution of such problems, based upon the use of finite differences and extrapolations, will be given in this section.*

* For a complete treatment of the subject, see, for example, L. Collatz, *Eigenwertprobleme und ihre numerische Behandlung*, Chelsea Publishing Company, New York, 1948.

Consider, for example, the Euler buckling problem of a beam, simply supported at the right end $(x = L)$ and built in at the left end $(x = 0)$, acted upon by compressive axial forces P (Fig. 4.5). The deflections y of the axis x of the beam are governed* by the characteristic value problem:

$$y^{IV} + \frac{P}{EI} y'' = 0,$$

$$y(0) = y'(0) = y(L) = y''(L) = 0,$$

(4.7.1)

where EI is the flexural rigidity of the beam.

The corresponding difference problem is obtained by substituting in the differential equation and the boundary conditions the central difference operators of Fig. 2.8a or Eqs. (2.7.16) for the derivatives.

To this purpose, introduce first the change of variable:

$$z = \frac{x}{L}; \qquad \frac{d}{dx} = \frac{1}{L}\frac{d}{dz}; \qquad x = 0, \quad z = 0; \qquad x = L, \quad z = 1,$$

and reduce Eq. (4.7.1) to the nondimensional form

$$y^{IV} + \frac{PL^2}{EI} y'' = 0,$$

(a)

where the derivatives are now taken with respect to z. Dividing the interval of definition $(0,1)$ of z in n equal parts of length $h = 1/n$ and multiplying Eq. (a) by h^4, the equation becomes:

$$h^4 y^{IV} + \frac{PL^2}{n^2 EI} (h^2 y'') = 0.$$

Substitution of $\delta^4 y_i$ for $h^4 y^{IV}$, and of $\delta^2 y_i$ for $h^2 y''$ gives the difference equation:

$$\delta^4 y_i + k_n \delta^2 y_i = 0,$$

(b)

where:

$$k_n = \frac{PL^2}{n^2 EI} = \frac{1}{n^2} K_n.$$

(4.7.2)

Using Eqs. (2.7.16) for $\delta^4 y_i$ and $\delta^2 y_i$, the finite difference equation becomes:

$$y_{ll} - 4y_l + 6y_i - 4y_r + y_{rr} + k_n(y_l - 2y_i + y_r) = 0$$

* See, for example, *Differential Equations*, Sec. 2.11.

and can finally be written in the form:

$$y_{ll} + (k_n - 4)y_l + (6 - 2k_n)y_i + (k_n - 4)y_r + y_{rr} = 0. \quad (4.7.3)$$

Equation (4.7.3) holds at the $n - 1$ internal pivotal points $i = 1$, $2, \ldots, n - 1$.

Conditions (4.7.1) must be satisfied at the ends of the beam: introduction in these conditions of the central difference Eqs. (2.7.16) transforms them into the difference Eqs. (4.1.1):

$$y_0 = 0; \quad y_{-1} = y_1; \quad y_n = 0; \quad y_{n+1} = -y_{n-1}, \quad (4.7.4)$$

where y_{-1} and y_{n+1} are the deflections at the pivotal points of the beam axis prolonged by h beyond the supports. The set of $n - 1$ linear algebraic, *homogeneous* equations (4.7.3) has the trivial solution $y_i = 0$, corresponding to the straight configuration of equilibrium of the beam, but may have a nonzero solution if and only if the determinant Δ of its coefficients (which is a function of k_n) is identically zero.* The determinantal equation

$$\Delta(k_n) = 0 \quad (4.7.5)$$

is an algebraic equation of, say, order p in k_n, whose roots are approximations to the first p characteristic values k and hence to the first p critical loads P. Since the first critical value is the only value of practical importance, the determinantal equation will be solved for its smallest root k.

It is convenient to start the solution with small values of n and to increase the value of n gradually, that is, to reduce the spacing h of the pivotal points as $1/n$.

Approximation $n = 2$. With $n = 2$ (Fig. 4.4a), Eq. (4.7.3) gives:

$$y_1 + (k_2 - 4) \cdot 0 + (6 - 2k_2)y_1 + (k_2 - 4) \cdot 0 - y_1 = 0,$$

or: $$(6 - 2k_2)y_1 = 0.$$

If y_1 is to be different from zero, $6 - 2k_2$ must vanish, $k_2 = 3$, and

$$K_2 = 2^2 k_2 = 12.$$

---

* See, for example, *Engineering Problems*, Sec. 4.7.

Approximation $n = 3$. With $n = 3$ (Fig. 4.4b), Eq. (4.7.3) gives:

at $z = \frac{1}{3}$ $y_1 + (6 - 2k_3)y_1 + (k_3 - 4)y_2 = 0,$

at $z = \frac{2}{3}$ $(k_3 - 4)y_1 + (6 - 2k_3)y_2 - y_2 = 0,$

or: $(7 - 2k_3)y_1 + (k_3 - 4)y_2 = 0$

$(k_3 - 4)y_1 + (5 - 2k_3)y_2 = 0.$

The determinant of this linear system equated to zero is a quadratic equation for k_3:

$$\begin{vmatrix} (7 - 2k_3) & (k_3 - 4) \\ (k_3 - 4) & (5 - 2k_3) \end{vmatrix} = (7 - 2k_3)(5 - 2k_3) - (k_3 - 4)^2$$

$$= 3k_3^2 - 16k_3 + 19 = 0,$$

whose smallest root equals 1.78475.   Hence

$$K_3 = 3^2 k_3 = 16.063$$

Approximation $n = 4$. With $n = 4$ (Fig. 4.4c), Eq. (4.7.3) gives:

at $z = \frac{1}{4}$ $y_1 + (6 - 2k_4)y_1 + (k_4 - 4)y_2 + y_3 = 0,$

at $z = \frac{1}{2}$ $(k_4 - 4)y_1 + (6 - 2k_4)y_2 + (k_4 - 4)y_3 = 0,$

at $z = \frac{3}{4}$ $y_1 + (k_4 - 4)y_2 + (6 - 2k_4)y_3 - y_3 = 0.$

The smallest root of the corresponding determinantal equation is $k_4 = 1.11075$, from which

$$k_4 = 4^2 \cdot 1.11075 = 17.772.$$

It may be proved* that the error in the characteristic value K of an equation with constant coefficients, obtained by central differences, is also of order h^2.   Hence h^2- and (h^2, h^4)-extrapolations evaluated by means of the coefficients of Sec. 2.9 may be used to improve the results of the computations.   Table 4.10 contains the values K_n, their extrapolations, and the percentage errors computed by means of the true value of $K = 20.187$.

* See M. G. Salvadori, "Numerical computation of buckling loads by finite differences," *Trans. ASCE*, **117** (1952).

The increase in accuracy, easily obtained by extrapolation, could be achieved only by consideration of a large number of pivotal points and solution of a high-degree determinantal equation.

Table 4.10

n	K_n	e (%)
2	12.000	−40.5′
3	16.063	−20.4
4	17.772	−12.0

n	h^2-extr.	e (%)
2,3	19.313	−4.3
3,4	19.969	−1.1

n	(h^2,h^4)-extr.	e (%)
2,3,4	20.189	0.01

4.8   The Use of Unevenly Spaced Pivotal Points

The finite difference operators used in the previous sections were all based upon the use of evenly spaced pivotal points, but many physical problems are naturally solved by means of unevenly spaced pivotal points.

As an example of application of formulas with unequal spacing, consider the buckling of a "stepped" beam, simply supported at the ends $x = 0$ and $x = L$, acted upon by compressive axial forces P, whose moment of inertia varies as indicated in Fig. 4.6.*

To solve the corresponding boundary value problem:*

$$y'' + \frac{P}{EI} y = 0, \qquad y(0) = y(L) = 0, \qquad (4.8.1)$$

the central portion of the beam is divided into two equal parts with pivotal points (2) at the quarter points, and the end portions have one pivotal point (0) at the ends and another (1) at two-thirds of

---

* See, for example, *Differential Equations*, Sec. 2.11.

their length from the ends.　In this division, the central portion
consists of two "lumps" of length $\frac{1}{2}(\frac{5}{7}L) = (\frac{5}{14})L$ with moment
of inertia $2I_0$, and each end portion consists of two "lumps" of
length $\frac{2}{3}(\frac{1}{7}L) = (\frac{2}{21})L$ with moment of inertia I_0, one-half of these
lumps being actually beyond the beam ends.

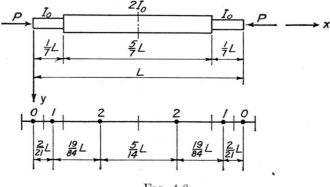

Fᴵɢ. 4.6

Since the spacing h between the pivotal points varies from point
to point, the second derivative appearing in Eq. (4.8.1) may be
approximated by Eq. (2.2.3):

$$h^2 y'' = \frac{2}{\alpha(\alpha + 1)} \, [\alpha y_l - (1 + \alpha) y_i + y_r], \tag{a}$$

in which:
$$h = x_i - x_l; \quad \alpha = \frac{x_r - x_i}{x_i - x_l}. \tag{b}$$

Equations (b) give in the present problem:

at (1)　　$h_1 = \frac{2}{21}L; \quad \alpha_1 = \dfrac{19\!/\!84}{2\!/\!21} = 2.375,$

at (2)　　$h_2 = \frac{19}{84}L; \quad \alpha_2 = \dfrac{5\!/\!14}{19\!/\!84} = 1.579.$

Hence, multiplying Eq. (4.8.1) by h_i^2 and substituting Eq. (a) for
$h^2 y''$, the difference equations become:

at (1)　　$\dfrac{2}{2.375(1 + 2.375)} \, [2.375 \cdot 0 - (1 + 2.375)y_1 + y_2]$

$$+ \frac{P}{EI_0} (\tfrac{2}{21}L)^2 y_1 = 0,$$

at (2) $\dfrac{2}{1.579(1 + 1.579)}$ $[1.579y_1 - (1 + 1.579)y_2]$

$$+ \dfrac{P}{E(2I_0)} \left(\tfrac{19}{84}L\right)^2 y_2 = 0$$

or: $(0.03635K - 3.375)y_1 + y_2 = 0,$

$$1.579y_1 + (0.05208K - 1.579)y_2 = 0,$$

where: $K = \dfrac{PL^2}{EI_0}.$ (c)

The corresponding determinantal equation:

$$\begin{vmatrix} 0.03635K - 3.375 & 1 \\ 1.579 & 0.05208K - 1.579 \end{vmatrix} = 0$$

has a smaller root $K = 19.01$, from which:

$$P_{cr} = 19.01 \, \dfrac{EI_0}{L^2}.$$

The value of P_{cr} obtained by the energy method, with an assumed sine deflection, which is known to be an upper bound for the buckling load, equals 19.04, so that the result obtained by unequal differences should be very near the true value.[*]

PROBLEMS

4.1 Express the initial conditions of Eq. (4.1.2) in terms of

(a) Forward differences with errors of order h.
(b) Forward differences with errors of order h^2.

Ans.   (a) $y_0 = 0$; $y_1 = y_0$; $y_2 = 2y_1 - y_0$; $y_3 = 3y_2 - 3y_1 + y_0$; $y_4 = 4y_3 - 6y_2 + 4y_1 - y_0$. (b) $y_0 = 0$; $y_2 = 4y_1 - 3y_0$; $y_3 = 4y_2 - 5y_1 + 2y_0$; $y_4 = (\tfrac{14}{3})y_3 - 8y_2 + 6y_1 - (\tfrac{5}{3})y_0$; $y_5 = (\tfrac{11}{2})y_4 - 12y_3 + 13y_2 - 7y_1 + (\tfrac{3}{2})y_0$.

4.2 Evaluate by forward integration and linear interpolation the pivotal values of the integrals of the following boundary value problems,

[*] For another numerical method of evaluation of buckling loads see N. M. Newmark, "Numerical Procedure for Computing Deflections, Moments and Buckling Loads," *Trans. ASCE*, **108** (1943).

using operators with errors of order h^2 and the number of subintervals indicated.

(a) $y'' + \dfrac{1}{x} y = 0$; $y(1) = 1$, $y(2) = 2$; $n = 2, 4$.

(b) $y'' + (\sin x)y = 0$; $y(0) = 0$, $y(1) = 1$; $n = 2, 4$.

Ans. (a) $n = 4$. $y_{-1} = 0.586$; $y_1 = 1.351$; $y_2 = 1.635$; $y_3 = 1.850$.

4.3 Evaluate by Taylor series the first three nonzero terms of the series expansion in the solution of the following problems, carrying θ'_0 and y'_0 as unknowns to be determined by the second boundary condition.

(a) $\theta'' + \sin \theta = 0$; $\theta(0) = 0$, $\theta(1) = 1$.
(b) $y'' + y^2 = x^2 + 1$; $y(0) = 0$, $y(1) = 0$.

Ans. (b) $y = \begin{cases} -0.5574x + 0.5x^2 + 0.0574x^4 \\ 12.56x + 0.5x^2 - 13.06x^4 \end{cases}$

4.4 Determine the values of y at the pivotal points of the interval $(0,1)$, if y satisfies the boundary value problem:

$$y'' + 4y = 4x^2 + 2; \qquad y(0) = 0, \quad y(1) = 1.$$

Use $n = 2$ and $n = 4$. Compare with the rigorous solution of the problem $(y = x^2)$, and state why the numerical solution coincides with the rigorous solution *whatever* n, when y'' is approximated by $\delta^2 y / h^2$.

4.5

(a) Solve the following boundary value problem by central difference formulas with errors of order h^2, using 2 and 4 subintervals.

$$y'' - 4y' + 4y = e^{3x}; \qquad y(0) = 0, \quad y(1) = -2.$$

Solve the system of simultaneous equations by Gauss's scheme.

(b) Apply the first term of Fox's correction to the values of y in the $n = 2$ approximation.

(c) Repeat (b) for $n = 4$.

(d) Using the uncorrected values of y for $n = 2, 4$, obtain by extrapolation improved values of y at $x = 0.5$.

(e) Repeat (d) for the corrected values of y (from parts b and c).

Ans. (a) $y_2{}^{(1)}(0.50) = -1.121$; $y_4{}^{(1)}(0.25) = -0.3473$; $y_4{}^{(1)}(0.50) = -0.9508$; $y_4{}^{(1)}(0.75) = -1.7257$. (b) $y_2{}^{(2)}(0.50) = -0.7840$. (c) $y_4{}^{(2)}(0.25) = -0.3294$; $y_4{}^{(2)}(0.50) = -0.9167$; $y_4{}^{(2)}(0.75) = -1.6884$. (d) $y_{2,4}{}^{(1)}(0.50) = -0.8941$. (e) $y_{2,4}{}^{(2)}(0.50) = -0.9256$.

4.6

(a) Solve the following boundary value problem by central difference formulas with errors of order h^2, using 2 and 4 subintervals.

$$y'' - 8y' + 8y = e^x; \qquad y(0) = 0, \quad y(3) = 4.$$

Solve the system of simultaneous equations by Cholesky's method.

(b) Apply the first term of Fox's correction to the values of y in the $n = 2$ approximation.

(c) Repeat (b) for $n = 4$.

(d) Using the uncorrected values of y for $n = 2, 4$, obtain by extrapolation improved values of y at $x = 1.5$.

(e) Repeat (d) for the corrected values of y.

4.7 Solve the heat-flow problem of Sec. 4.3 assuming $L = 100$ cm, $R = 1$ cm, $k = 1$ cal/sec °C cm²/cm, $k_1 = 6 \cdot 10^{-4}$, $u_0 = 0$, $u_n = 1$, and $U(x)$ to be given by the following table:

$z = x/L$	0	0.25	0.50	0.75	1.00
$F(z) = U(x)/u_n$	1.00	1.10	1.35	1.15	1.00

Ans. $v_0 = 0$; $v_1 = 0.658$; $v_2 = 0.984$; $v_3 = 1.035$.

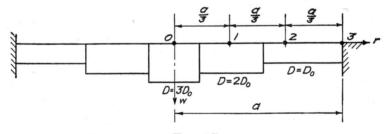

FIG. 4.7

4.8 The circular stepped plate of radius a in Fig. 4.7, built in along its edge, deflects under a uniform load q.

(a) Determine its slope $\varphi(r)$ by means of the equation*

$$\varphi'' + \frac{1}{r}\varphi' - \frac{1}{r^2}\varphi = \frac{-qr}{2D}$$

---

* See, for instance, S. Timoshenko, *Theory of Plates and Shells*, McGraw-Hill Book Company, Inc., New York, 1940, pp. 55 ff.

and the boundary conditions

$$\varphi(0) = 0; \quad \varphi(a) = 0,$$

where r is the radial distance and D is the flexural rigidity of the plate.

(b) Determine its center deflection by numerical integration using the trapezoidal rule.

4.9 Solve Problem 4.8 for the case of a simply supported plate, whose boundary conditions are:

$$\varphi(0) = 0; \quad \varphi' + \frac{\mu}{r}\varphi \bigg]_{r=a} = 0,$$

assuming the value $\mu = 0.3$ for Poisson's ratio.

Ans. $\varphi(a/3) = 0.046 \dfrac{qa^3}{D_0}; \quad \varphi(2a/3) = 0.085 \dfrac{qa^3}{D_0}; \quad \varphi(a) = 0.097 \dfrac{qa^3}{D_0}; \quad w_0 = 0.60 \dfrac{qa^4}{D_0}.$

4.10 Determine the values of y at the pivotal points of the interval $(0,1)$, if y satisfies the boundary value problem:

$$y''' + 2y = 12x^2 + 2; \qquad y(0) = 0, \quad y(1) = y'(1) = 0.$$

(a) Use $n = 2$ and approximate y' by averaged central differences, y''' by the unsymmetrical expression of Eq. (2.2.2).

(b) Use $n = 3$ and approximate y''' at $x = \frac{1}{3}$ by Eq. (2.2.2), at $x = \frac{2}{3}$ by averaged central differences.

Ans. (a) $y_1 = \frac{5}{34} = 0.147$.   (b) $y_1 = 0.186$, $y_2 = 0.149$.

4.11 Determine the values of y at the pivotal points of the interval $(0,1)$, if y satisfies the boundary value problem:

$$y^{IV} + 81y = 81x^2; \quad y(0) = y(1) = y''(0) = y''(1) = 0.$$

Use $n = 3$ and symmetrical approximations for the derivatives.

4.12 Determine the values of y at the pivotal points of the interval $(0,1)$, if y satisfies the boundary value problem:

$$y^{IV} + 81y = f(x); \qquad y(0) = y'(0) = y''(1) = y'''(1) = 0.$$

Use $n = 3$ and symmetrical approximations for the derivatives.

(a) Assume $f(x) = 729x^2$.

(b) Solve the same problem when the function $f(x)$ at the right-hand member of the differential equation is given by the following table:

x	$\frac{1}{3}$	$\frac{2}{3}$	1
$f(x)$	81	162	243

Ans. (a) $y_1 = 1.1539$; $y_2 = 3.9231$; $y_3 = 7.4615$.   (b) $y_1 = 0.6154$; $y_2 = 1.6923$; $y_3 = 2.8462$.

4.13

(a) Evaluate the deflection at the pivotal points of the beam of Fig. 4.8, using 4 subintervals and lumping the distributed load at the pivotal points. Use central difference expressions with errors of order h^2.

(b) Evaluate the bending moments at the pivotal points ($M = -EIy''$).

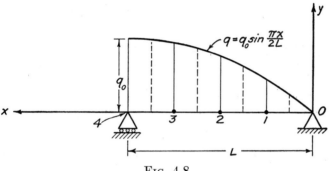

FIG. 4.8

4.14

(a) Evaluate the deflection at the pivotal point of the beam of Fig. 4.9, using 4 subintervals and lumping the distributed load at the pivotal points. Use central difference expressions with errors of order h^2.

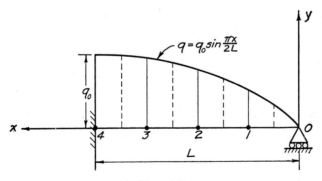

FIG. 4.9

(b) Evaluate the bending moment at the built-in end $(M = -EIy'')$.

Ans. $y_3 = -0.0009883qL^4/EI$; $y_2 = -0.001154qL^4/EI$;
    $y_1 = -0.0005710qL^4/EI$; $M_4 = -0.01828qL^2$.

4.15

(a) Evaluate the deflection at the pivotal points of the beam of Fig. 4.10 using 4 subintervals and lumping the distributed load at the pivotal points. Use central difference expressions with errors of order h^2.

(b) Evaluate the bending moments at the pivotal points $(M = -EIy'')$.

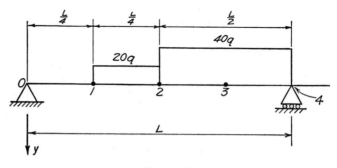

FIG. 4.10

4.16   Evaluate the deflections at the pivotal points of a uniformly loaded simply supported beam whose moment of inertia varies linearly from I_0 at its left end to $5I_0$ at its right end. Use central difference expressions with errors of order h^2 and 4 subintervals.

Ans. $y_1 = 0.003621qL^4/EI_0$; $y_2 = 0.004883qL^4/EI_0$;
    $y_3 = 0.003377qL^4/EI_0$.

4.17

(a) Evaluate the deflections at the pivotal points of a beam on an elastic foundation (see Sec. 4.6) uniformly loaded and simply supported at both ends with $k = 16$. Use central difference formulas with errors of order h^2 with $n = 2, 4$. Extrapolate the value of the deflection at the center.

(b) Evaluate the bending moment at the mid-span section by 2 and 4 subintervals and extrapolate $(M = -EIy'')$.

4.18   A simply supported beam of constant moment of inertia I and length L buckles under the action of two equal longitudinal compressive loads P. Evaluate the lowest critical value of P using $n = 2, 3,$ and 4

subintervals and extrapolation.   *Hint*: The characteristic value problem
is defined by the following equations:

$$y'' + \frac{P}{EI} y = 0; \qquad y(0) = y(L) = 0.*$$

Ans. $K = \frac{PL^2}{EI}$; $K_2 = 8$; $K_3 = 9$; $K_4 = 9.3726$; $K_{2,3} = 9.8$; $K_{3,4}$
$= 9.85164$; $K_{2,3,4} = 9.86881$.

4.19   A simply supported slender beam of length L, whose moment of
inertia is given by:

$$I(x) = I_0(1 + 2x/L) \qquad 0 \leq x \leq L/2,$$

$$I(x) = I_0(3 - 2x/L) \qquad L/2 \leq x \leq L,$$

buckles under the action of two longitudinal compressive loads P.   Determine the lowest critical value of P, using $n = 2$, 3, and 4 subintervals and
extrapolations of the h^2- and (h^2,h^4)-type.   (See Problem 4.18.)

4.20   A cantilever beam of narrow rectangular cross section is built in
at $x = 0$ and loaded by a transverse load P at $x = L$.   Determine the
lowest critical value of P for which the beam buckles laterally using $n = 2$,
3, and 4 subintervals and an (h^2,h^4)-extrapolation.   *Hint:* The rotation β
satisfies the following characteristic value problem:

$$\beta'' + \frac{P^2L^2}{BC} (1 - x/L)^2\beta = 0; \quad \beta(0) = 0; \quad \beta'(L) = 0.\dagger$$

Ans. $P_2 = 4 \sqrt{BC/L^4}$; $P_3 = 3.933 \sqrt{BC/L^4}$; $P_4 = 3.959 \sqrt{BC/L^4}$; $P_{2,3,4}$
$= 4.030 \sqrt{BC/L^4}$; $P = 4.013 \sqrt{BC/L^4}$.

4.21   A beam of narrow rectangular cross section is simply supported
at $x = \pm L/2$, while the rotation of its ends around the axis of the beam
is prevented.   The beam buckles laterally under the action of a vertical
load P at $x = 0$.   Determine the lowest critical value of P in terms of:
B, the smallest flexural rigidity of the beam in its principal plane; C, the
torsional rigidity; L, the length of the beam.   Use $n = 2$, 3, and 4 subintervals and extrapolation for $P_{2,4}$.   *Hint:* The rotation β satisfies the
following characteristic value problem:

$$\beta'' + \frac{P^2L^2}{4BC} \left(\frac{1}{2} - \frac{x}{L}\right)^2 \beta = 0; \quad \beta\left(\frac{L}{2}\right) = \beta\left(-\frac{L}{2}\right) = 0.\ddagger$$

---

* See Sec. 4.8.
† See, for example, S. Timoshenko, *Theory of Elastic Stability*, pp. 245 ff;
see also Problem 4.21.
‡ See, for example, S. Timoshenko, *Theory of Elastic Stability*, pp. 250 ff.

4.22 A circular plate of radius R and flexural rigidity D, clamped at the edge, buckles under a uniform compression N per unit of length. Determine the lowest critical value of N, using $n = 2$ and 3 subintervals and extrapolation. The slope ϕ of the plate satisfies the following characteristic value problem:

$$\phi'' + \frac{1}{r}\phi' + \left(\frac{N}{D} - \frac{1}{r^2}\right)\phi = 0; \qquad \phi(0) = \phi(R) = 0.*$$

Ans. $N_2 = 12.00D/R^2$; $N_3 = 13.50D/R^2$; $N_{2,3} = 14.70D/R^2$;
$N = 14.68D/R^2$.

4.23 The modes and frequencies of a shear beam with a linearly varying spring constant are governed by the following characteristic value problem:†

$$\frac{d^2x}{dz^2} + \frac{K^2}{z}x = 0; \qquad x(1) = 0; \quad \frac{dx}{dz}\bigg]_{0.5} = 0,$$

where $K^2 = \dfrac{\omega^2 L^2 m_0}{\alpha^2 k_0}$; m_0 and k_0, the unit mass and unit spring constant, are equal to $m\Big]_{z=0}$ and $k\Big]_{z=0}$; L = the length of the beam; and α = the complementary slope of the spring-constant line. Evaluate the lowest three values of ω^2, using $n = 1, 2, 3$, and 4 subintervals and extrapolation.

4.24 A slender strut of length L, moment of inertia I, and weight per unit of length q, built in at $x = 0$ and free at $x = L$, buckles under its own weight. Determine the critical value of q using $n = 1, 2$ and extrapolation. The deflection y of the strut is governed by the following characteristic value problem‡:

$$y^{\mathrm{IV}} + \frac{qL}{EI}\left(1 - \frac{x}{L}\right)y'' - \frac{qL}{EI}\frac{1}{L}y' = 0;$$

$$y(0) = y'(0) = y''(L) = y'''(L) = 0.$$

Let $k_n = q_n L^3/EI$.

Ans. $k_1 = 4.0000$; $k_2 = 6.7624$; $k_{1,2} = 7.6832$; $k = 7.83$.

4.25 Evaluate the lowest natural frequency of the free oscillations of a simply supported beam of length L, using $n = 2, 3$, and 4 subintervals

* See, for example, S. Timoshenko, *Theory of Elastic Stability*, pp. 367 ff.
† See, for instance, M. G. Salvadori, "Earthquake Stresses in Shear Buildings," *Trans. ASCE*, **118** (1953).
‡ See, for example, S. Timoshenko, *Theory of Elastic Stability*, pp. 115 ff.

and extrapolation. *Hint:* The differential equation of motion of the beam is $EI\partial^4 y/\partial x^4 + \rho A \partial^2 y/\partial t^2 = 0,$* where EI = flexural rigidity, ρ = density, A = cross section of beam. Substitute $y(x,t) = X(x) \sin \omega t$ in this equation and state that the beam is simply supported at the ends: $X(0) =$

$X(L) = 0; X''(0) = X''(L) = 0.$ Let $w = \dfrac{\omega L^2}{\sqrt{EI/\rho A}}$

Ans. $w_2 = 8; w_3 = 9; w_4 = 9.3726; w_{2,3} = 9.8; w_{3,4} = 9.8516; w_{2,3,4} = 9.8688.$

4.26 Evaluate the lowest natural frequency of the free oscillations of a beam of length L, built in at $x = 0$ and free at $x = L$, using $n = 2$ subintervals. *Hint:* See Problem 4.25.

4.27 Determine the values of y at the pivotal points of the interval $(0,1)$, if y satisfies the boundary value problem: $y'' + 2y = f(x); y(0) = y(1) = 0,$ and $f(x)$ is given by the following table:

x	0	0.15	0.40	0.75	1.00
$f(x)$	0	16	30	20	0

Use unsymmetrical approximations of y'' with errors of order h.

Ans. $y_1 = -1.8021; y_2 = -3.8260; y_3 = -2.7060.$

4.28 Evaluate the buckling load P of the simply supported beam of Fig. 4.11, using unequal differences of order h and the indicated subdivisions. (See Problem 4.18.)

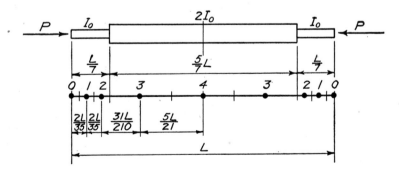

FIG. 4.11

*See, for example, S. Timoshenko, *Vibration Problems in Engineering,* 2d ed., D. Van Nostrand Company, Inc., New York, 1937, pp. 332 ff.

4.29   The circular stepped plate of Fig. 4.12, built in along its edge, deflects under a uniform load q.

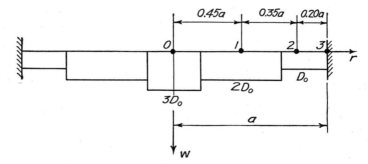

Fig. 4.12

(a) Determine its slope $\varphi(r)$ by means of unsymmetrical approximations φ'' with errors of order h.   (See Problem 4.8.)

(b) Determine its center deflection by numerical integration.

Ans. $\varphi(0.45a) = 0.0163qa^3/D_0$; $\varphi(0.8a) = 0.0177qa^3/D_0$;
$\qquad w_0 = 0.0114qa^4/D_0$.

4.30   Solve Problem 4.29 for the case of a simply supported plate. (See Problem 4.9.)

CHAPTER V

The Numerical Solution of Partial Differential Equations

5.1 Partial Difference Operators in Cartesian Coordinates

Processes of numerical integration have found their widest application in the solution of partial differential equations.

The transformation of a partial differential equation into the corresponding partial difference equation is obtained, essentially, by the same methods and expansions developed in previous chapters for ordinary differential equations, since partial derivatives are evaluated by the same limiting process used for ordinary derivatives, keeping all but one variable constant. Thus, indicating by D_x, D_y, . . . the partial derivatives of a function $z = f(x, y, . . .)$ with respect to x, y, . . . , respectively, the central difference expansions for D_x, D_y, . . . may be obtained directly from Eqs. (2.7.16).

For example, calling h the constant spacing of the pivotal points in the x direction and $\delta_x{}^n z_i$ the nth central difference of z at i taken in the x direction:

$$2hD_x z_i = z_r - z_l + \epsilon_{1x},$$

$$\left[\epsilon_{1x} = \mu\left(-\frac{\delta_x{}^3}{6} + \frac{\delta_x{}^5}{30} - \ldots\right)z_i\right] \quad (5.1.1)$$

$$h^2 D_x{}^2 z_i = z_r - 2z_i + z_l + \epsilon_{2x},$$

$$\left[\epsilon_{2x} = \left(-\frac{\delta_x{}^4}{12} + \frac{\delta_x{}^6}{90} - \ldots\right)z_i\right] \quad (5.1.2)$$

$$2h^3 D_x{}^3 z_i = z_{rr} - 2z_r + 2z_l - z_{ll} + \epsilon_{3x},$$

$$\left[\epsilon_{3x} = \mu\left(-\frac{\delta_x{}^5}{4} + \frac{7\delta_x{}^7}{120} - \ldots\right)z_i\right] \quad (5.1.3)$$

$$h^4 D_x{}^4 z_i = z_{rr} - 4z_r + 6z_i - 4z_l + z_{ll} + \epsilon_{4x},$$

$$\left[\epsilon_{4x} = \left(-\frac{\delta_x{}^6}{6} + \frac{7\delta_x{}^8}{240} - \ldots\right)z_i\right]. \quad (5.1.4)$$

Similarly, calling k the constant spacing of the pivotal points in the y direction and $\delta_y{}^n z_i$ the nth central difference of z at i taken in the y direction, and indicating the pivotal points adjoining z_i vertically by z_{aa}, z_a, z_b, and z_{bb}, as shown in Fig. 5.1 (the subscripts

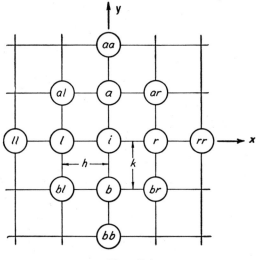

Fig. 5.1

a and b stand for "above" and "below"), the partial derivatives with respect to y are given by:

$$2kD_y z_i = z_a - z_b + \epsilon_{1y},$$

$$\left[\epsilon_{1y} = \mu \left(-\frac{\delta_y{}^3}{6} + \frac{\delta_y{}^5}{30} - \ldots \right) z_i \right] \quad (5.1.5)$$

$$k^2 D_y{}^2 z_i = z_a - 2z_i + z_b + \epsilon_{2y},$$

$$\left[\epsilon_{2y} = \left(-\frac{\delta_y{}^4}{12} + \frac{\delta_y{}^6}{90} - \ldots \right) z_i \right] \quad (5.1.6)$$

$$2k^3 D_y{}^3 z_i = z_{aa} - 2z_a + 2z_b - z_{bb} + \epsilon_{3y},$$

$$\left[\epsilon_{3y} = \mu \left(-\frac{\delta_y{}^5}{4} + \frac{7\delta_y{}^7}{120} - \ldots \right) z_i \right] \quad (5.1.7)$$

$$k^4 D_y{}^4 z_i = z_{aa} - 4z_a + 6z_i - 4z_b + z_{bb} + \epsilon_{4y},$$

$$\left[\epsilon_{4y} = \left(-\frac{\delta_y{}^6}{6} + \frac{7\delta_y{}^8}{240} - \ldots \right) z_i \right]. \quad (5.1.8)$$

The expression for the second mixed derivative of z with respect to x and y, D_{xy}, is obtained by applying the operator giving D_x to the operator giving D_y, that is, by the "product" $D_x D_y$:

$$D_{xy} z_i = \frac{1}{2k}\left[\frac{1}{2h}(z_r - z_l)_a - \frac{1}{2h}(z_r - z_l)_b\right] + \frac{1}{4hk}\epsilon_{1,xy},$$

or:

$$4hk D_{xy} z_i = z_{ar} - z_{al} - z_{br} + z_{bl} + \epsilon_{1,xy}$$
$$[\epsilon_{1,xy} = (\epsilon_{1,x})_a - (\epsilon_{1,x})_b]. \qquad (5.1.9)$$

Similarly, the fourth mixed derivative $\partial^4 z/\partial x^2 \partial y^2 = D_{xxyy}$ is the operational product of $D_x{}^2$ and $D_y{}^2$ or:

$$h^2 k^2 D_{xxyy} z_i = (z_r - 2z_i + z_l)_a - 2(z_r - 2z_i + z_l)_i$$
$$+ (z_r - 2z_i + z_l)_b + \epsilon_{2,xy}$$
$$= (z_{ar} + z_{al} + z_{br} + z_{bl}) - 2(z_a + z_b + z_r + z_l) + 4z_i$$
$$+ \epsilon_{2,xy} \qquad [\epsilon_{2,xy} = (\epsilon_{2,x})_a - 2(\epsilon_{2,x})_i + (\epsilon_{2,x})_b]. \qquad (5.1.10)$$

The *Laplacian* (or *harmonic*) *operator* ∇^2*

$$\nabla^2 \equiv \frac{\partial^2}{\partial x^2} + \frac{\partial^2}{\partial y^2} = D_x{}^2 + D_y{}^2$$

becomes by Eqs. (5.1.2), (5.1.6) for a *rectangular lattice* of *mesh sizes h,k*:

$$h^2 k^2 \nabla^2 z_i = k^2(z_r - 2z_i + z_l) + h^2(z_a - 2z_i + z_b)$$
$$+ k^2 \epsilon_{2x} + h^2 \epsilon_{2y} \qquad (5.1.11)$$

and for the particular case of equal spacing of the pivotal points in the x and y directions, that is, for a *square lattice* of mesh size h:

$$h^2 \nabla^2 z_i = z_a + z_b + z_r + z_l - 4z_i + \epsilon_{2x} + \epsilon_{2y}, \qquad (5.1.12)$$

where ϵ_{2x} and ϵ_{2y} are given by Eqs. (5.1.2) and (5.1.6), respectively. The *biharmonic operator*

$$\nabla^4 \equiv \nabla^2(\nabla^2) = \frac{\partial^4}{\partial x^4} + \frac{2\partial^4}{\partial x^2 \partial y^2} + \frac{\partial^4}{\partial y^4}\dagger$$

---

* The operator ∇^2 should not be confused with the second backward difference.

† The operator ∇^4 should not be confused with the fourth backward difference.

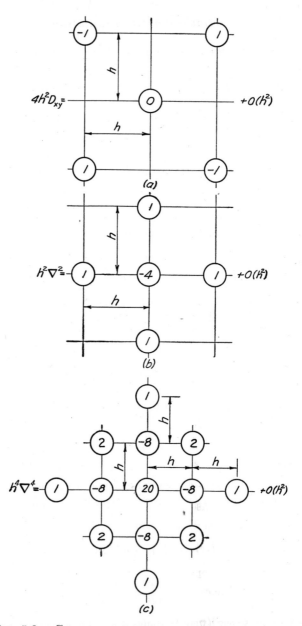

$$4h^2 D_{xy} = \quad +0(h^2)$$

(a)

$$h^2 \nabla^2 = \quad +0(h^2)$$

(b)

$$h^4 \nabla^4 = \quad +0(h^2)$$

(c)

Fig. 5.2.   Central difference partial operators.

170

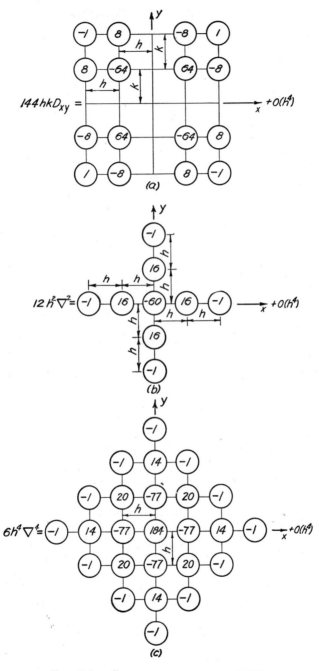

FIG. 5.3. SECOND-ORDER OPERATORS.

becomes, for a square lattice

$$h^4\nabla^4 z_i = h^4\nabla^2(\nabla^2 z_i) = h^4[\nabla^2 z_a + \nabla^2 z_b + \nabla^2 z_r + \nabla^2 z_l - 4\nabla^2 z_i]$$
$$= (z_{aa} + z_{bb} + z_{rr} + z_{ll}) + 2(z_{al} + z_{ar} + z_{br} + z_{bl})$$
$$- 8(z_a + z_b + z_r + z_l) + 20z_i + \epsilon, \quad (5.1.13)$$

where ϵ is obtained by means of ϵ_{4x}, ϵ_{4y}, and $\epsilon_{4,xy}$.

The partial operators D_{xy}, ∇^2, and ∇^4 for square lattices are conveniently represented by the "molecules" of Fig. 5.2a, b and c, respectively.

By means of the central difference operators of Fig. 2.8b, we obtain similarly the operators of the "molecules" in Fig. 5.3 with errors of order h^4, which may be used to obtain more refined solutions.

Three-dimensional operators are obtained in a perfectly analogous manner, and have been used in the solution of heat flow and elasticity problems.

5.2   Numerical Double Integration

[a]   The Trapezoidal Rule

The double integral

$$V = \int_a^b \int_c^d f(x,y) \, dx \, dy \qquad (5.2.1)$$

extended to a rectangle $x = a$, $x = b$, $y = c$, $y = d$, can be evaluated numerically by two successive integrations in the x and y directions, using the trapezoidal rule of Sec. 2.8a.

For this purpose, divide the rectangle (a,b), (c,d) into a number $m \cdot n$ of rectangles of sides $h = (b - a)/m$, $k = (d - c)/n$ and consider the values f_{ij} of f at the pivotal points (Fig. 5.4):

$$x_i = ih, \quad (i = 0,1,2, \ldots ,m);$$
$$y_j = jk, \quad (j = 0,1,2, \ldots ,n).$$

The value B_1 of the integral extended over one rectangle of sides

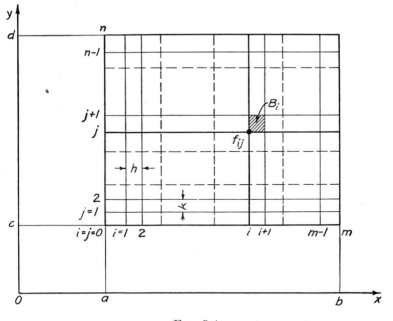

FIG. 5.4

h,k with its lower left corner at i,j becomes by the trapezoidal rule [Eq. (2.8.1)]:

$$B_1 = \int_{y_i}^{y_{j+1}} dy \int_{x_i}^{x_{i+1}} f(x,y)\, dx \doteq \int_{y_j}^{y_{j+1}} \left\{ \frac{h}{2} [f_i(y) + f_{i+1}(y)] \right\} dy$$

$$\doteq \frac{h}{2} \left[\frac{k}{2} (f_{i,j} + f_{i,j+1}) + \frac{k}{2} (f_{i+1,j} + f_{i+1,j+1}) \right]$$

$$= \frac{hk}{4} [f_{ij} + f_{i,j+1} + f_{i+1,j} + f_{i+1,j+1}]. \tag{5.2.2}$$

Adding the values of B_1 corresponding to each rectangle of the domain and noting that each internal pivotal value is counted four times, and each boundary pivotal value is counted twice, with the exception of the corner values, which are counted only once, the value of V may be conveniently represented by the operator or "molecule" of Fig. 5.5.

To evaluate the error in the operator for double integration by the trapezoidal rule, it must be remembered that the error in the

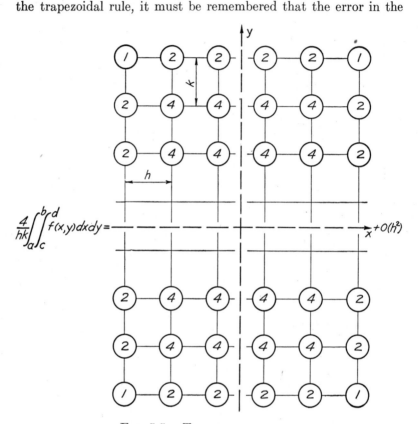

FIG. 5.5.   TRAPEZOIDAL RULE.

formula for single integration by the trapezoidal rule is of order h^2 (Sec. 2.8a).   Hence the area of each section of the volume V, obtained by means of a plane parallel to xz at $y = y_j$, has an error of order h^2:

$$A(y_j) = \int_a^b f(x,y_j) \, dx = A_j + K_j h^2. \tag{a}$$

By means of Eq. (a) and the trapezoidal rule applied in the y direction, the double integral V becomes:

$$V = k(\tfrac{1}{2}A_0 + A_1 + \ldots + A_{n-1} + \tfrac{1}{2}A_n)$$
$$+ k(\tfrac{1}{2}K_0 + K_1 + \ldots + K_{n-1} + \tfrac{1}{2}K_n)h^2 + K'k^2,$$

where the last term is the error due to the integration along the y-axis. Substituting $(d - c)/n$ for k in the second term of this equation and setting

$$\bar{K} = \frac{(d - c)}{n}\left(\frac{1}{2}K_0 + K_1 + K_2 + \ldots + K_{n-1} + \frac{1}{2}K_n\right),$$

we see that the error in the double integral is of the type

$$\epsilon_t = \bar{K}h^2 + K'k^2$$

or, calling α the ratio k/h,

$$\epsilon_t = (\bar{K} + \alpha^2 K')h^2. \qquad (5.2.3)$$

Equation (5.2.3) shows that the error in the trapezoidal rule for double integration is of order h^2, and that therefore the h^2-extrapolation formula (Sec. 2.9) may be used to improve the results of the numerical integration.

The trapezoidal rule will be now applied to the evaluation of the integral

$$V = \int_1^2 \int_1^2 \frac{dx\,dy}{x + y}$$
$$= \int_1^2 \left[\ln(x + y)\right]_1^2 dy = \int_1^2 [\ln(x + 2) - \ln(x + 1)]\,dy$$
$$= \left[(x + 2)[\ln(x + 2) - 1] - (x + 1)[\ln(x + 1) - 1]\right]_1^2$$
$$= \ln \tfrac{1024}{729} = \ln 1.4046639 = 0.339798. \qquad (b)$$

With $n = 2$ and $h = k = 0.5$, the values of $f(x,y) = \dfrac{1}{x + y}$ at the pivotal points of the field of integration become:

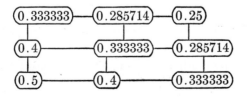

and the approximate value of V given by the operator of Fig. 5.5 using four significant figures, is:

$$V_{t,2} = \frac{0.5 \cdot 0.5}{4} \{(0.3333 + 0.5 + 0.3333 + 0.25)$$
$$+ 2(0.4 + 0.4 + 0.2857 + 0.2857) + 4(0.3333)\} = 0.3433$$

with an error of -1.0 per cent. With $n = 4$ and $h = k = 0.25$, we obtain similarly

$$V_{t,4} = 0.3406$$

with an error of -0.24 per cent. Using the h^2-extrapolation, with the coefficients $\alpha_2 = 1.3333$, $\alpha_1 = 0.3333$ from Table 2.9 corresponding to the ratio $n_2/n_1 = 2$, we obtain the value

$$V_t \Big]_{2,4} = 1.3333 \cdot 0.3406 - 0.3333 \cdot 0.3433 = 0.3397$$

with an error of $+0.03$ per cent.

[b]   Simpson's rule

By means of two successive applications of Simpson's $\frac{1}{3}$ rule [Eq. (2.8.3)] in the x and y directions, the value of the double integral

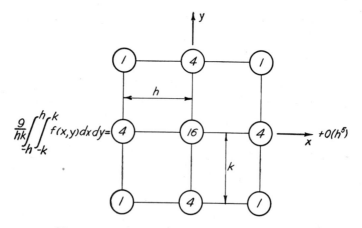

Fig. 5.6.   Simpson's rule for 4 squares.

V extended to four adjacent rectangles of sides h,k meeting at x_i, y_j becomes:

$$B_2 = \int_{y_{i-1}}^{y_{i+1}} dy \int_{x_{i-1}}^{x_{i+1}} f(x,y)\, dx \doteq \int_{y_{i-1}}^{y_{i+1}} \frac{h}{3} [f_{i-1}(y) + 4f_i(y) + f_{i+1}(y)]\, dy$$

$$\doteq \frac{hk}{9} [f_{i-1,j-1} + f_{i+1,j-1} + f_{i-1,j+1} + f_{i+1,j+1}$$

$$+ 4(f_{i,j+1} + f_{i,j-1} + f_{i-1,j} + f_{i+1,j}) + 16f_{ij}]. \quad (5.2.4)$$

The operator B_2 appears in the "molecule" of Fig. 5.6.

Adding the values B_2 corresponding to each rectangle of the domain, we obtain the operator or "molecule" of Fig. 5.7.

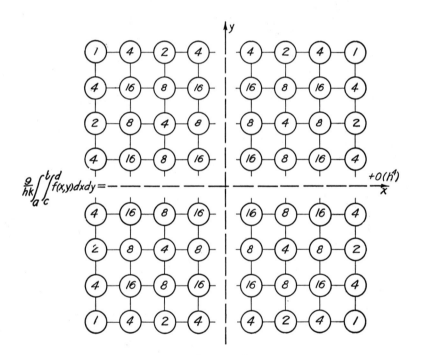

FIG. 5.7.   SIMPSON'S RULE.

By a process similar to the one used in part (a) of this section, it is easy to prove that the error in Simpson's rule for double integration is of order h^4, and that therefore h^4-extrapolations (Sec. 2.9) may be used in connection with the two-dimensional Simpson's rule.

The evaluation of the integral (b) of this section by Simpson's rule gives, for $n = 2$:

$$V_{s,2} = \frac{0.5 \cdot 0.5}{9} [0.5 + 0.333333 + 0.25 + 0.333333$$
$$+ 4(0.4 + 0.4 + 0.285714 + 0.285714) + 16 \cdot 0.333333]$$
$$= 0.339881$$

with an error of -0.0024 per cent.

5.3   The Solution of Laplace's Equation by Iteration

A large variety of two-dimensional physical problems are

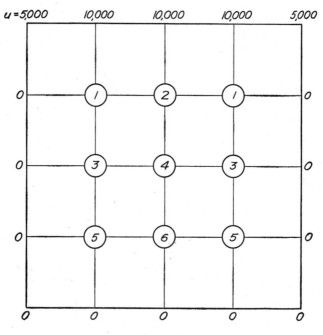

FIG. 5.8

governed by the so-called *Laplacian equation*

$$\nabla^2 u = \frac{\partial^2 u}{\partial x^2} + \frac{\partial^2 u}{\partial y^2} = 0 \tag{5.3.1}$$

with appropriate boundary conditions; among these are steady-state heat problems. It may be proved,* in fact, that the tem-

* See, for example, *Partial Differential Equations*, Sec. 8.

perature $u(x,y)$ in a two-dimensional body (insulated thin plate, or infinitely long cylinder) satisfies Eq. (5.3.1), whenever u is independent of the time.

As an example of solution of the Laplacian equation by numerical methods, consider the problem of determining the steady-state temperature u at the pivotal points of a square lattice of mesh size h in a thin square plate of sides L, completely insulated. Substituting in Eq. (5.3.1) for $\nabla^2 u$ the operator of Fig. 5.2b, and using the symbols of Fig. 5.1 to indicate the pivotal points, Eq. (5.3.1) becomes the *Laplacian difference equation*:

$$u_a + u_b + u_r + u_l - 4u_i = 0. \qquad (5.3.2)$$

For $h = L/4$, with the temperature on the plate boundary given by Fig. 5.8 and pivotal points numbered as in the same figure, Eq. (5.3.2) leads to the system of six linear equations:

Point	u_1	u_2	u_3	u_4	u_5	u_6	c	
1	-4	1	1				$-10,000$	
2	2	-4		1			$-10,000$	
3	1		-4	1	1		0	(a)
4		1	2	-4		1	0	
5			1		-4	1	0	
6				1	2	-4	0	

whose roots, evaluated by Gauss's scheme, are

$$\begin{aligned} u_1 &= 4286, & u_2 &= 5268, & u_3 &= 1875, \\ u_4 &= 2500, & u_5 &= 714, & u_6 &= 982. \end{aligned} \qquad (b)$$

The Laplacian equations are also conveniently solved by iteration (Sec. 1.9). Solving Eq. (5.3.2) for u_i:

$$u_i = \tfrac{1}{4}(u_a + u_b + u_r + u_l), \qquad (5.3.3)$$

it is seen that the temperature at i is the average of the four temperatures at the adjoining corners of the lattice. Starting with any tentative values for u at the pivotal points and averaging successively the temperatures at four adjoining corners, iterated values for u_i are obtained in a very simple manner.

In order to have rapid convergence of the iteration process, which is known as *Liebman's procedure* in this particular case, it is important to start with good initial values. These are usually obtained by means of a lattice with larger mesh size. Thus with $h = L/2$, the initial value at the center of the plate becomes by Eq. (5.3.3):

$$u_4^{(0)} = \tfrac{1}{4}(10{,}000 + 0 + 0 + 0) = 2500.$$

The initial values at points 1 and 5 may now be obtained by averaging the four values *diagonally* adjoining these points, since the

Table 5.1

n	u_1	u_2	u_3	u_4	u_5	u_6
0	4375	5312	1875	2500	625	938
1	4296	5273	1855	2480	698	969
2	4282	5261	1865	2490	708	976
3	4281	5263	1869	2494	711	979
4	4283	5265	1872	2497	712	980
5	4284	5266	1873	2498	713	981
6	4284	5266	1873	2498	713	981

diagonals of a square lattice constitute another square lattice, and the operator ∇^2 is invariant with respect to a rotation of the coordinate axes. Thus:

$$u_1^{(0)} = \tfrac{1}{4}(10{,}000 + 2500 + 0 + 5000) = 4375$$

$$u_5^{(0)} = \tfrac{1}{4}(0 + 2500 + 0 + 0) = 625.$$

The initial values at points 2, 3, and 6 are obtained by averaging the four adjoining values of the original lattice:

$$u_2^{(0)} = \tfrac{1}{4}(4375 + 10{,}000 + 4375 + 2500) = 5312$$

$$u_3^{(0)} = \tfrac{1}{4}(0 + 4375 + 2500 + 625) = 1875$$

$$u_6^{(0)} = \tfrac{1}{4}(625 + 2500 + 625 + 0) = 938.$$

Table 5.1 gives the successive values of the u_i obtained by Liebman's averaging process, which check the solution by Gauss's scheme within two units in the last figure.

5.4 Solution of Laplace's Equation by Relaxation

The solution of Laplace's equation $\nabla^2 u = 0$, which is of great importance in field theory (electromagnetism, heat conduction, elasticity, etc.), may be also conveniently obtained by relaxation (Sec. 1.10).

The residual R_i in the Laplacian difference operator (5.3.2) due to approximate values for the u's,

$$u_a + u_b + u_r + u_l - 4u_i = R_i,$$

shows that a change δu_i in the pivotal value u_i will decrease R_i by $4\delta u_i$ and increase the four adjoining R's by δu_i. The relaxation operations thus involve equal integral multipliers at each pivotal point, and may be performed without the use of a calculating machine.

Table 5.2

(1)		(2)	
4375	−313	5312	2
−80	1	−40	−158
−8	−33	−4	2
−1	1	5268	−14
4286	5		2
	−1		

(3)		(4)	
1875	0	2500	0
	−80		−40
	8		4
	1		

(5)		(6)	
625	313	938	2
80	7	40	158
8	33	4	2
1	1	982	14
714	5		2
	1		

Table 5.2 shows the relaxation of the six equations (a) of Sec. 5.3, starting with the initial values of the first row of Table 5.1. The largest residual is systematically reduced to zero at every step, and since the temperature is symmetrical about the middle axis of the plate, only six pivotal points have been used. Note that, because of symmetry (Fig. 5.8), a change δu at 1, 3, and 5 will increase the residuals at 2, 4, and 6, respectively, by $2\delta u$. In this type of problem, relaxation is often the simplest and fastest method of solution.

5.5 Solution of Poisson's Equation by Relaxation

Another fundamental equation of mathematical physics, the *Poissonian equation*

$$\nabla^2 z = \frac{\partial^2 z}{\partial x^2} + \frac{\partial^2 z}{\partial y^2} = f(x,y),$$

which governs phenomena in electricity, magnetism, elasticity, etc., can also be conveniently solved by relaxation. It is applied here to a problem in elasticity.

Consider a perfectly flexible thin membrane evenly stretched over a horizontal square hole of side L and slightly deflected (up or down) by a constant pressure p (Fig. 5.9). Let S be the *constant* tension per unit of length in the membrane, and z its ordinates above the plane of the hole, taken as the x,y-plane. The forces acting on an element $dx\,dy$ of the membrane are: (1) the pressure $p\,dx\,dy$, (2) the resultant of the tension S applied to the sides dy, (3) the resultant of the tension S applied to the sides dx. The weight of the membrane is considered negligible.

Assuming the slope of the membrane to be everywhere very small (Fig. 5.10), the resultant in the vertical direction of the tension S applied to the sides dy of the element equals:

$$-S\,dy\,\frac{\partial z}{\partial x} + S\,dy\left(\frac{\partial z}{\partial x} + \frac{\partial}{\partial x}\frac{\partial z}{\partial x}\,dx\right) = S\,\frac{\partial^2 z}{\partial x^2}\,dx\,dy.$$

Similarly, the resultant of the tension S on the sides dx of the element equals:

$$-S\,dx\,\frac{\partial z}{\partial y} + S\,dx\left(\frac{\partial z}{\partial y} + \frac{\partial}{\partial y}\frac{\partial z}{\partial y}\,dy\right) = S\,\frac{\partial^2 z}{\partial y^2}\,dx\,dy.$$

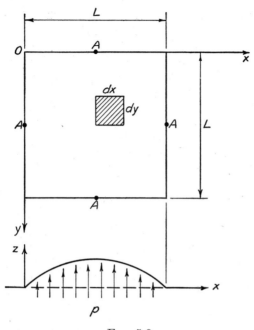

F<small>IG</small>. 5.9

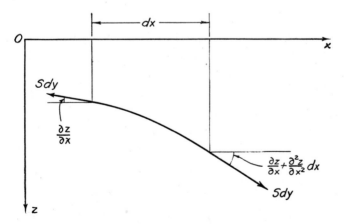

F<small>IG</small>. 5.10

Hence the differential equation of equilibrium of the membrane in the z direction reduces, after division by $S\ dx\ dy$, to

$$\frac{\partial^2 z}{\partial x^2} + \frac{\partial^2 z}{\partial y^2} + \frac{p}{S} = 0, \tag{5.5.1}$$

a Poissonian equation with $f(x,y) = -p/S = $ constant. The boundary conditions require that

$$z = 0 \quad \text{on the boundary.} \tag{5.5.2}$$

To obtain a numerical solution of the membrane problem in nondimensional form, let

$$x = \xi L; \quad y = \eta L; \quad z(x,y) = \frac{pL^2}{S} \phi(\xi,\eta) \tag{5.5.3}$$

in Eqs. (5.5.1) and (5.5.2):

$$\frac{\partial^2 z}{\partial x^2} + \frac{\partial^2 z}{\partial y^2} + \frac{p}{S} = \frac{pL^2}{S}\left[\frac{\partial^2 \phi}{L^2 \partial \xi^2} + \frac{\partial^2 \phi}{L^2 \partial \eta^2}\right] + \frac{p}{S} = 0,$$

$$\frac{pL^2}{S}\phi = 0 \quad \text{on the boundary.}$$

The function ϕ is thus found to be a solution of the boundary value problem:

$$\frac{\partial^2 \phi}{\partial \xi^2} + \frac{\partial^2 \phi}{\partial \eta^2} + 1 = 0$$

$$\phi(0,\eta) = \phi(1,\eta) = \phi(\xi,0) = \phi(\xi,1) = 0 \tag{5.5.4}$$

To transform the first of Eqs. (5.5.4) into a difference equation using a square lattice of mesh size $h = 1/n$, the equation is multiplied through by $h^2 = 1/n^2$, and the molecule of Fig. 5.2b is substituted for $h^2 \nabla^2$. The difference equations,

$$\phi_a + \phi_b + \phi_r + \phi_l - 4\phi_i + \frac{1}{n^2} = 0, \tag{5.5.5}$$

together with the conditions (5.5.4) on the boundary, are the numerical equations for the membrane problem. Once the values of ϕ have been obtained, the actual membrane deflections may be computed by means of Eq. (5.5.3).

Starting with $n = 2$ (Fig. 5.11a) and remembering that $\phi = 0$ on the boundary, Eq. (5.5.5) gives:

$$0 + 0 + 0 + 0 - 4\phi_1 + \tfrac{1}{4} = 0$$

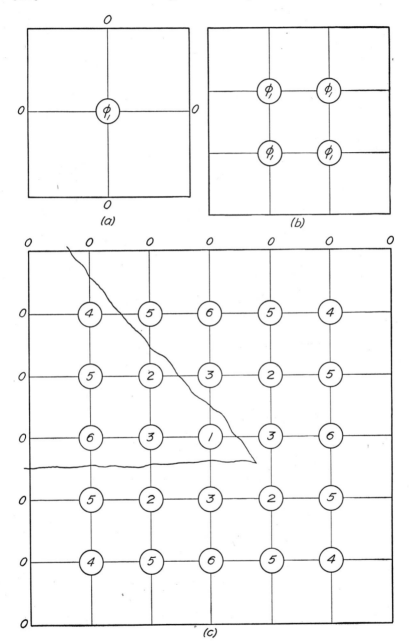

Fig. 5.11

Table 5.3

δRᵢ / δφᵢ	$i = 1$	2	3	4	5	6
$i = 1$	−4	0	+1	0	0	0
2	0	−4	+2	0	+1	0
3	+4	+2	−4	0	0	+1
4	0	0	0	−4	+1	0
5	0	+2	0	+2	−4	+2
6	0	0	+1	0	+1	−4

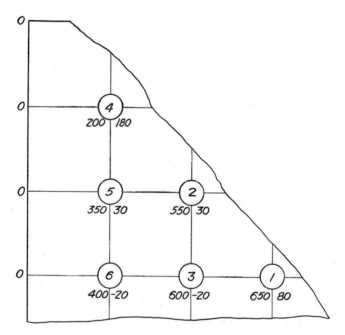

Fig. 5.12

or $\phi_1 = 0.0625$. For $n = 3$ (Fig. 5.11b), Eq. (5.5.5) gives:

$$0 + 0 + \phi_1 + \phi_1 - 4\phi_1 + \tfrac{1}{9} = 0,$$

or $\phi_1 = 0.0556$.

For $n = 6$, Eq. (5.5.5), multiplied through by 10^4 to avoid the decimal point, gives:

$$\phi_a + \phi_b + \phi_r + \phi_l - 4\phi_i + 278 = 0. \tag{5.5.6}$$

Due to symmetry, only one-eighth of the membrane and six values of ϕ are considered, as shown in Fig. 5.11c. Also because of

Table 5.4

①		②		③		④		⑤		⑥	
65	8	55	-2	60	8	20	18	35	8	40	-2
6	-16 3		4 3		5 5		-2 3		8 2		4
	-4 0		10 1		11 1		4 0		-4 -2		-4 -1
			-2 0		-4 5				4 1		0
71		58		1 26				2		42	
				64				38			
710	-2	580	-2	640	8	260	-2	380	18	420	-2
10	38 8		14 10		24 4		14 8		-14 7		14
1.5	-2 2		-18 2		-16 0.5		-2 2		-16 0.5		24
	8 0.5		-2		-9		2		-2		-4
	0		6		4		0		5		8
			-2		5				-3		2
721.5		2		-3 264.5				-1		0	
		0		-1.5				-0.5			
				-0.5				0 427.5			
	590.5			0				0.5			
				652.0				390.0			

symmetry, the changes δR in the residuals due to changes $\delta \phi = 1$ in the ϕ have the values indicated in Table 5.3.

The initial values of ϕ are computed by interpolation at sight from the values $10^4 \phi_1 = 625$ for $n = 2$, and $10^4 \phi_1 = 556$ for $n = 3$; they appear in Fig. 5.12 together with the corresponding residuals.

The relaxation Table 5.4 gives, first, the values of ϕ to two figures evaluated by rounded-off residuals (the largest residual is reduced at each step principally by overrelaxation); two more figures in the ϕ's are then computed by relaxing the residuals due to the ϕ values with two figures (again overrelaxation is used principally).

The actual membrane deflections are computed by means of the ϕ values of Table 5.4 and Eq. (5.5.3).

5.6 Elastic Torsion

It is proved in the theory of elasticity* that the tangential stress τ_z in a twisted prismatic bar of constant cross section, whose axis is taken to be the z-axis, may be expressed in terms of the derivatives of a "torsion function" ψ by the equations:

$$\tau_{xz} = G\theta \frac{\delta\psi}{\delta y}, \qquad \tau_{yz} = -G\theta \frac{\delta\psi}{\delta x}. \qquad (5.6.1)$$

Here τ_{xz} and τ_{yz} are the components of τ_z in the x- and y-directions, respectively, G is the shear modulus, θ is the angle of twist per unit length, and the function ψ satisfies the Poissonian equation

$$\nabla^2\psi + 2 = 0 \qquad (5.6.2)$$

and the boundary condition

$$\psi = 0 \qquad \text{on the boundary,} \qquad (5.6.3)$$

if the bar has a solid cross section.

The torque M_t producing the stresses of Eqs. (5.6.1) is expressed in terms of ψ by the equation

$$M_t = 2G\theta \int\int \psi \, dx \, dy, \qquad (5.6.4)$$

where the double integral is extended over the cross section of the bar.

We wish to evaluate numerically the maximum stress in a prismatic bar of square cross section with sides L parallel to the x- and y-axes, when the bar is acted upon by a torque M_t producing stresses within the elastic limit.

To obtain a numerical solution in nondimensional form, take the origin at one of the corners of the cross section and let in Eqs. (5.6.2), (5.6.3):

* See, for example, S. Timoshenko, *Theory of Elasticity*, McGraw-Hill Book Company, Inc., New York, 1934, pp. 228 ff.

$$\phi(\xi,\eta) = \frac{1}{L^2} \psi\ (x,y)$$

$$\xi = \frac{x}{L}, \qquad \eta = \frac{y}{L},$$

(5.6.5)

thus obtaining the boundary problem for ϕ:

$$\frac{\partial^2 \phi}{\partial \xi^2} + \frac{\partial^2 \phi}{\partial \eta^2} + 2 = 0$$

$$\phi(0,\eta) = \phi(1,\eta) = \phi(\xi,0) = \phi(\xi,1) = 0.$$

(5.6.6)

Comparison of Eqs. (5.6.6) with Eqs. (5.5.4) proves that the nondimensional torsion function ϕ of this section satisfies the same

Table 5.5

Point	1	2	3
$10^4 \cdot \phi$	1443	1181	1304
Point	4	5	6
$10^4 \cdot \phi$	529	780	855

obundary value problem as the nondimensional membrane deflection ϕ of Sec. 5.5, except for a factor of 2 in the constant of the equation. Since the differential equations in Eqs. (5.5.4) and (5.6.6) are linear, their solutions are proportional to the constant; hence the values of the nondimensional torsion function ϕ of Eqs. (5.6.6) are twice the values of the membrane deflection ϕ of Table 5.4. In other words, the membrane deflection is an *analogue* of the torsion function.

Table 5.5 gives the values of the nondimensional torsion function ϕ, obtained from the membrane relaxation solution for $n = 6$ of Table 5.4.

In terms of ϕ [Eqs. (5.6.5)], the stresses [Eqs. (5.6.1)] and the torque [Eq. (5.6.4)] take the form:

$$\tau_{xz} = G\theta L \frac{\partial \phi}{\partial \eta}, \qquad \tau_{yz} = -G\theta L \frac{\partial \phi}{\partial \xi}, \qquad (5.6.7)$$

$$M_t = 2G\theta L^4 \iint \phi\ d\xi\ d\eta \equiv 2G\theta L^4 V, \qquad (5.6.8)$$

and show that the stress components are proportional to the *slope* of the ϕ membrane in the x and y directions, and the torque is proportional to the volume V under the membrane ϕ.

In particular, the maximum stress occurs at the middle point A of the cross-section side (Fig. 5.9):

$$|\tau_{\max}| = G\theta L \left|\frac{\partial\phi}{\partial\xi}\right|_A. \tag{5.6.9}$$

The value of the maximum slope $\partial\phi/\partial\xi$ at A may be obtained by the forward difference expansion of the first derivative of Eq. (2.5.4), using the differences of the ϕ values of Table 5.5 and $h = \frac{1}{6}$.

Table 5.6

n	ϕ	$\Delta\phi$	$\Delta^2\phi$	$\Delta^3\phi$	$\Delta^4\phi$	$\Delta^5\phi$	$\Delta^6\phi$
0	0	855	-406	96	-64	0	0
1	855	449	-310	$+32$	-64	0	
2	1304	$+139$	-278	-32	-64		
3	1443	-139	-310	-96			
4	1304	-449	-406				
5	855	-855					
6	0						

Table 5.6 gives the successive forward differences of ϕ along the middle axis of the cross section, by means of which Eq. (2.5.4) yields

$$\left.\frac{\partial\phi}{\partial\xi}\right]_{\max} = \frac{1}{\frac{1}{6}}\left[855 - \tfrac{1}{2}(-406) + \tfrac{1}{3}(96) - \tfrac{1}{4}(-64)\right] = 6636.$$

Hence by Eq. (5.6.9), and remembering the factor 10^4 used in Table 5.5,

$$|\tau_{\max}| = 0.6636G\theta L.$$

This value differs by 1.7 per cent from the value $0.675G\theta L$ obtained by Timoshenko using a power series expansion for ϕ.*

* S. Timoshenko, *Theory of Elasticity*, McGraw-Hill Book Company, Inc., New York, 1934, p. 248.

The corresponding value of the torque M_t is obtained by evaluating the double intergral of Eq. (5.6.8) by means of Simpson's rule, applying the operator B_2 of Fig. 5.6 once at 1, four times at 4, and four times at 6 (Fig. 5.11c), or using the operator of Fig. 5.7:

$$\iint \phi \, d\xi \, d\eta = \frac{1}{9 \cdot 36} \{4 \cdot 1181 + 4 \cdot 4 \cdot 1304 + 16 \cdot 1443$$

$$+ \, 4[0 + 0 + 0 + 1181 + 4(0 + 0 + 780 + 780) + 16 \cdot 529]$$

$$+ \, 4[0 + 0 + 1181 + 1181 + 4(0 + 780 + 780 + 1304) + 16 \cdot 855]\}$$

$$= 685.8.$$

Hence: $M_t = 2 \cdot 685.8 \cdot 10^{-4} G\theta L^4 = 0.1372 G\theta L^4.$ (a)

This value is 2.42 per cent smaller than the value $0.1406 G\theta L^4$ computed by Timoshenko by means of a power series*.

5.7   Solution of a Problem in Plastic Torsion by Relaxation

The numerical solution of the torsion problem for stresses *beyond the elastic limit*, that is, in the plastic range, is easily obtained by means of the membrane analogy of the previous section.

To this purpose, notice first of all that the solution of the elastic torsion problem by finite differences and relaxation is analogous to the substitution of an elastic net for the continuous membrane. The net is loaded at the nodes, which correspond to the pivotal points, and the residual equation corresponding to Eq. (5.6.6),

$$R_i = (\phi_a + \phi_b + \phi_r + \phi_l - 4\phi_i) + \frac{2}{n^2} \qquad (5.7.1)$$

contains a term in parentheses proportional to the resultant of the tensions in the four wires meeting at the ith node, and the term $2/n^2$, which is proportional to the applied load. The residual thus represents the *unbalanced* force at the ith node, which must vanish for equilibrium.

Let us now assume that the material of the bar under torsion behaves elastically up to a value τ_0 of the shear stress τ and plastically from then on, that is, that an increase in shear strain γ will

---

* S. Timoshenko, *Theory of Elasticity*, McGraw-Hill Book Company, Inc., New York, 1934, p. 248.

not increase the shear stress τ beyond τ_0 (Fig. 5.13).   Calling M_0 the value of the torque producing a stress τ_0 at the middle points A of the edge (Fig. 5.14) where the stress is maximum, an increase of the torque beyond M_0 will cause the penetration of the plastic stress τ_0 into the section, so that in certain plastic regions around the points A the stress will be everywhere equal to τ_0.   It is easy to visualize these regions with the help of the membrane analogy.   As the torque M increases, the analogue of M, that is, the membrane

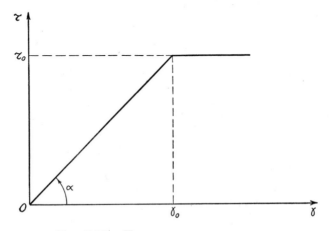

FIG. 5.13.   ELASTO-PLASTIC MATERIAL.

volume V, increases due to an increase in the pressure p.   The membrane is blown up and its slope increases.   Imagine a glass "roof" of constant slope m, corresponding to the maximum stress τ_0, set over the membrane.   As the membrane is blown up, it will touch the roof, starting at the points A, and as the pressure is increased, the contact between the membrane and the roof will be extended to larger and larger "plastic" regions as shown in Fig. 5.14. At the limit, when the whole section is in the plastic range, the membrane touches the roof everywhere and has the shape of a pyramid.

It is now clear that, while in the elastic region the external load p is equilibrated by the tension S in the membrane, in the plastic regions any unbalanced force is automatically equilibrated by the

reaction of the roof.   This observation of Southwell gives a simple
means of solving the plastic torsion problem.

Let us assume that the nondimensional deflections ϕ of the
"membrane" determined in Table 5.5 correspond to the value M_0

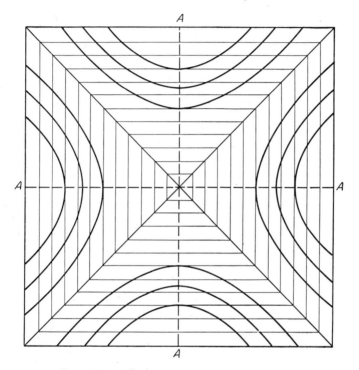

FIG. 5.14.   PLASTIC REGIONS IN TORSION.

of the torque, and that therefore the "slope" of the ϕ surface at A
corresponds to the plastic stress τ_0.   Approximating slopes by first
differences, the constant slope of the plastic roof must be taken
equal to the height 855 of the membrane at the pivotal point 6
divided by $h = \frac{1}{6}$ (Fig. 5.11c).   The heights of the points on the
roof are then equal to 855 for the points 4, 5, and 6, to $855 \cdot 2 = 1710$
for the points 2 and 3, and to $855 \cdot 3 = 2565$ for point 1 (Fig. 5.15).

On the other hand, since τ is proportional to M_t, if the torque reached a value of, say, $1.5M_0$ and the material still behaved elastically, the heights of the membrane would be 1.5 times the elastic heights computed in Table 5.5, and would have the values given in Fig. 5.16. Whenever the ordinates in Fig. 5.16 are higher

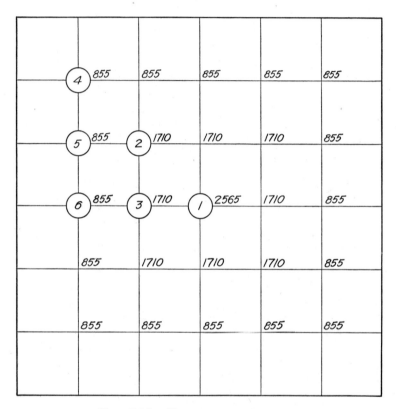

FIG. 5.15. PLASTIC ROOF HEIGHTS.

than those in Fig. 5.15, the roof will prevent the displacement of the membrane; hence the membrane must be brought *down* to the level of the roof at points 2, 3, 5, and 6 by means of the negative displacements of Table 5.7. The residuals due to these displacements are evaluated by means of Eq. (5.7.1), and appear in Table 5.8. Remembering that residuals represent unbalanced forces and

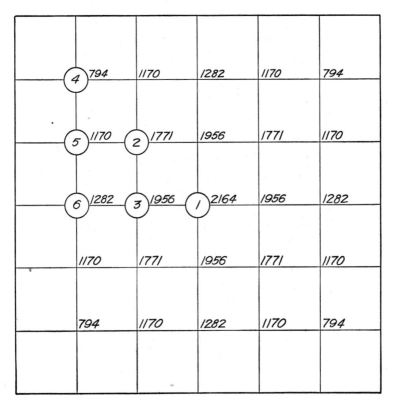

Fig. 5.16.   Elastic heights $(M_2 = 1.5M_0)$.

Table 5.7

Point	2	3	5	6
Displacement	1710 − 1771 = −61	1710 − 1956 = −246	855 − 1170 = −315	855 − 1282 = −427

Table 5.8

Lowering of Membrane to Roof

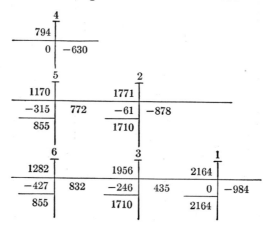

Table 5.9

Relaxation of Negative Residuals ($M_2 = 1.5M_0$)

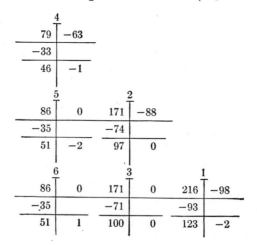

noting that positive residuals represent *upward* unbalanced forces equilibrated by the roof, the positive residuals are neglected and the *negative* residuals only are relaxed. This relaxation is performed in Table 5.9, which gives the new heights of the membrane to three figures. The height at point 6, corresponding to the plastic stress τ_0, is now 51, and the plastic region is seen to have reached

Table 5.10

Relaxation of Negative Residuals ($M_1 = 1.25M_0$)

```
           4
      66 │ −24
     ─────
     −13 │
      53 │  0


        5             2
      86 │  0      148 │ −24
     ─────        ─────
     −14          −28
      72 │  0      120 │  0


        6             3              1
      86 │  0      163 │ −21      180 │ 0
     ─────        ─────          ─────
     −15          −30            −30
      71 │  1      133 │ −2       150 │ 0
```

beyond point 5 and almost points 2 and 3, where the roof height is $2 \cdot 51 = 102$.

Table 5.10 gives the same calculations for $M = 1.25M_0$. Here the height at point 6 corresponding to the plastic stress is 71 and the plastic region has reached beyond points 5 and 6 but not points 2 and 3. Figure 5.17 gives the plastic regions corresponding to $M = 1.25M_0$ and $M = 1.5M_0$.

It is now possible to compute by Simpson's rule (Sec. 5.2b) the integral V of the elastoplastic ϕ function, as was done in Sec. 5.6 for the elastic ϕ function. For $M_1 = 1.25M_0$ and $M_2 = 1.5M_0$ we obtain, respectively, $V_1 = 651.8$ and $V_2 = 499.8$, and hence by Eq. (5.6.8) (remembering that the ϕ's were multiplied by 10^4):

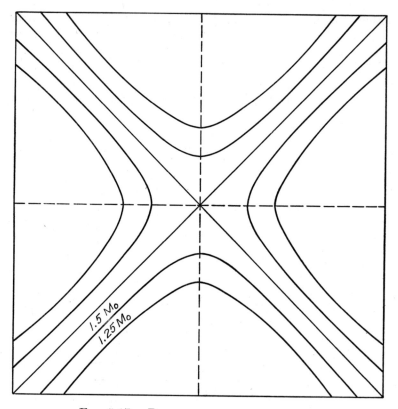

FIG. 5.17.   PLASTIC REGIONS IN TORSION.

$$1.25M_0 = 2 \cdot 10^{-4} \cdot 651.8G\theta_1L^4 = 0.1304G\theta_1L^4 \qquad \text{(a)}$$

$$1.5M_0 = 2 \cdot 10^{-4} \cdot 499.8G\theta_2L^4 = 0.09996G\theta_2L^4, \qquad \text{(b)}$$

where θ_1 and θ_2 are the values of θ corresponding to M_1 and M_2, respectively.

Since it was found in Sec. 5.6 that for the elastic case [Eq. (a)]:

$$M_0 = 0.1372G\theta_0L^4, \qquad \text{(c)}$$

taking the ratios of Eqs. (a) and (b) to (c), we see that

$$\frac{\theta_1}{\theta_0} = 1.32 \quad \text{for} \quad \frac{M_1}{M_0} = 1.25; \qquad \frac{\theta_2}{\theta_0} = 2.06 \quad \text{for} \quad \frac{M_2}{M_0} = 1.5.$$

Figure 5.18 gives the graph of M/M_0 versus θ/θ_0 and shows the nonlinear relation between torque and angle of twist in the plastic problem.

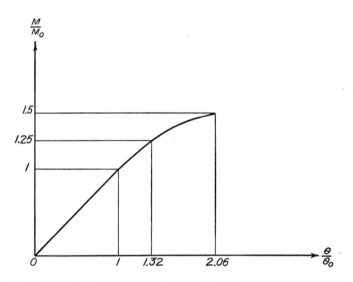

FIG. 5.18. TORQUE VS. TWIST IN PLASTIC TORSION OF SQUARE SECTION.

5.8 A Boundary Value Problem Involving $\nabla^4 z$

The boundary value problem for the deflections w of a square plate of sides a, built in all around, is given by*

$$\nabla^4 w = \frac{q}{D}; \quad w = \frac{\partial w}{\partial \nu} = 0 \quad \text{on the boundary,} \qquad (5.8.1)$$

where: q = load per unit area of plate,

$D = \dfrac{Eh^3}{12(1 - \mu^2)}$ = flexural rigidity of plate,

h = plate thickness,

E, μ = Young's modulus and Poisson's ratio, respectively, of the plate material,

ν = direction of the normal to the boundary.

* See, for example, S. Timoshenko, *Theory of Plates and Shells*, p. 222.

The problem (5.8.1) is reduced to nondimensional form by the transformation:

$$x = \xi a, \quad y = \eta a; \quad w(x,y) = \frac{qa^4}{D} z(\xi,\eta), \qquad \text{(a)}$$

giving:

$$\nabla^4 z = 1; \quad z = \frac{\partial z}{\partial \nu} = 0 \quad \text{on the boundary,} \qquad (5.8.2)$$

where the operator ∇^4 is taken with respect to ξ and η.

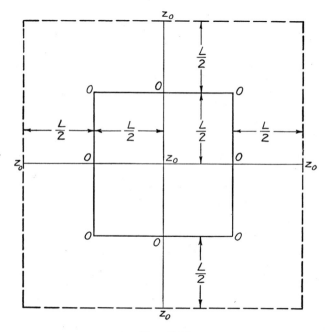

FIG. 5.19

The numerical solution of the problem (5.8.2) is obtained by substituting for $\nabla^4 z$ the central difference operator of Fig. 5.2c with a square lattice of mesh size $1/n$.

The boundary conditions, by Eq. (4.1.1), state that the values of z at pivotal points immediately outside the boundary are equal to the values of z at points immediately inside the boundary on the same normal.

Starting with $n = 2$ (Fig. 5.19), Eq. (5.8.2) gives

$$(z_0 + z_0 + z_0 + z_0) + 2 \cdot 0 - 8 \cdot 0 + 20 z_0 = \frac{1}{2^4},$$

from which:

$$z_0]_2 = \frac{1}{2^4 \cdot 24} = \frac{1}{384}.$$

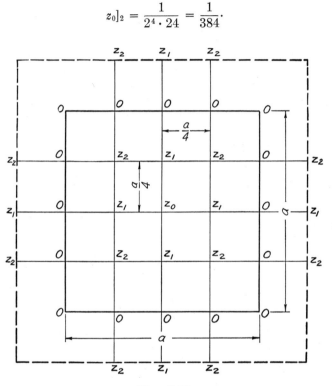

FIG. 5.20

For $n = 4$, Eq. (5.8.2) applied at the points of Fig. 5.20 gives

at (0) $\qquad 20 z_0 - 32 z_1 + 8 z_2 = \dfrac{1}{4^4},$

at (1) $\qquad -8 z_0 + 26 z_1 - 16 z_2 = \dfrac{1}{4^4},$

at (2) $\qquad 2 z_0 - 16 z_1 + 24 z_2 = \dfrac{1}{4^4},$

from which, for example, by Gauss's scheme:

$$z_0]_4 = \frac{0.461}{4^4}; \qquad z_1]_4 = \frac{0.309}{4^4}; \qquad z_2]_4 = \frac{0.209}{4^4}.$$

For $n = 8$, it is similarly found that $z_0]_8 = 5.857/8^4$.

The deflection at the center of the plate for $\mu = 0.3$ and with $n = 2, 4, 8$ becomes, by Eq. (a):

$$w_0]_2 = \frac{12(1 - 0.3^2)}{384} \frac{qa^4}{Eh^3} = 0.0284 \frac{qa^4}{Eh^3} \qquad (e = 106\%),$$

$$w_0]_4 = \frac{12(1 - 0.3^2) \cdot 0.461}{256} \frac{qa^4}{Eh^3} = 0.0197 \frac{qa^4}{Eh^3} \qquad (e = 43\%),$$

$$w_0]_8 = \frac{12(1 - 0.3^2) \cdot 5.857}{4096} \frac{qa^4}{Eh^3} = 0.0156 \frac{qa^4}{Eh^3} \qquad (e = 13\%).$$

The percentage errors e are computed from the series solution value $(w_0 = 0.0138qa^4/Eh^3)$ given by Timoshenko.[*] Extrapolations of the h^2-type can be used on the approximate values (see Sec. 2.9) and give:

$$w_0]_{2,4} = 0.0167 \frac{qa^4}{Eh^3} \qquad (e = 21\%),$$

$$w_0]_{4,8} = 0.0142 \frac{qa^4}{Eh^3} \qquad (e = 2.9\%),$$

$$w_0]_{2,4,8} = 0.0140 \frac{qa^4}{Eh^3} \qquad (e = 1.4\%).$$

5.9   Two-Dimensional Characteristic Value Problems

Consider a square plate of side a, simply supported along two opposite edges and built in along the other two edges. The plate is acted upon by a uniform compressive force N per unit of length, perpendicular to the simply supported edges and acting in the plane of the plate (Fig. 5.21). Choosing the x-axis parallel to the built-in edges, with origin at the center of the plate, it may be proved that the deflection w of the plate at a point (x,y) satisfies the differential

[*] See, S. Timoshenko, *Theory of Plates and Shells*, p. 228.

equation*

$$\nabla^4 w + \frac{N}{D}\frac{\partial^2 w}{\partial x^2} = 0, \tag{5.9.1}$$

where D is the flexural rigidity of the plate.   We wish to find the lowest value of the compression N for which the plate will buckle,

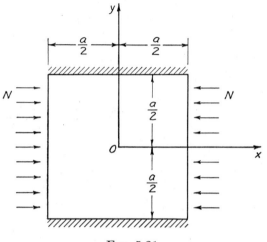

Fɪɢ. 5.21

that is, for which the deflection w will not be identically zero, while satisfying the boundary conditions of simple support:

$$w = 0, \quad \frac{\partial^2 w}{\partial x^2} = 0 \quad \text{at} \quad x = \pm\frac{a}{2} \tag{5.9.2}$$

and the conditions for complete lack of rotation:

$$w = 0, \quad \frac{\partial w}{\partial y} = 0 \quad \text{at} \quad y = \pm\frac{a}{2}. \tag{5.9.3}$$

Equation (5.9.1) is first reduced to nondimensional form by the transformation:

$$\xi = \frac{x}{a}, \quad \eta = \frac{y}{a}$$

* See, for instance, S. Timoshenko, *Theory of Elastic Stability*, p. 337.

and, multiplied through by a^4, becomes:

$$\nabla^4 w + \frac{Na^2}{D}\frac{\partial^2 w}{\partial \xi^2} = 0,\qquad (5.9.4)$$

where $\nabla^4 w$ is taken with respect to ξ and η. The plate is then covered with a square lattice of mesh size $1/n$. Multiplying the equation through by $h^4 = 1/n^4$, and using the operator of Fig. 5.2c for $h^4\nabla^4 w$ and the operator of Eq. (5.1.2) for $\partial^2 w/\partial \xi^2$, the difference equation corresponding to Eq. (5.9.4) is obtained in molecular form:

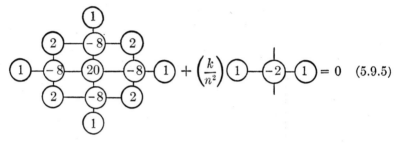

$$+ \left(\frac{k}{n^2}\right) \qquad = 0 \quad (5.9.5)$$

where:

$$k = \frac{Na^2}{D}.\qquad (5.9.6)$$

The application of Eq. (5.9.5) at the internal pivotal points gives rise to a set of homogeneous linear algebraic equations in the unknown pivotal displacements w_i, whose determinant must be identically zero if the w_i are to be different from zero. The lowest value of N making the determinant of Eqs. (5.9.5) equal to zero is the lowest critical value of the compressive force.

In order to apply Eq. (5.9.5) at the pivotal points immediately inside the boundary, the deflection must be known at fictitious pivotal points immediately *outside* the boundary. These deflections are given in terms of the deflections at the pivotal points immediately inside the boundary by the boundary conditions. In fact, by Eqs. (4.1.1), Eqs. (5.9.2) become:

$$w_i = 0, \quad w_l = -w_r \qquad \text{at } \xi = \pm\tfrac{1}{2}, \qquad (5.9.7)$$

while Eqs. (5.9.3) give:

$$w_i = 0, \quad w_a = w_b \qquad \text{at } \eta = \pm\tfrac{1}{2}. \qquad (5.9.8)$$

Starting with $n = 2$ and the deflections of Fig. 5.22, we obtain by Eqs. (5.9.5):

$$(-w_0 + w_0 - w_0 + w_0) + 2(0) - 8(0) + 20w_0$$

$$+ \frac{k_2}{4} (0 - 2w_0 + 0) = 0,$$

or:
$$w_0 \left(20 - \frac{k_2}{2} \right) = 0,$$

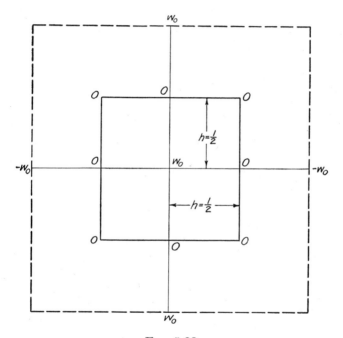

Fɪɢ. 5.22

from which the value of k_2 and the corresponding percentage error (obtained from Timoshenko's value* for Poisson's ratio $\mu = 0.25$, $k = 7.69\pi^2$) become

$$k_2 = 40 = 4.053\pi^2 \qquad (e = +47.3\%). \qquad \text{(a)}$$

* See, S. Timoshenko, *Theory of Elastic Stability*, p. 345.

With $n = 3$ and the deflections of Fig. 5.23, we obtain similarly:

$$(-w_1 + w_1 + 0 + 0) + 2(0 + 0 + 0 + w_1)$$
$$- 8(0 + 0 + w_1 + w_1) + 20w_1 + \frac{k_3}{9}(0 - 2w_1 + w_1) = 0,$$

or:
$$w_1\left(6 - \frac{k_3}{9}\right) = 0,$$

from which:

$$k_3 = 54 = 5.471\pi^2 \qquad (e = 28.9\%). \tag{b}$$

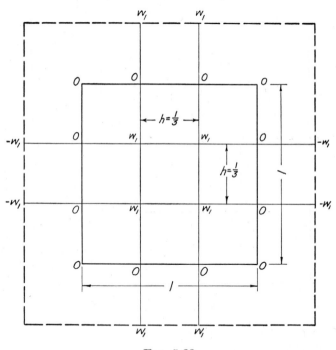

Fig. 5.23

With $n = 4$ and the deflections: of Fig. 5.24, we obtain the four equations of Table 5.11, in which

$$\gamma = \frac{k}{16}.$$

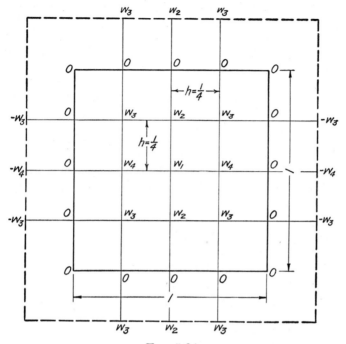

Fɪɢ. 5.24

Table 5.11

w_1	w_2	w_3	w_4	c
$20 - 2\gamma$	-16	8	$2\gamma - 16$	0
-8	$22 - 2\gamma$	$2\gamma - 16$	4	0
2	$\gamma - 8$	$22 - 2\gamma$	-8	0
$\gamma - 8$	4	-16	$20 - 2\gamma$	0

Setting their determinant equal to zero we obtain as lowest root $\gamma = 3.9884$ and hence:

$$k_4 = 63.814 = 6.466\pi^2 \qquad (e = 16.0\%). \qquad (c)$$

By means of h^2-extrapolations (Table 2.9) applied to the values (a), (b), and (c), we obtain the following extrapolated values of k, with the percentage errors indicated in parentheses:

$$k_{2,3} = 6.605\pi^2 \quad (+14\%), \qquad k_{3,4} = 7.744\pi^2 \quad (-0.65\%).$$

[The error in k is not rigorously of the h^2-type, as also indicated by the poor approximation of the extrapolation $k_{2,3,4} = 8.1252$ ($e = 5.66\%$).]

5.10   The Solution of Partial Differential Equations by Separation of the Variables and Finite Differences

The classical method of the separation of the variables and modern numerical procedures may often be advantageously combined to solve partial differential equations.   This mixed approach will be illustrated by its application to the buckling problem of the preceding section.

Since two sides of the square plate are simply supported and a rectangular simply supported plate of sides a and b is known to buckle into squares whenever b is a multiple of a, it is logical to assume the deflection w in the form:

$$w(x,y) = Y(y) \cos \frac{\pi}{a} x, \tag{5.10.1}$$

where $Y(y)$ is an unknown function of y only.   This deflection function w satisfies the boundary conditions on the simply supported boundaries [Eqs. (5.9.2)], and when substituted in the equilibrium equation [Eq. (5.9.1)], reduces it to the *ordinary* differential equation in Y:

$$Y^{\mathrm{IV}} - 2\frac{\pi^2}{a^2} Y'' + \left(\frac{\pi^4}{a^4} - \frac{N}{D}\frac{\pi^2}{a^2}\right) Y = 0. \tag{5.10.2}$$

Substitution of Eq. (5.10.1) in the boundary conditions along the built-in edges [Eqs. (5.9.3)] gives the boundary conditions for Y:

$$Y = 0, \quad Y' = 0 \quad \text{at} \quad y = \pm\frac{a}{2}. \tag{5.10.3}$$

The partial characteristic value problem of Eqs. (5.9.1), (5.9.2), and (5.9.3) has thus been reduced to the ordinary characteristic value problem of Eqs. (5.10.2) and (5.10.3).

To solve this last problem in nondimensional form, we use the transformation:

$$y = a\eta,$$

obtaining:

$$\frac{d^4Y}{d\eta^4} - 2\pi^2 \frac{d^2Y}{d\eta^2} + \left(\pi^4 - \pi^2 \frac{Na^2}{D}\right) Y = 0 \qquad (5.10.4)$$

$$Y(\eta) = 0, \quad \frac{dY}{d\eta} = 0 \quad \text{at} \quad \eta = \pm\tfrac{1}{2}. \qquad (5.10.5)$$

Multiplying Eq. (5.10.4) by $h^4 = 1/n^4$ and substituting central difference expressions for the derivatives of Y [Eqs. (2.7.16)], we obtain the difference equation in Y:

$$Y_{bb} - \left(\frac{2\pi^2}{n^2} + 4\right) Y_b + \left(6 + \frac{4\pi^2}{n^2} + \frac{\pi^4}{n^4} - \frac{\pi^2 k}{n^4}\right) Y_i - \left(\frac{2\pi^2}{n^2} + 4\right) Y_a$$
$$+ Y_{aa} = 0, \qquad (5.10.6)$$

where k is given by Eq. (5.9.6). The boundary conditions require that:

$$Y_a = Y_b \quad \text{at} \quad \eta = \pm\tfrac{1}{2}. \qquad (5.10.7)$$

Starting with $n = 2$ and the values Y of Fig. 5.25a, in which the

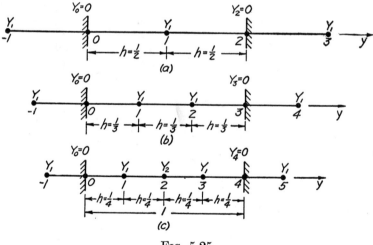

(a)

(b)

(c)

FIG. 5.25

y-axis is plotted horizontally for convenience, Eq. (5.10.6) gives:

$$Y_1 + 0 + \left(6 + \frac{4\pi^2}{4} + \frac{\pi^4}{16} - \frac{\pi^2}{16} k_2\right) Y_1 + 0 + Y_1 = 0,$$

from which: $\quad k_2 = 3.935\pi^2 \quad (e = +49\%)$. $\hspace{2cm}$ (a)

With $n = 3$ and the values Y of Fig. 5.25b, Eq. (5.10.6) gives:

$$Y_1 + 0 + \left(6 + \frac{4\pi^2}{9} + \frac{\pi^4}{81} - \frac{\pi^2}{81} k_3\right) Y_1 - \left(\frac{2\pi^2}{9} + 4\right) Y_1 + 0 = 0,$$

from which: $\quad k_3 = 5.318\pi^2 \quad (e = +31\%)$. $\hspace{2cm}$ (b)

With $n = 4$ and the values Y of Fig. 5.25c, we obtain the two equations:

$$Y_1 + 0 + \left(6 + \frac{4\pi^2}{16} + \frac{\pi^4}{256} - \frac{\pi^2}{256} k_4\right) Y_1 - \left(\frac{2\pi^2}{16} + 4\right) Y_2 + Y_1 = 0$$

$$0 - \left(\frac{2\pi^2}{16} + 4\right) Y_1 + \left(6 + \frac{4\pi^2}{16} + \frac{\pi^4}{256} - \frac{\pi^2}{256} k_4\right) Y_2$$

$$- \left(\frac{2\pi^2}{16} + 4\right) Y_1 + 0 = 0.$$

The smallest root of the determinant of these equations equals:

$$k_4 = 6.252\pi^2 \quad (e = +19\%). \hspace{2cm} (c)$$

The h^2-extrapolations applied to Eqs. (a), (b), and (c) give the following results with the percentage errors indicated in parentheses:

$$k_{2,3} = 7.45\pi^2 \quad (e = +3.1\%);$$
$$k_{3,4} = 7.797\pi^2 \quad (e = -1.4\%).$$

The solution by separation of the variables gives results of the same order of accuracy as the finite difference solution in two dimensions of Sec. 5.9, but requires much less labor, since the evaluation of k_4, for example, involves a determinant of the second order in the one-dimensional solution and a determinant of the fourth order in the two-dimensional solution.

5.11   Membrane Vibrations

The technique used in the preceding section to solve two-dimensional buckling problems may be used to solve two-dimensional vibration problems.

The differential equation for the free vibrations of a membrane is obtained by adding to the equilibrium equation (5.5.1) the inertia forces $-m \dfrac{\partial^2 z}{\partial t^2}$, where m is the membrane mass per unit of area, and by setting the external pressure p equal to zero:

$$\frac{\partial^2 z}{\partial x^2} + \frac{\partial^2 z}{\partial y^2} - \frac{m}{S}\frac{\partial^2 z}{\partial t^2} = 0. \tag{5.11.1}$$

To find the natural frequencies ω of a membrane, the function $z(x,y,t)$ is assumed to represent a harmonic vibration:

$$z(x,y,t) = Z(x,y) \sin \omega t \tag{a}$$

and is substituted in Eq. (5.11.1), which becomes, after division by $\sin \omega t$:

$$\frac{\partial^2 Z}{\partial x^2} + \frac{\partial^2 Z}{\partial y^2} + \frac{m\omega^2}{S} Z = 0. \tag{5.11.2}$$

To solve the problem in nondimensional form for the case of a square membrane of side L supported on a flat boundary, the usual transformation

$$x = \xi L, \qquad y = \eta L \tag{b}$$

is introduced in Eq. (5.11.2), which thus becomes:

$$\frac{\partial^2 Z}{\partial \xi^2} + \frac{\partial^2 Z}{\partial \eta^2} + K^2 Z = 0, \tag{5.11.3}$$

with:

$$K = \frac{mL^2}{S}\omega^2, \tag{5.11.4}$$

and Eq. (5.11.3) is then transformed into a finite difference equation by the operator of Fig. 5.2b with $h^2 = 1/n^2$:

$$Z_a + Z_b + Z_r + Z_l + \left(\frac{K}{n^2} - 4\right) Z_i = 0. \tag{5.11.5}$$

The conditions on the boundary require that:

$$Z = 0 \text{ on the boundary.} \tag{5.11.6}$$

For $n = 2$ and 3 (Fig. 5.26a, b), Eq. (5.11.5) gives:

$$n = 2; \quad \left(\frac{K_2}{4} - 4\right) Z_1 = 0; \quad K_2 = 16 \quad (e = -19\%)$$

$$n = 3; \quad Z_1 + 0 + Z_1 + 0 + \left(\frac{K_3}{9} - 4\right) Z_1 = 0; \quad K_3 = 18$$

$$(e = -9\%)$$

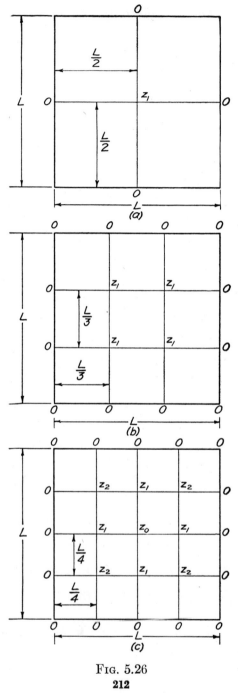

FIG. 5.26

The determinantal equation for $n = 4$ (Fig. 5.26c) is:

$$\begin{vmatrix} \dfrac{K_4}{16} - 4 & 2 & 0 \\[2mm] 2 & \dfrac{K_4}{16} - 4 & 1 \\[2mm] 0 & 4 & \dfrac{K_4}{16} - 4 \end{vmatrix} = 0$$

and its smallest root is:

$$K_4 = 18.75 \qquad (e = -5\%).$$

The extrapolated values of K are:

$$K_{2,3} = 19.60 \quad (-0.7\%), \qquad K_{3,4} = 19.71 \quad (-0.15\%),$$

$$K_{2,3,4} = 19.75 \quad (+0.051\%).$$

The true value of K is 19.739.

5.12   Pivotal Points Near Curved Boundaries

In all the problems of the preceding sections the pivotal points inside the rectangular domains and on their boundaries fell on the corners of a rectangular lattice and were evenly spaced in the x and the y directions.   When a two-dimensional domain covered by a rectangular lattice is bounded by curves, instead, some or all of its pivotal boundary points do not fall on the corners of the lattice, and special formulas must be used at pivotal points adjoining the boundaries.

Consider, for example, the steady-state temperature problem of the plate of Fig. 5.27, a square plate of sides L with two corners rounded off by arcs of circle of radius $L/2$.   The temperature u in the plate satisfies the Laplacian equation $\nabla^2 u = 0$ (Sec. 5.3).   This equation can be transformed into a difference equation by the operator of Fig. 5.2b at points (1), (2), and (3), but point (4) is not evenly spaced from the adjoining pivotal points, and must be dealt with by means of a special equation.

The difference equation $\nabla^2 u = 0$ at the upper point (4) may be obtained, for example, by means of Eq. (2.2.3), which in the present case becomes:

$$\frac{\partial^2 u}{\partial x^2} = \frac{1}{h^2} \frac{2}{\alpha(\alpha + 1)} [\alpha u_l - (1 + \alpha)u_i + u_r] + 0(h) \qquad \text{(a)}$$

$$\alpha = \frac{x_r - x_i}{h} = \frac{x_5 - x_4}{L/4}, \qquad \text{(b)}$$

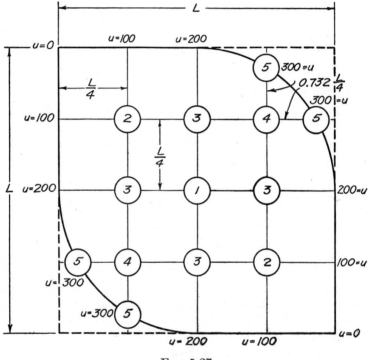

Fig. 5.27

and by the corresponding equation in the y direction:

$$\frac{\partial^2 u}{\partial y^2} = \frac{1}{h^2} \frac{2}{\beta(\beta + 1)} [\beta u_b - (1 + \beta)u_i + u_a] + 0(h) \qquad \text{(c)}$$

$$\beta = \frac{y_a - y_i}{h} = \frac{y_5 - y_4}{L/4}. \qquad \text{(d)}$$

Adding up Eqs. (a) and (c), the operator $\nabla^2 u$ is obtained in the form:

$$\frac{h^2}{2}\alpha(1+\alpha)\beta(1+\beta)\nabla^2 u = \beta(1+\beta)[\alpha u_l - (1+\alpha)u_i + u_r]$$
$$+ \alpha(1+\alpha)[\beta u_b - (1+\beta)u_i + u_a], \quad (5.12.1)$$

which is also given in the molecule of Fig. 5.28.

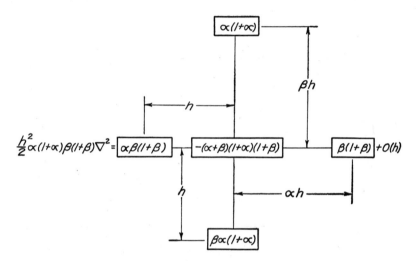

Fig. 5.28. ∇^2 operator for unevenly spaced points.

In the problem of Fig. 5.27, $\alpha = \beta$ and the operator of Fig. 5.28 becomes, after division by $\alpha(1+\alpha)$, the operator of Fig. 5.29.

If this operator is applied at point (4) with $\alpha = \sqrt{3} - 1 = 0.732$, and the operator of Fig. 5.2b is applied at the points (1), (2), and (3), one obtains the system of linear equations for the u_i of Table 5.12, whose roots are

$$u_1 = 203.7; \quad u_2 = 151.9; \quad u_3 = 203.7; \quad u_4 = 259.3.$$

The operator in Fig. 5.29 has an error of order h, while the operator of Fig. 5.2b has an error of order h^2. To have consistent errors throughout the domain one may express $\nabla^2 u$ by means of the operator of Eq. (2.3.6), but in the present example this does not change the first four figures of the u_i (see Problem 5.31).

The type of difference formulas used in this section are also applied in problems involving so-called *graded nets*. These lattices, with different values of the mesh size in different regions of the domain, are used whenever the function to be determined varies

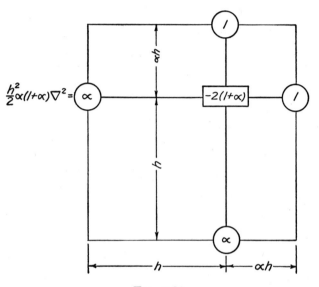

Fig. 5.29

Table 5.12

Point	u_1	u_2	u_3	u_4	c
1	-4	0	4	0	0
2	0	-4	2	0	-200
3	1	1	-4	1	-200
4	0	0	2	-1.464	-600

rapidly in a given region, since a smaller mesh size gives better accuracy at points where it is needed. While the detailed technique of graded nets goes beyond the scope of this book, the reader may consult Southwell's books and papers on this particular subject.*

* See, for example, R. V. Southwell, *Relaxation Methods in Theoretical Physics*, Oxford University Press, London, 1946, p. 50.

5.13   A Transient Problem in Two-Dimensional Heat Flow

A square plate of side L, initially at zero temperature, has two opposite sides suddenly raised to a constant temperature u_0, while the other two are kept at zero temperature (Fig. 5.30). The

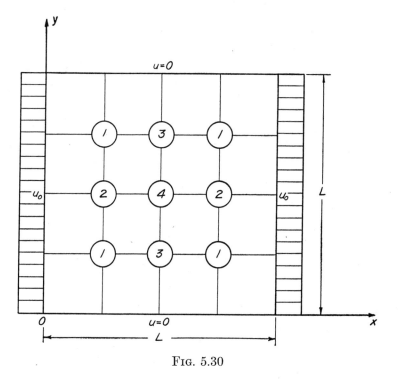

Fig. 5.30

variation of the temperature with time is to be determined for points inside the plate.

The differential equation satisfied by the temperature $u(x,y,t)$ at a point x, y of the plate at a time t may be shown to be*

$$\frac{k}{c\delta}\left(\frac{\partial^2 u}{\partial x^2} + \frac{\partial^2 u}{\partial y^2}\right) = \frac{\partial u}{\partial t}, \qquad (5.13.1)$$

where k is the thermal conductivity, c is the specific heat and δ is the density of the plate (mass per unit area). The temperature

* See, for example, *Partial Differential Equations*, Sec. 8.

must moreover satisfy the conditions:

$$u(0,y,t) = u(L,y,t) = u_0,$$
$$u(x,0,t) = u(x,L,t) = 0, \quad \Bigg\}$$
$$u(x,y,0) = 0.$$

(5.13.2)

The problem is thus of the boundary value type for the space variables and of the initial value type for the time variable, and may be solved by finite differences, following a suggestion of Bender and Schmidt.

Cover the square plate by means of a square lattice of mesh size $h = L/n$ and use a time interval $\Delta t = \tau$. Using the *central* difference operator of Fig. 5.2b for $\nabla^2 u$, and the *forward* difference operator of Fig. 2.5a for the derivative $\partial u/\partial t$, Eq. (5.13.1) reduces to the following difference equation:

$$u_a(t) + u_b(t) + u_r(t) + u_l(t) - 4u_i(t)$$
$$= \frac{\delta c h^2}{k\tau} [u_i(t + \tau) - u_i(t)]. \quad (5.13.3)$$

If the time interval τ is chosen so as to make $\delta c h^2/k\tau = 4$, that is, if

$$\tau = \frac{\delta c}{4k} h^2, * \quad (5.13.4)$$

Eq. (5.13.3) reduces to

$$u_i(t + \tau) = \tfrac{1}{4}[u_a(t) + u_b(t) + u_r(t) + u_l(t)]. \quad (5.13.5)$$

The temperature at a point i at a time $t + \tau$ is thus seen to become the average of the temperatures at the four adjoining pivotal points at time t. As shown by Eq. (5.13.4), a refinement in the temperature-time variation, requiring a decrease in the value of τ, entails a decrease in h and hence an increase in the number of pivotal points considered, so that a very fine mesh is needed to obtain accurate temperatures for small values of t.

The square plate of the present example was covered by a lattice of mesh size $h = L/4$, so that the time interval τ has the value

$$\tau = \frac{\delta c L^2}{64k}. \quad (a)$$

---

* It may be proved that the finite difference solution of the partial differential equation (5.13.1) does not converge towards the true solution if $\tau > \delta c h^2/4k$.

Table 5.13

② $x = L/4$, $y = L/2$ ④ $x = L/2$, $y = L/2$

$n = t/\tau$	u	6250	∞		$n = t/\tau$	u	5000	∞
0	0	6242	19		0	0	4990	19
1	2500	6240	18		1	0	4985	18
2	3750	6235	17		2	1250	4980	17
3	4375	6230	16		3	2500	4970	16
4	5000	6220	15		4	3125	4960	15
5	5312	6210	14		5	3750	4941	14
6	5625	6191	13		6	4062	4921	13
7	5781	6171	12		7	4375	4882	12
8	5937	6132	11		8	4531	4843	11
9	6015	6093	10		9	4687	4765	10
			$n = t/\tau$					$n = t/\tau$

① $x = L/4$, $y = L/4$ ③ $x = L/2$, $y = L/4$

$n = t/\tau$	u	5000	∞		$n = t/\tau$	u	3750	∞
0	0	4995	19		0	0	3742	19
1	2500	4992	18		1	0	3741	18
2	3125	4990	17		2	1250	3735	17
3	3750	4985	16		3	1875	3730	16
4	4062	4980	15		4	2500	3720	15
5	4375	4970	14		5	2812	3710	14
6	4531	4960	13		6	3125	3691	13
7	4687	4941	12		7	3281	3671	12
8	4765	4921	11		8	3437	3632	11
9	4843	4882	10		9	3515	3593	10
			$n = t/\tau$					$n = t/\tau$

The initial temperature on the opposite sides $x = 0$, $x = L$ was assumed equal to 10,000; the successive values of the temperature at the pivotal points, appearing in Table 5.13 for one-quarter of the plate, were computed by successive averaging according to Eq. (5.13.5), noticing that the temperature distribution is symmetrical about $x = L/2$ and $y = L/2$. The values of the temperature in Table 5.13 must be read moving downward up to $t = 9\tau$ and upward from then on. The last value of the temperature, corresponding to $t = \infty$, is the steady-state value and was computed by relaxation, using the methods of Sec. 5.3.

The table shows numerically how an accurate determination of the temperature variation immediately after $t = 0$ would require the use of a very fine mesh.

5.14   The Laplacian Operator in Skew Coordinates

Difference operators in Cartesian coordinates are well adapted to the solution of problems involving rectangular domains. When the domain to be considered is a parallelogram it may be often more accurate and simpler to use coordinates parallel to the sides of the parallelogram, or *skew coordinates*.

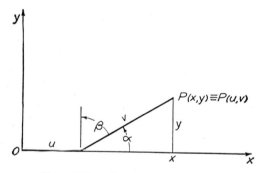

FIG. 5.31.   SKEW COORDINATES.

A point of Cartesian coordinates (x,y) (Fig. 5.31) is located in the plane by skew coordinates (u,v) given by the transformation:

$$x = u + v \cos \alpha; \qquad y = v \sin \alpha, \qquad (5.14.1)$$

where α is the complement of the *angle of skew* β.

Indicating partial derivatives by subscripts, the partial derivatives of x and y with respect to u and v are given by:

$$x_u = 1; \quad x_v = \cos \alpha; \quad y_u = 0; \quad y_v = \sin \alpha. \qquad (a)$$

Consider now a function $z(u,v)$ in which u, v are related to x, y by means of Eqs. (5.14.1). The first derivatives of z with respect to u and v are obtained by the rule for the differentiation of composite functions:

$$z_u = z_x x_u + z_y y_u = z_x$$

$$z_v = z_x x_v + z_y y_v = z_x \cos \alpha + z_y \sin \alpha.$$

The second derivatives of z with respect to u and v are obtained

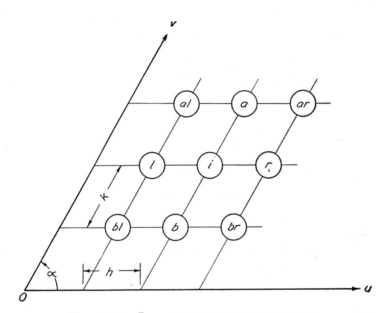

FIG. 5.32.   LATTICE IN SKEW COORDINATES.

by "squaring" the operators z_u and z_v and by means of their "product":

$$z_{uu} = z_{xx} \tag{b}$$

$$z_{vv} = z_{xx} \cos^2 \alpha + 2z_{xy} \sin \alpha \cos \alpha + z_{yy} \sin^2 \alpha \tag{c}$$

$$z_{uv} = z_{xx} \cos \alpha + z_{xy} \sin \alpha. \tag{d}$$

Substituting Eqs. (b) and (d) in Eq. (c):

$$z_{vv} = z_{uu} \cos^2 \alpha + 2 \cos \alpha(z_{uv} - z_{uu} \cos \alpha) + z_{yy} \sin^2 \alpha,$$

z_{yy} is obtained in terms of z_{uu}, z_{vv}, z_{uv}:

$$z_{yy} = \frac{1}{\sin^2 \alpha} (z_{vv} - 2z_{uv} \cos \alpha + z_{uu} \cos^2 \alpha)$$

and the *Laplacian operator in skew coordinates* becomes, by Eq. (b)

$$(\sin^2 \alpha)\nabla^2 z = z_{uu} - 2z_{uv} \cos \alpha + z_{vv}. \qquad (5.14.2)$$

For $\alpha = \pi/2$, Eq. (5.14.2) reduces to $\nabla^2 z = z_{xx} + z_{yy}$.

The ∇^2 operator in skew coordinates is transformed into the

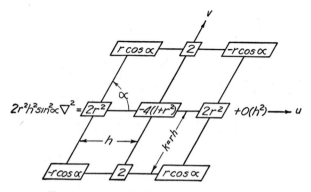

FIG. 5.33. ∇^2 IN SKEW COORDINATES.

corresponding difference operator by substituting for the derivatives z_{uu}, z_{uv}, z_{vv} their expressions given by Fig. 2.8a. With the symbols of Fig. 5.32:

$$h^2 z_{uu} = z_r - 2z_i + z_l; \quad k^2 z_{vv} = z_a - 2z_i + z_b$$

$$4hk z_{uv} = z_{ar} - z_{br} - z_{al} + z_{bl},$$

and the ∇^2 operator takes the form of the molecule in Fig. 5.33, in which $r = k/h$.

The operator of Fig. 5.33 may be used, for example, to determine the center deflection w of a skew plate of sides $a = b$ with an angle of skew of 30° ($\alpha = 60°$), simply supported all around its boundary and uniformly loaded.   The corresponding problem may be shown[*] to reduce to the integration of the two equations:

$$\nabla^2 M = -q; \quad \nabla^2 w = -M/D \qquad (e)$$

[*] See, for example, S. Timoshenko, *Theory of Plates and Shells*, Sec. 36.

with the conditions:

$$M = 0 \qquad w = 0 \qquad \text{on the boundary.} \tag{f}$$

With $a = b$, $r = 1$, $n = 2$, $\alpha = 60°$, the operator of Fig. 5.33 becomes the operator of Fig. 5.34, and with $h = a/2$, gives at the

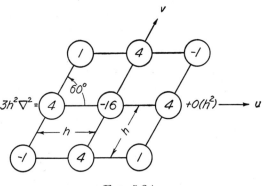

FIG. 5.34

center of the plate, for the first of Eqs. (e):

$$\frac{-16}{3(a/2)^2} M_0 = -q \qquad \therefore \qquad M_0 = \tfrac{3}{64}qa^2,$$

and for the second of Eqs. (e):

$$\frac{-16}{3(a/2)^2} w_0 = -\tfrac{3}{64}\frac{qa^2}{D} \qquad \therefore \qquad w_0]_2 = 0.00220 \frac{qa^4}{D}.$$

Using $n = 4$, and solving the corresponding system of five simultaneous equations, it is found that $w_0]_4 = 0.00241qa^4/D$, and an h^2-extrapolation gives:

$$w_0]_{2,4} = 0.00248 \frac{qa^4}{D}.$$

It is simple to obtain the operator ∇^4 in skew coordinates in each numerical case, once ∇^2 is known. For example, using the ∇^2 of Fig. 5.34:

$$9h^4\nabla^4z_i = (\nabla^2z_{al} - \nabla^2z_{ar} + \nabla^2z_{br} - \nabla^2z_{bl})$$
$$+ 4(\nabla^2z_a + \nabla^2z_b + \nabla^2z_r + \nabla^2z_l) - 16\nabla^2z_i,$$

and ∇^4 becomes the operator of Fig. 5.35.

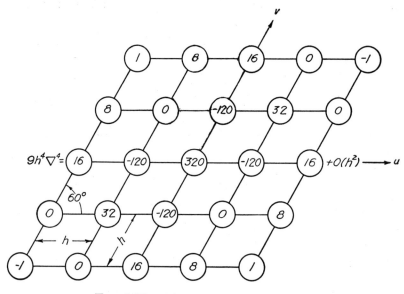

FIG. 5.35. ∇^4 IN SKEW COORDINATES:
$(\alpha = 60°, h = k)$.

5.15   The Laplacian Operator in Polar Coordinates

Polar coordinates (Fig. 5.36) are used in connection with circular domains and are obtained from Cartesian coordinates through the transformations:

$$x = \rho \cos \theta \qquad y = \rho \sin \theta,$$

$$\rho = +(x^2 + y^2)^{1/2} \qquad \theta = \tan^{-1}\frac{y}{x}. \tag{5.15.1}$$

The partial derivatives of ρ and θ with respect to x and y are, by Eqs. (5.15.1):

$$\rho_x = \tfrac{1}{2} \frac{2x}{(x^2 + y^2)^{1/2}} = \frac{x}{\rho} = \cos\theta; \qquad \rho_y = \tfrac{1}{2} \frac{2y}{(x^2 + y^2)^{1/2}} = \sin\theta;$$

$$\theta_x = -\frac{y/x^2}{1 + (y/x)^2} = -\frac{y}{\rho^2} = -\frac{\sin\theta}{\rho}; \tag{a}$$

$$\theta_y = \frac{1/x}{1 + (y/x)^2} = \frac{x}{\rho^2} = \frac{\cos\theta}{\rho}.$$

Consider a function $z(\rho, \theta)$, in which ρ and θ are functions of x and y through Eqs. (5.15.1). The first partial derivatives of z with

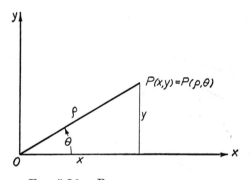

FIG. 5.36.   POLAR COORDINATES.

respect to x and y, by the rule for the differentiation of composite functions and Eqs. (a), are given by

$$z_x = z_\rho \rho_x + z_\theta \theta_x = z_\rho \cos\theta - z_\theta \frac{\sin\theta}{\rho}$$

$$z_y = z_\rho \rho_y + z_\theta \theta_y = z_\rho \sin\theta + z_\theta \frac{\cos\theta}{\rho}. \tag{b}$$

"Squaring" the first of Eqs. (b), we obtain

$$z_{xx} = \left(\frac{\partial}{\partial\rho} \cos\theta - \frac{\partial}{\partial\theta} \frac{\sin\theta}{\rho} \right) \left(z_\rho \cos\theta - z_\theta \frac{\sin\theta}{\rho} \right)$$

$$= z_{\rho\rho} \cos^2\theta + z_\rho \frac{\sin^2\theta}{\rho} + z_{\theta\theta} \frac{\sin^2\theta}{\rho^2} - 2z_{\rho\theta} \frac{\sin\theta\cos\theta}{\rho}$$

$$+ 2z_\theta \frac{\sin\theta\cos\theta}{\rho}. \tag{c}$$

To obtain z_{yy}, either "square" the second of Eqs. (b) or change $\cos \theta$ into $\sin \theta$ and $\sin \theta$ into $-\cos \theta$ in Eq. (c), obtaining:

$$z_{yy} = z_{\rho\rho} \sin^2 \theta + z_\rho \frac{\cos^2 \theta}{\rho} + z_{\theta\theta} \frac{\cos^2 \theta}{\rho^2} + 2z_{\rho\theta} \frac{\cos \theta \sin \theta}{\rho}$$
$$- 2z_\theta \frac{\cos \theta \sin \theta}{\rho}. \quad \text{(d)}$$

Adding Eqs. (c) and (d), the Laplacian in polar coordinates becomes:

$$\nabla^2 z = z_{\rho\rho} + \frac{1}{\rho} z_\rho + \frac{1}{\rho^2} z_{\theta\theta}. \quad (5.15.2)$$

By means of the operators of Fig. 2.8a and with the symbols of

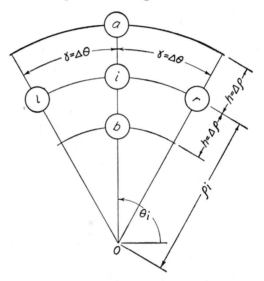

FIG. 5.37.   LATTICE IN POLAR COORDINATES.

Fig. 5.37, the derivatives of Eq. (5.15.2) are approximated by

$$z_{\rho\rho} = \frac{1}{h^2} (z_a - 2z_i + z_b)$$

$$z_\rho = \frac{1}{2h} (z_a - z_b)$$

$$z_{\theta\theta} = \frac{1}{\gamma^2} (z_r - 2z_i + z_l),$$

where: $h = \Delta\rho,$ $\gamma = \Delta\theta$ (5.15.3)

and the Laplacian operator takes the form given in Fig. 5.38.

When the problem is symmetrical about the origin, and hence z

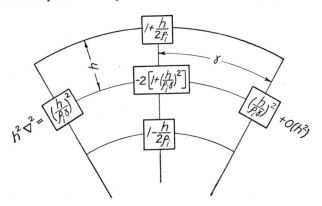

FIG. 5.38. ∇^2 IN POLAR COORDINATES.

does not depend on θ, the ∇^2 operator becomes the ordinary operator
of Fig. 5.39.

The operator of Fig. 5.39 may be used to determine the deflections w at the pivotal points of an annular membrane of internal
radius a and external radius $2a$, under uniform pressure p (Fig. 5.40).

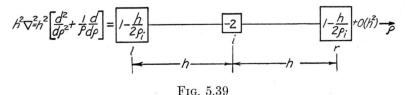

FIG. 5.39

In this case, due to symmetry, Eq. (5.5.1), governing the deflections
of the membrane, reduces to

$$\frac{d^2w}{d\rho^2} + \frac{1}{\rho}\frac{dw}{d\rho} + \frac{p}{S} = 0,$$ (e)

and letting:

$$\rho = ax; \quad w = \frac{pa^2}{S}z; \quad h = \frac{1}{n},$$ (f)

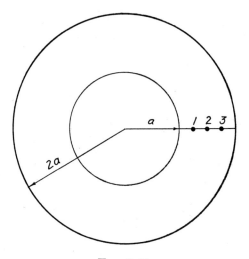

Fɪɢ. 5.40

the corresponding difference equation becomes:

$$\left(1 - \frac{1}{2nx_i}\right) z_l - 2z_i + \left(1 + \frac{1}{2nx_i}\right) z_r = -\frac{1}{n^2}. \qquad (g)$$

Dividing the width of the membrane into four equal parts of width $\frac{1}{4}$, Eq. (g) gives:

at $x = \frac{5}{4}$ $0 - 2z_1 + \left(1 + \dfrac{1}{8\left(\frac{5}{4}\right)}\right) z_2 = -\frac{1}{16}$

at $x = \frac{3}{2}$ $\left(1 - \dfrac{1}{8\left(\frac{3}{2}\right)}\right) z_1 - 2z_2 + \left(1 + \dfrac{1}{8\left(\frac{3}{2}\right)}\right) z_3 = -\frac{1}{16}$

at $x = \frac{7}{4}$ $\left(1 - \dfrac{1}{8\left(\frac{7}{4}\right)}\right) z_2 - 2z_3 + 0 = -\frac{1}{16},$

or:

$$-2z_1 + \tfrac{11}{10}z_2 = -\tfrac{1}{16}$$

$$\tfrac{11}{12}z_1 - 2z_2 + \tfrac{13}{12}z_3 = -\tfrac{1}{16}$$

$$\tfrac{13}{14}z_2 - 2z_3 = -\tfrac{1}{16}.$$

The roots of this system are:

$$z_1 = 0.100, \quad z_2 = 0.126, \quad z_3 = 0.090,$$

and the corresponding membrane deflections are:

$$w_1 = 0.100 pa^2/S; \quad w_2 = 0.126 pa^2/S; \quad w_3 = 0.090 pa^2/S.$$

5.16   The Laplacian Operator in Triangular Coordinates

One of the non-Cartesian lattices most commonly used to cover domains of irregular shape is the *triangular lattice* (Fig. 5.41). The

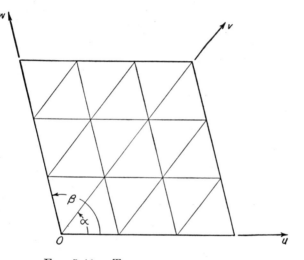

FIG. 5.41.   TRIANGULAR LATTICE.

Laplacian may be expressed in terms of the pivotal points of a triangular lattice by the use of *triangular coordinates*, which locate a point in a plane by means of three coordinates u, v, and w (Fig. 5.42). A constant ratio v/u, w/u, or w/v is maintained among the three coordinates, so that only two coordinates are essential.

Assuming the direction u coincident with the x-axis, and calling α and β the angles between v and u, and w and u, the transformation from Cartesian to triangular coordinates becomes:

$$x = u + v \cos \alpha + w \cos \beta$$
$$y = v \sin \alpha + w \sin \beta. \tag{5.16.1}$$

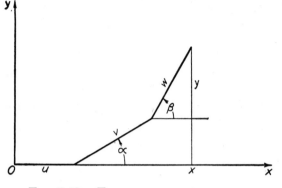

$$\text{FIG. 5.42.} \quad \text{TRIANGULAR COORDINATES.}$$

The partial derivatives of x and y with respect to u, v, and w are therefore:

$$x_u = 1; \quad x_v = \cos \alpha; \quad x_w = \cos \beta;$$
$$y_u = 0; \quad y_v = \sin \alpha; \quad y_w = \sin \beta. \tag{a}$$

A function $z(x,y)$ may be considered a function of u, v, w through the intermediate functions x, y defined by Eqs. (5.16.1), and its derivatives may be computed by the rule for the differentiation of composite functions. Thus by Eqs. (a):

$$z_u = z_x x_u + z_y y_u = z_x$$
$$z_v = z_x x_v + z_y y_v = z_x \cos \alpha + z_y \sin \alpha$$
$$z_w = z_x x_w + z_y y_w = z_x \cos \beta + z_y \sin \beta,$$

and, "squaring" these operators:

$$z_{uu} = z_{xx} \tag{b}$$

$$z_{vv} = z_{xx} \cos^2 \alpha + 2z_{xy} \sin \alpha \cos \alpha + z_{yy} \sin^2 \alpha \tag{c}$$

$$z_{ww} = z_{xx} \cos^2 \beta + 2z_{xy} \sin \beta \cos \beta + z_{yy} \sin^2 \beta. \tag{d}$$

Substituting Eq. (b) in Eqs. (c) and (d), and eliminating z_{xy} between these last two equations, z_{yy} becomes:

$$z_{yy} = \frac{z_{uu} \, 2 \cos \alpha \cos \beta \sin (\beta - \alpha) - z_{vv} \sin 2\beta + z_{ww} \sin 2\alpha}{2 \sin \alpha \sin \beta \sin (\beta - \alpha)},$$

and hence, by Eq. (b):

$$\nabla^2 z = z_{xx} + z_{yy} = z_{uu} + z_{yy}$$

$$= \frac{z_{uu} \sin 2(\beta - \alpha) - z_{vv} \sin 2\beta + z_{ww} \sin 2\alpha}{2 \sin \alpha \sin \beta \sin (\beta - \alpha)}. \qquad (5.16.2)$$

For the commonly used *equilateral triangular lattice*, with

$$\alpha = 60°, \quad \beta = 120°, \quad \beta - \alpha = 60°$$

$$\sin \alpha = \sin \beta = \sin (\beta - \alpha) = \sin 2\alpha = \sin 2(\beta - \alpha) = \frac{\sqrt{3}}{2}$$

$$\sin 2\beta = -\frac{\sqrt{3}}{2},$$

Eq. (5.16.2) reduces to:

$$\nabla^2 z = \tfrac{2}{3}(z_{uu} + z_{vv} + z_{ww}). \qquad (5.16.3)$$

The corresponding ∇^2 difference operator in *equilateral triangular coordinates* obtained by means of the operator $h^2 D^2$ of Fig. 2.8a applied in the u, v, and w directions appears in Fig. 5.43.

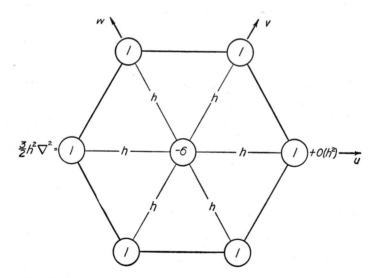

FIG. 5.43. ∇^2 IN EQUILATERAL TRIANGULAR COORDINATES.

"Squaring" the operator of Fig. 5.43 we obtain the ∇^4 *operator in equilateral triangular coordinates*, given in Fig. 5.44.

The operator of Fig. 5.43 may be used, for example, to determine the values of the harmonic function z, whose values on a hexagonal

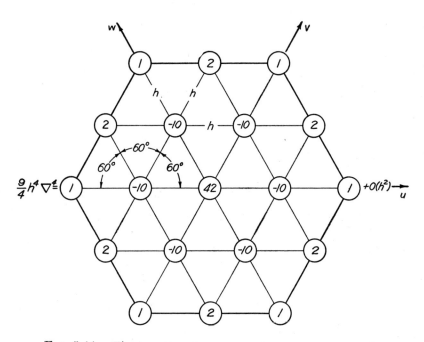

FIG. 5.44. ∇^4 IN EQUILATERAL TRIANGULAR COORDINATES.

boundary are given in Fig. 5.45.   A harmonic function satisfies, by definition, the Laplacian equation $\nabla^2 z = 0$.   Hence the values of z at the pivotal points of the hexagonal domain satisfy the system of equations:

at (1) $2z_2 + 4z_3 - 6z_1 = 0,$

at (2) $z_1 + 2z_3 - 6z_2 + 200 + 200 + 300 = 0,$

at (3) $z_1 + z_2 + z_3 - 6z_3 + 50 + 100 + 200 = 0,$

whose roots are:

$$z_1 = 156; \quad z_2 = 189; \quad z_3 = 139.$$

The z_i could be interpreted as the values of the temperature inside a hexagonal plate, whose boundaries are kept at the temperatures of Fig. 5.45, or as the ordinates of a pressureless membrane, whose ordinates on the boundary are given by Fig. 5.45.

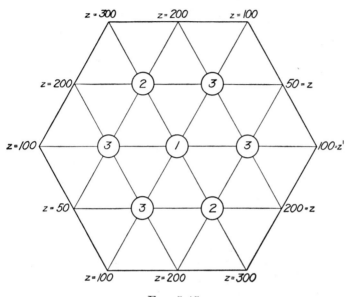

FIG. 5.45

The skew plate considered in Sec. 5.14, having an angle of skew of $30°$ ($\alpha = 60°$), may also be covered by an equilateral triangular lattice. For $n = 4$, for example, the operator of Fig. 5.43 must be applied at the four points of Fig. 5.46 in order to solve the two Poissonian equations (a) of Sec. 5.14. Solution of the corresponding systems[*] gives a central deflection:

$$w_0]_4 = 0.00283 \frac{qa^4}{D},$$

while the deflections obtained with $n = 8$ and $n = 10$ are, respectively,

$$w_0]_8 = 0.00262 \frac{qa^4}{D}; \qquad w_0]_{10} = 0.00260 \frac{qa^4}{D}.$$

[*] See F. L. Ehasz, "Structural Skew Plates," *Trans. ASCE*, **111**, 1011 (1946).

The extrapolated values of the deflection are:

$$w_0]_{4,8} = 0.00255 \, \frac{qa^4}{D}; \qquad w_0]_{8,10} = 0.00256 \, \frac{qa^4}{D};$$

$$w_0]_{4,8,10} = 0.00256 \, \frac{qa^4}{D}.$$

Assuming the coefficient 0.00256 to be correct, it is interesting to notice that it was obtained by solving at least sixteen simultaneous

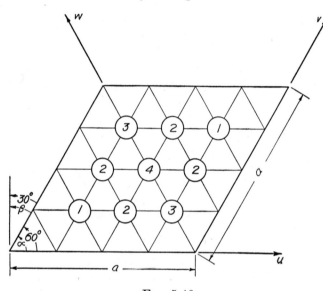

Fig. 5.46

equations, while the results obtained by skew coordinates with only four pivotal points and extrapolation (0.00248) is only 3 per cent off.

These results indicate that each domain should be covered with the lattice of pivotal points best adapted to the solution of the problem, in order to attain the greatest numerical efficiency.

PROBLEMS

5.1 Derive the difference operators corresponding to the following differential operators in terms of forward differences with error of order h^2:

(a) $h^2 \, D_{xy}$. (b) $h^2 \nabla^2$. (c) $h^4 \, D_{xx\dot{y}\dot{y}}$.

Sketch the corresponding molecules.

Ans. See Fig. 5.47.

5.2 Determine the finite difference operators corresponding to the following differential operators, in terms of backward differences with errors of order h^2:

  (a) $h^2 D_{xy}$.   (b) $h^2 \nabla^2$.   (c) $h^4 D_{xxyy}$.

Sketch the corresponding molecules.

Ans. See Fig. 5.48.

5.3

  (a) Determine the first term of the error in the operators of Problem 5.1(a), (b), (c).

  (b) Determine the first term of the error in the operators of Problem 5.2(a), (b).

5.4 Show that the error in Simpson's rule for double integration is of order h^4.

5.5 Evaluate the following integrals to four significant figures by the trapezoidal formula, using square lattices with $n = 2$ and 4 subintervals and extrapolation.

  (a) $\displaystyle\int_2^4 dy \int_4^6 \ln xy^2 \, dx.$ (b) $\displaystyle\int_0^{\pi/2} dy \int_0^{\pi/2} \sin \sqrt{2xy} \, dx.$

  (c) $\displaystyle\int_1^5 dy \int_1^5 \frac{dx}{(x^2 + y^2)^{\frac{1}{2}}}.$ (d) $\displaystyle\int_0^1 dy \int_0^1 e^{-(x^2+y^2)} \, dx.$

Ans. (a) $A_2 = 14.95$; $A_4 = 15.02$; $A_{2,4} = 15.05$.   (c) $A_2 = 4.134$; $A_4 = 3.997$; $A_{2,4} = 3.952$.

5.6 Evaluate the integrals of Problem 5.5 to four significant figures by Simpson's rule, using square lattices with $n = 2$ and 4 subintervals and extrapolation.

Ans. (b) $A_2 = 1.585$; $A_4 = 1.724$; $A_{2,4} = 1.733$.   (c) $A_2 = 3.962$; $A_4 = 3.963$; $A_{2,4} = 3.963$.

5.7 Evaluate the following integral to four significant figures, using rectangular lattices with $n = 2$ and 4 subintervals and extrapolation

  (a) by the trapezoidal rule,

  (b) by Simpson's rule.

$$\int_0^1 dy \int_0^{0.5} \sinh (x^2 y) \, dx$$

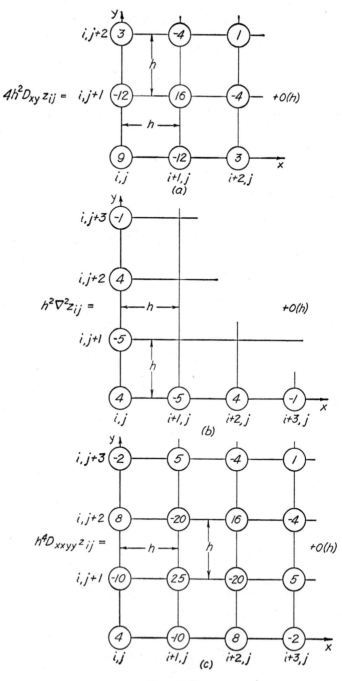

FIG. 5.47

236

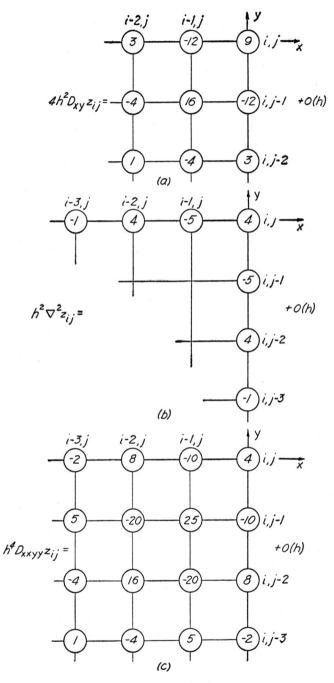

FIG. 5.48

5.8   Determine, by Liebman's procedure, the steady-state temperature at the pivotal points of the rectangular plate of sides a and $b = 2a$ of Fig.

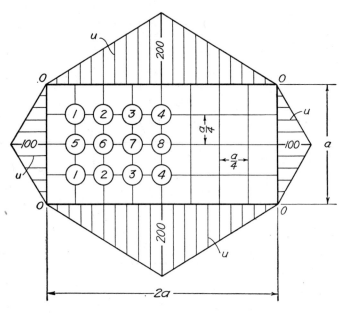

Fɪɢ. 5.49

5.49, if the sides have the temperature indicated in the figure.   Use the operator of Fig. 5.2b.

Ans.	(1)	(2)	(3)	(4)	(5)	(6)	(7)	(8)
	72	102	132	151	87	104	127	139

5.9   Determine by iteration the values, at the pivotal points of the square of Fig. 5.50, of the harmonic function whose boundary values are given in the figure.   Use the operator of Fig. 5.2b, $n = 2$ and 4 subintervals and extrapolation.

5.10   Determine by relaxation the steady-state temperature at the pivotal points of the plate of Fig. 5.51 if its sides are kept at the temperature indicated in the figure.   Use the operator of Fig. 5.2b.

Ans. $u_1 = 433$; $u_2 = 267$; $u_3 = 267$; $u_4 = 233$.

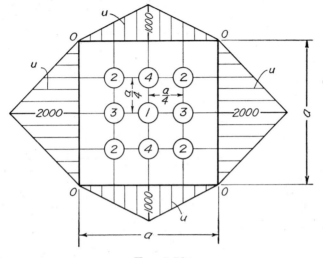

Fig. 5.50

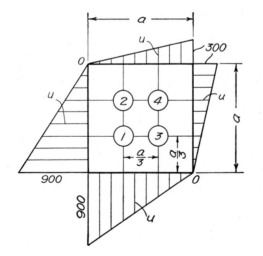

Fig. 5.51

5.11 Determine by relaxation the steady-state temperature at the pivotal points of the plate of Fig. 5.52 if its sides are kept at the temperature indicated in the figure. Use the operator of Eq. (5.1.11).

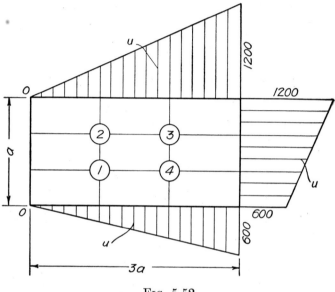

Fig. 5.52

5.12 Determine the lateral deflection at the pivotal points of a square membrane of side L, assuming $PL^2/S = 16,000$, and $n = 4$ subintervals (see Sec. 5.5). Use the operator of Fig. 5.2b.

Ans. $u_1 = 1125$; $u_2 = 875$; $u_3 = 687.5$.

5.13 A simply supported square plate of side a is loaded with a uniform load q. Determine the deflection and the bending moment at the center of the plate, assuming Poisson's ratio $\mu = 0.3$. Use $n = 2$ and $n = 4$ subintervals and extrapolation. *Hint:* The differential equation of the plate $\nabla^4 w = q/D$ (see Sec. 5.8) may be split into two equations of the second order by setting $M = (M_x + M_y)/(1 + \mu)$* where M_x and M_y are the bending moments per unit of length on sections normal to the x- and y-axes. The equations in M and w are $\nabla^2 M = -q$; $\nabla^2 w = -M/D$. The boundary conditions for both w and M are $w = 0$; $M = 0$ on the

---

* See, for example, S. Timoshenko, *Theory of Plates and Shells*, pp. 99 ff.

boundary.   Use the operator of Fig. 5.2b and solve the set of simultaneous equations in the pivotal values of w and M by Gauss's scheme.

Ans. $M_2 = 0.0406qa^2$; $w_2 = 0.00391qa^4/D$; $M_4 = 0.0457qa^2$;
$w_4 = 0.00403qa^4/D$; $M_{2,4} = 0.0474qa^2$; $w_{2,4} = 0.00406qa^4/D$.
$M = 0.0479qa^2$; $w = 0.00405qa^4/D$.

5.14   Determine by iteration the value of the function z, satisfying the equation $\nabla^2 z = 1$, if $z = 0$ on the boundary of a square of side a.   Use the operator of Fig. 5.2b, $h = a/2$ and $a/4$, and extrapolate the value of z at the center of the square.

5.15   Evaluate z at the pivotal points of a square of sides $a = 4h = 2$, if $\nabla^2 z = x^2 y^2$ and $z = 0$ on the boundary.   Assume the origin at the center of the square and use the operator of Fig. 5.2b.

Ans. $u_1 = u_3 = -0.00391$; $u_2 = -0.00586$.

5.16

(a) Determine by relaxation the pivotal values of the function ϕ satisfying the torsional equation $\nabla^2 \phi + 2 = 0$ and having zero values on the boundaries of the section of Fig. 5.53a.   Use the operator of Fig. 5.2b.

(b) Repeat for Fig. 5.53b.

(c) Determine the torsional rigidity of the section of Fig. 5.53a (see Sec. 5.6).

(d) Repeat for Fig. 5.53b.
Use the trapezoidal rule for integration.

Ans.   (a) $\phi_1 = \phi_4 = 0.9756a^2$; $\phi_2 = \phi_5 = 0.9268a^2$; $\phi_3 = \phi_6 = 0.7317a^2$

5.17

(a) Determine the values of the torsion function ϕ for the elastoplastic case considered in Sec. 5.7, assuming $M = 1.35M_0$, and $n = 6$ subintervals.

(b) Determine the corresponding value of θ/θ_0.

5.18   Determine the value ϕ_0 of the function ϕ at the center of a square of side a, if ϕ satisfies the equation $\nabla^4 \phi = 0$ inside the square and the conditions

$$\phi = 0, \qquad \frac{d\phi}{d\nu} = 1$$

on the boundary of the square.   Use the operator of Fig. 5.2c and $n = 2$ and 4 subintervals.   *Note:* ν is the outside normal to the square.

Ans. $n = 2$: $\phi_0 = -0.1667a$; $n = 4$: $\phi_0 = -0.2191a$.

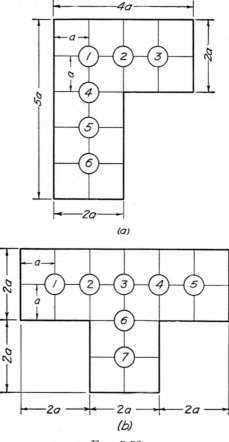

Fig. 5.53

5.19 A uniformly loaded rectangular plate of sides a, $2a$ is built in along its short sides and simply supported along its long sides. Determine the deflection at the center of the plate, using $h = a/2$ (see Sec. 5.8). *Hint:* The boundary conditions along the simply supported edges are: $w = 0$; $d^2w/dv^2 = 0$.

5.20 A simply supported square plate of side a buckles under a uniform pressure N per unit of length of boundary. Determine the lowest buckling value of N using $n = 2$, 3, and 4 subintervals and extrapolation (see Sec. 5.9). *Hint:* The problem is governed by the equations* $\nabla^4 w +$

* See S. Timoshenko, *Theory of Plates and Shells*, pp. 324 ff.

$\dfrac{N}{D} \nabla^2 w = 0$; $w = 0$, $\nabla^2 w = 0$ on the boundary. Let $\nabla^2 w = z$ and use the operator of Fig. 5.2b.

Ans. $N_2 = 16D/a^2$; $N_3 = 18D/a^2$; $N_4 = 18.75D/a^2$; $N_{2,3} = 19.6D/a^2$; $N_{3,4} = 19.71D/a^2$; $N_{2,3,4} = 19.75D/a^2$; $N = 19.74D/a^2$.

5.21   A simply supported rectangular plate of sides $2a$ parallel to x, and a parallel to y, buckles under a uniform compression N per unit of boundary length. Determine the lowest buckling value of N by rectangular coordinates, using $n = 2$, 3, and 4 subintervals and extrapolation (see Sec. 5.9 and Problem 5.20).

5.22   A built-in rectangular plate of sides $2a$ and a, parallel to x and y, respectively, buckles under a uniform pressure N per unit of boundary length. Determine the lowest buckling value of N, using $n = 2$ and 3 subintervals and extrapolation (see Sec. 5.9).

Ans. $N_2 = 16.8D/a^2$; $N_3 = 26.55D/a^2$; $N_{2,3} = 34.35D/a^2$.

5.23   A simply supported square plate buckles under a uniform pressure N per unit length applied to two opposite sides. Determine the lowest buckling value of N, using $n = 2$, 3, and 4 subintervals (see Sec. 5.9).

Ans. $N_2 = 32D/a^2$; $N_3 = 36D/a^2$; $N_4 = 37.514D/a^2$; $N_{2,3} = 39.20D/a^2$; $N_{3,4} = 39.46D/a^2$; $N_{2,3,4} = 39.54D/a^2$; $N = 39.478D/a^2$.

5.24   Solve Problem 5.23 by separation of the variables, letting $w = Y(y) \sin \dfrac{\pi}{a} x$ and using $n = 2$, 3, and 4 subintervals.

5.25   A simply supported square plate of side a vibrates freely. Determine its lowest frequency by finite difference operators with errors of order h^2, using $n = 2$, 3, and 4 subintervals and extrapolation. *Hint:* The differential equation for the free vibration of a plate is $D\nabla^4 w + m\partial^2 w/\partial t^2 = 0$, where m is the mass per unit of area. Substitute $w(x,y,t) = z(x,y) \sin \omega t$.

5.26   A built-in rectangular plate of sides a and $2a$ vibrates freely. Determine its lowest frequency by finite differences using $n = 2$ and 3 subintervals and extrapolation (see Problem 5.25).

Ans. $\omega_2 = (12.962/a^2) \sqrt{D/m}$; $\omega_3 = (17.283/a^2) \sqrt{D/m}$; $\omega_{2,3} = (20.740/a^2) \sqrt{D/m}$.

5.27   A rectangular plate is built-in along its sides $2a$ parallel to x and simply supported along its sides a, parallel to y. The plate vibrates freely. Determine its lowest frequency by separation of the variables and finite differences for $n = 2$, 3, and 4 subintervals and extrapolate. *Hint:* Let

$w(x,y,t) = Y(y) \sin \dfrac{\pi}{2a} x \sin \omega t$ in the plate equation of Problem 5.25. Let $W = \omega a^2 \sqrt{m/D}$.

Ans. $W_2 = 13.175$; $W_3 = 17.132$; $W_4 = 19.373$; $W_{2,3} = 20.298$; $W_{3,4} = 22.254$; $W_{2,3,4} = 22.906$.

5.28 Evaluate to three significant figures the potential V at the pivotal points of Fig. 5.54, when the boundary values of V are as indicated

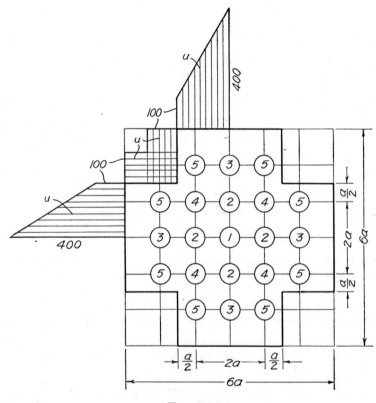

Fig. 5.54

in the figure. Use the difference operator of Fig. 5.28. *Hint:* The potential V satisfies the Laplacian equation.

5.29 Evaluate the steady-state temperature at the pivotal points of the plate of Fig. 5.55, when the boundaries are kept at the indicated temperatures.   Use $\nabla^2 u$ operator of Fig. 5.28 at all points.

Ans. $u_1 = 4833$; $u_2 = 6056$; $u_3 = 8278$.

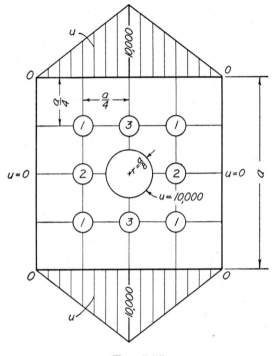

Fɪɢ. 5.55

5.30 Determine the lowest frequency of vibration of an elliptic membrane of semiaxes a and $2a/3$, by means of a rectangular lattice with $h = a/3$ and $k = a/2$.   Use difference formulas with errors of order h (see Sec. 5.11).

5.31 Determine the lowest frequency of vibration of a membrane whose boundary has the shape of Fig. 5.27, using the pivotal points of this figure (see Sec. 5.11).   Use a ∇^2 operator with error of order h at point 4, and ∇^2 operators with error of order h^2 at the other pivotal points.

Ans. $\omega = (4.490/L)\sqrt{S/m}$.

5.32 The plate of Fig. 5.27 is a square of side L with two corners rounded off by arcs of a circle of radius $L/2$. Determine the temperature u at the pivotal points when the boundary has the temperatures indicated in the figure. Use operators for $\nabla^2 u$ with error of order h^2 at all pivotal points.

5.33 The square plate of Fig. 5.56, initially at zero temperature, has two opposite sides suddenly raised to a temperature of 10,000°, and the

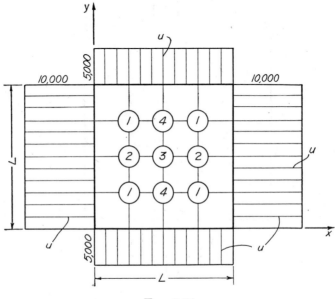

Fig. 5.56

other two sides raised to a temperature of 5,000°. Determine the variation of temperature with time by the Bender-Schmidt method, using a mesh size $h = L/4$, for $n = t/\tau$ varying between 0 and 10.

$n = t/\tau$	u_1	u_2	u_3	u_4
1	3750	2500	0	1250
2	4687	4375	1875	3125
5	6562	6718	5625	5468

Ans.

5.34 Determine by relaxation, the steady-state temperature at the pivotal point of the skew plates: (a) of Fig. 5.57; (b) of Fig. 5.58, when their sides are kept at the indicated temperatures.

Ans. (a) $u_1 = 99.6$; $u_2 = 139.0$; $u_3 = 160.9$; $u_4 = 152.2$.

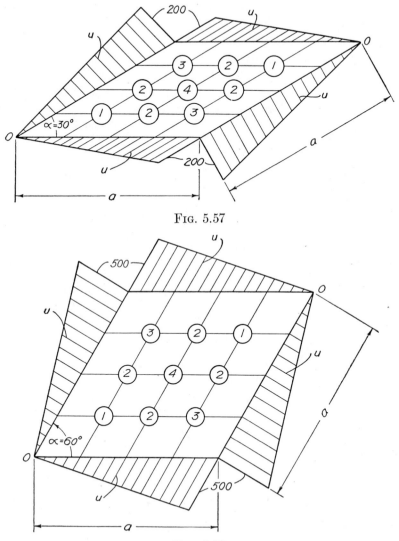

FIG. 5.57

FIG. 5.58

5.35 Determine the lateral deflections at the center of a skew membrane of angle $\alpha = 60°$ and equal sides a, when the ratio of pressure P to tension S equals 16,000.   Use $n = 2$ and 4 subintervals and extrapolation (see Sec. 5.5).

5.36 Determine the lowest frequency of vibration of a skew membrane of equal sides a and angle $\alpha = 60°$, using skew coordinates with $n = 2$ and 3 subintervals, and extrapolation (see Sec. 5.11).

Ans. $\omega_2 = (4.619/a)\ \sqrt{S/m};\ \omega_3 = (4.880/a)\ \sqrt{S/m};$
$\omega_{2,3} = (5.088/a)\ \sqrt{S/m}.$

5.37 A simply supported 45° skew plate, with sides L and $\sqrt{2}\,L$, buckles under a uniform compression N per unit of boundary length. Evaluate the lowest critical value of N using $n = 2$, 3, and 4 subintervals and extrapolations (see Problem 5.20).

Ans. $N_2 = 24D/L^2;\ N_3 = 26.63D/L^2;\ N_4 = 27.15D/L^2;$
$N_{2,3} = 28.730D/L^2;\ N_{3,4} = 27.820D/L^2;\ N_{2,3,4} = 27.510D/L^2.$

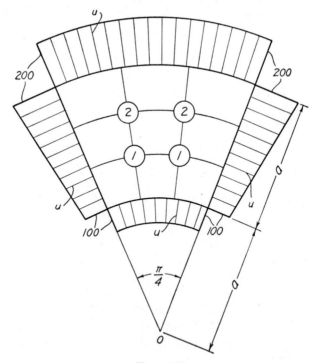

FIG. 5.59

5.38 Determine the pivotal value of the potential ϕ in the circular sector of Fig. 5.59, when its boundary values are as indicated in the figure. Use $n = 2$ and 3 subintervals. *Hint:* The potential ϕ satisfies the Laplacian equation $\nabla^2 \phi = 0$.

Ans. $n = 2 : \phi = 155$. $\quad n = 3 : \phi_1 = 138; \ \phi_2 = 171$.

5.39 Determine the deflections at the pivotal points of an annular membrane of internal radius a and external radius $3a$, under a uniform pressure P and uniform tension S. Use $n = 2$ and 4 subintervals and extrapolation at the center line of the membrane (see Sec. 5.5).

5.40 Determine the lowest frequency of vibration of the membrane of Problem 5.39, using $n = 2, 3$, and 4 subintervals and extrapolation (see Sec. 5.11). Let $w = \omega a \sqrt{m/S}$.

Ans. $w_2 = 1.4142; \quad w_3 = 1.4893; \quad w_4 = 1.5153; \quad w_{2,3} = 1.5495; \quad w_{3,4} = 1.5487$.

5.41 The function $u(x,y)$ satisfies the equation $\nabla^2 u = 0$ in the interior of a hexagon of side a, and has the values indicated in Fig. 5.60, on its boundary. Determine by iteration to 3 significant figures the values of u at the pivotal points indicated in the figure.

Ans. $u_1 = 233; \ u_2 = 276; \ u_3 = 212$.

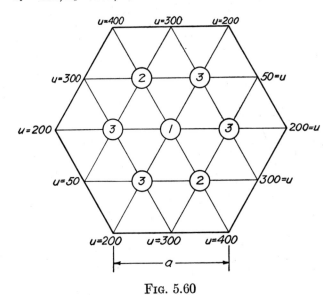

FIG. 5.60

5.42 Determine the elastic torsional stress function ϕ, satisfying the equation $\nabla^2\phi + 2 = 0$, at the pivotal points of an equilateral triangular cross section, using $n = 4$, 5, and 6 subintervals; ϕ is zero on the boundary (see Sec. 5.6).

5.43 Determine the lowest frequency of vibration of an equilateral triangular membrane of sides a, using $n = 3$, 4, and 5 subintervals and extrapolation (see Sec. 5.11).

Ans. $\omega_3 = (6/a)\sqrt{S/m}$; $\omega_4 = (6.532/a)\sqrt{S/m}$; $\omega_5 = (6.788/a)\sqrt{S/m}$;
$\omega_{3,4} = (7.216/a)\sqrt{S/m}$; $\omega_{4,5} = (7.243/a)\sqrt{S/m}$; $\omega = (7.255/a)\sqrt{S/m}$.

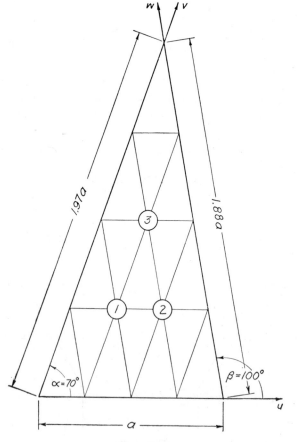

Fig. 5.61

5.44 Determine the lowest frequency of vibration of a regular hexagonal membrane of sides a. Use $n = 1, 2$, and 3 subintervals and extrapolation (see Sec. 5.11).

5.45 Determine the lowest frequency of vibration of the triangular membrane of Fig. 5.61. Use $n = 3$ and 4 subintervals and extrapolation. *Hint:* Derive the ∇^2 operator in triangular coordinates for $\alpha = 70°$, $\beta = 100°$, and let the deflection

$$z(u,v,w,t) = z(u,v,w) \sin \omega t$$

(see Sec. 5.11).

Ans. $\omega_3 = (4.701/a) \sqrt{S/m};\ \omega_4 = (4.859/a) \sqrt{S/m};$
     $\omega_{3,4} = (5.062/a) \sqrt{S/m}.$

5.46 A simply supported equilateral triangular plate of sides a is acted upon by a uniform load q. Determine the lateral deflection at the pivotal points of the plate, using $n = 3, 4, 5$, and 6 subintervals and extrapolate the center deflection w_0 (see Problem 5.13).

Ans. $n = 3;\ w_0 = 0.00077qa^4/D.$ $n = 4;\ w_1 = 0.00055qa^4/D.$ $n = 5;$
   $w_1 = 0.00036qa^4/D,\ w_2 = 0.00054qa^4/D.$ $n = 6;\ w_1 = 0.000241qa^4/D,$
   $w_2 = 0.000434qa^4/D,\ w_0 = 0.000627qa^4/D.$ $w_{3,6} = 0.000579qa^4/D.$

5.47 A simply supported equilateral triangular plate of sides a buckles under a uniform compression N per unit of boundary length. Determine the lowest buckling value of N using $n = 3, 4$, and 5 subintervals and extrapolation (see Problem 5.20).

5.48 A simply supported hexagonal plate of sides a buckles under a uniform compression N per unit of boundary length. Determine the lowest buckling value of N, using $n = 1, 2$, and 3 subintervals and extrapolation (see Problem 5.20).

Ans. $N_1 = 4D/a^2;\ N_2 = 6.28D/a^2;\ N_3 = 6.77D/a^2;\ N_{1,2} = 7.04D/a^2;$
   $N_{2,3} = 7.16D/a^2;\ N_{2,3,4} = 7.18D/a^2.$

Accumulation of errors, 121–124
Adams's method, for first-order equations, 101–104, 125, 126
 for simultaneous first-order equations, 108–109, 127
Adams-Störmer's method, for complete equations, 109–111, 127, 128, 129
 for incomplete equations, 111–113, 128, 129
Algebraic equations, 1–13
 complex roots of, 8–13, 38
  by Friedman's method, 11, 38
  by Graeffe's method, 13
  by synthetic division, 9
  by trial and error, 9
 real roots of, 1–8, 37, 38
  almost repeated, 7, 38
  by Newton's method, 4, 37, 38
  by synthetic division, 3, 37, 38
  by tangents, 4
  by trial and error, 2
  repeated, 7
 roots of, checking by Newton's relations, 13
Angle of twist, of square section: elastic, 188
 plastic, 198
Atmospheric pressure, 91, 106
 continuing solution of, by Runge-Fox's method, 106
 linearized equation of, 93
 starting solution of, 91
Averager operator, 66

Backward differences, 51–58
 derivatives in terms of, 56, 58, 83, 84, 235
 expansions in terms of derivatives, 54
 tabulation of, 52
Beams, buckling loads:
 of constant cross-section, 151, 162, 163
 of cantilever under own weight, 164
 of variable cross-section 155, 163, 165
Beams, deflections:
 of constant cross-section, 161, 162
 on elastic foundation, 148, 162
 of variable cross-section, 162
Beams, lateral buckling:
 of cantilever, 163
 of simply supported, 163
Beams, vibrations:
 of cantilever with constant cross-section, 165
 of simply supported, 164

Bender-Schmidt's method, 218, 246
Bickley's formulas, 47
Bi-harmonic functions, 169, 199, 203, 224, 232, 241, 242, 243
Boundary conditions, by central differences, 133, 200
 by forward differences, 157
Body falling in air:
 friction proportional to V^2, 125
 friction proportional to $V^{3/2}$, 126
Boundary value problems, integration of, 133–166
 higher-order ordinary, 148, 161, 162
 second-order ordinary:
  by central differences, 135, 158
  by forward integration, 134, 157
Buckling loads:
 by unequal differences, 155, 165
 improvement of, by extrapolation, 154, 162, 163, 164, 207, 242, 243, 248, 251
 lateral, 163
 of beams, 152, 155, 162, 163, 164
 of cantilever under own weight, 164
 of variable cross-section, 155, 163, 165
 of plates:
  circular, 164
  hexagonal, 251
  rectangular, 243
  skew, 248
  square, 202, 242, 243
  triangular, 251

Central differences, 63–70
 averaged, 65
 derivatives in terms of, 67, 69, 86, 167–172
 expansions in terms of derivatives, 67
 tabulation of, 65
 unaveraged, 64
  expansions in terms of derivatives, 67
Characteristic value problems:
 solution of ordinary:
  by central differences, 151, 162, 163, 164
  by unequal differences, 155, 165
 solution of partial:
  by finite differences, 202–208, 242, 243, 248, 249, 250, 251
  by separation of variables and finite differences, 208–210, 243
Check sums, in Cholesky's method, 27
 in Gauss's scheme, 17

Cholesky's method, 23–28, 41, 42
  figures lost in, 26
  for symmetrical systems, 25, 28
  number of operations in, 25
  time required by, 25
Convergence:
  in step-by-step integration, 122–124
  minimum h for, in Noumerov-Fox's method, 124
  when $h^2y'' = \delta^2 y$, 132
Coordinates, polar, 224–229, 249
  rectangular, 167–172
  skew, 220–224, 247, 248
  triangular, 229–234, 249, 250–251
Corrections, in Fox's method, 114, 116, 117, 130
  in Noumerov-Fox's method, 118, 121
  in Runge-Fox's method, 105, 107, 126
Crout's method, 23

Derivatives, evaluation of, by backward differences, 56–58, 83–84
  with errors of order h, 56, 58, 83
  with errors of order h^2, 57, 58, 84
  by central differences, 67, 86, 167–172
  with errors of order h^2, 68, 69, 86, 170
  with errors of order h^4, 69, 86, 171
  by interpolating parabolas, 46–48, 81, 83, 86
  with evenly spaced points, 46, 81, 83, 86
  with unevenly spaced points, 47, 81
  by forward differences, 59–60, 84, 85
  with errors of order h, 60, 84
  with errors of order h^2, 60, 85
  by Taylor series, 48–51, 81–83
  with evenly spaced points, 51, 81, 82, 83, 84, 86
  with unevenly spaced points, 48–51, 83
Descartes' rule of signs, 2
Determinants, evaluation of, by pivotal condensation, 22
Difference equations, rigorous solution of, 122
Differences, backward, 51–58
  central, 63–70
  forward, 58–61
Differentiation, numerical, 86, 87, 88
Doolittle's method, 17
∇^2-operator, in polar coordinates, 227
  by rectangular lattice, 169
  in skew coordinates, 222
  by square lattice:
    with error of order h^2, 169–170
    with error of order h^4, 171
  by unequal differences, 215–216

∇^2-operator (*cont.*):
  in triangular coordinates:
    equilateral, 231
    non-equilateral, 251
∇^4-operator, in skew coordinates, 224
  by square lattice, 169–172
  in triangular coordinates, 232

Elastic torsion, stresses in, 188
  by membrane analogy, 189
  of square section:
    by relaxation, 188
  of triangular section, 250
Electric circuits, L, C in series, with variable C, 119
  R, L, C in parallel, 114
    in series, 131
  R, L in series, with iron core, 94
    continuing solution by Adams' method, 102
    linearized equation of, 97
    starting solution of, 95
  R, L in series, with variable R, 126
Electron motion, 129
Electrostatic attraction, 129
Equations, algebraic, complex roots of, 8–13, 38
  linear simultaneous, 16–37, 39–44
  real roots of, 1–8, 37, 38
Equations, transcendental, 13–16, 38, 39
  real roots of, 14–16
    by linear interpolation, 14, 38
    by Newton's method, 14, 38
    by series expansion, 16, 39
Error, accumulation of, in step-by-step integration, 121–124
  detection of, by differences, 52, 84
  in derivatives, 48, 57, 60, 68
    by backward differences, 57
    by central differences, 68
    by forward differences, 60
    by Taylor series, 48
  in double integration:
    by Simpson's rule, 177
    by trapezoidal rule, 175
  in Fox's method, 114
  in Noumerov-Fox's method, 118, 121–124
  in partial derivatives:
    by central differences, 169–172
  in Runge-Fox's method, 106
  in single integration:
    by Simpson's rule, 74
    by trapezoidal rule, 71
  truncation, 121
Error equations, 20, 40

Extrapolations, by Gregory-Newton formulas, 63
h^2-type, 76
(h^2, h^4)-type, 78
h^4-type, 79
(h^4, h^6)-type, 88
Richardson's, 75–81

First-order equations, starting solution of, 91–97
linear, by Runge-Fox's method, 104–107, 126, 127
non-linear, by Adams' method, 101–104, 125, 126
simultaneous, 108–109, 127
starting integration of, by Taylor series, 91, 124, 125
step-by-step integration of, by Adams' method, 101–104
Forward differences, 58–60
derivatives in terms of, 59, 60, 84, 85, 234
expansions in terms of derivatives, 60
tabulation of, 59
Forward integration:
accumulation of error in, 121
by Adams' method, 101, 125, 126
by Adams-Störmer's method, 109, 127, 128, 129
by Noumerov-Fox's method, 118, 130
by Runge-Fox's method, 104, 126, 127
Fox's method, 113–118, 130, 131
Friedman's method, 11, 38

Gauss's scheme, 17–20, 39, 40, 140
number of operations in, 25
Gauss-Seidel iteration method, 28–31, 42, 43
Graeffe's method, 13
Gregory-Newton interpolation formulas, 61–63, 85, 86

Harmonic equation, 169, 178, 181, 215, 232, 238, 240, 244, 245, 246, 247, 249
Heat flow, in square plate, 217, 246
in wires, 135, 159
Hertz problem, dynamic, 128
Higher-order boundary value problems, 148, 161, 162

Initial conditions, by central differences, 130
Initial value problems, 91–132
Integration, numerical, 70–75, 172–178
double, by Simpson's rule, 176–178, 235

Integration, numerical (*cont.*):
double, by trapezoidal rule, 172–176, 235
single, by Simpson's rule, 72, 89, 90
by trapezoidal rule, 70, 89, 90
Integration, step-by-step, 101, 104, 108, 109, 118, 134, 157
Interpolating parabolas, 46–48, 81, 83, 86
Interpolation formulas, backward, 62, 85, 86
forward, 61, 85, 86
Richardson's, 75–81, 88
Interpolation, linear, 3

Laplace's equation, solution of, 178, 181, 215, 232, 238, 240, 244, 245, 246, 247, 249
by iteration, 178, 238
by relaxation, 181, 240, 247
by square lattice, 179
Laplacian operator:
in polar coordinates, 227
in rectangular coordinates, 169
in skew coordinates, 222
in triangular coordinates:
equilateral, 231
non-equilateral, 251
Lateral buckling, of cantilever beam, 163
of simply supported beam, 163
Lattices, in polar coordinates, 226
rectangular, 168
square, 168
in skew coordinates, 221
in triangular coordinates, 229
Liebmann's procedure, 180, 238
Linear differential equations, integration of:
by Fox's method, 113–118, 130, 131
by Noumerov-Fox's method, 118–121, 130
by Runge-Fox's method, 104–107, 126, 127
by Taylor series, 91–94, 124
Linear interpolation, 3
Linearized equations, first-order, 97
second-order, 99, 100

Matrices, 20–23, 41
multiplication of, 21, 41
unit triangular, 23
Membrane analogy, elastic, 189
plastic, 191
Membrane, deflections of:
annular, 227, 249
rectangular, 182, 240
skew, 248
Membrane equation, non-dimensional form of, 184
solution of by relaxation, 184–187

Membrane, vibrations of, 210–213
  annular, 249
  by non-equilateral triangular coordinates, 251
  by unequal differences, 245
  elliptic, 245
  hexagonal, 251
  skew, 248
  triangular, 250
Method of tangents, 4

Newton's method, 4, 37, 38
Newton's relations, 13
Nonlinear differential equations, integration of:
  by Adam's method, 101–104, 125, 126
  by Taylor series, 94–101, 124, 125
Nonlinear oscillations, 129
Noumerov-Fox's method, 118–121, 121–124, 130
Number of operations, in Gauss's scheme, 25
  in Cholesky's method, 25
Numerical differentiation, 86, 87, 88
Numerical integration, double, 172–178
  by Simpson's rule, 176, 235
  by trapezoidal rule, 172, 235
  improvement of, by extrapolation, 77, 79, 175, 177, 235
  single, 70–75
    by Simpson's rule, 72, 89, 90
    by trapezoidal rule, 70, 89, 90

Operators, partial:
  by backward differences, 235
  by central differences, 167–171
  by forward differences, 234
Order of error, in derivatives, 48, 49, 57, 58, 60, 69, 81, 82, 83, 84, 85, 167–172, 234, 235
  by Taylor series, 48, 49, 81, 82, 83
  in partial derivatives, 167–172, 234, 235
    by central differences, 167–172

Parabolas, interpolating, 46–48, 81
Partial derivatives, evaluation of:
  by backward differences, 235
  by central differences, 167–171
  by forward differences, 234
Partial differential equation, of Laplace, 178
  of Poisson, 182
Partial operators, by backward differences, 235
  by central differences, 167–171
  by forward differences, 234

Pendulum oscillations, by Adams-Störmer's method, 111, 112, 129
  damped, 99–101, 112, 125, 129, 131
    linearized equation of, 100
    starting solution of, 99
  undamped, 97–99, 111, 130
    linearized equation of, 99
    starting solution of, 97
Pivotal condensation, 22
Pivotal points:
  evenly spaced, 46, 51, 81, 82, 83, 133, 168
  near curved boundaries, 213
  unevenly spaced, 48, 50, 81, 83, 155, 213
Pivotal values, 45, 81, 82, 83, 168
Plastic roof, 192–195
Plastic torsion:
  by membrane analogy, 191–199, 241
  of square section, by relaxation, 191–199, 241
Plates, buckling load of:
  circular, built-in, 164
  hexagonal, 251
  rectangular, 243
  skew, 248
  square, 202, 242, 243
  triangular, 251
Plates, deflections of:
  circular-stepped, built-in, 159
    by unequal differences, 166
  circular-stepped, simply supported, 160
    by unequal differences, 166
  rectangular, 242
  skew:
    in skew coordinates, 222
    in triangular coordinates, 233
  square, built-in, 199
  square, simply supported, 240
  triangular, 251
Plates, vibrations of:
  rectangular, 243
  square, 243
Points, pivotal:
  evenly spaced, 46, 51, 81, 82, 83, 133, 168
  unevenly spaced, 48, 50, 81, 83, 155, 213
Poisson's equation, 182, 188, 241, 250
Polar coordinates, 224–229, 249
Polynomials, evaluation of, by synthetic division, 3
Potential, 244, 249
  in circular sector, 249

Quadratic factors, synthetic division by, 9

Rectangular lattices, 168
Relaxation, 31–37, 44, 143, 181, 182, 191
  block, 36
  by rounded-off coefficients, 34, 44
  group, 36
  over-, 36
  residuals, 31
  under-, 36
Richardson's extrapolations, 75–81, 88
Rocket launching, 128
Roof analogy, in plastic torsion, 192–195
Roots:
  almost repeated, 7, 38
  complex, 8–13, 38
    by Friedman's method, 11, 38
    by iteration, 9
    by synthetic division, 9
  real, 1–8, 37, 38
  repeated, 7
Runge-Fox's method:
  for first-order linear equations, 104–107, 126
  for simultaneous first-order equations, 109, 127

Second-order boundary value problems:
  improvement of solution by corrections, 140–145
    by Fox's correction and relaxation, 143
    by Fox's corrections and Gauss's scheme, 142
  improvement of solution by extrapolations, 145–148
    by Fox's correction and extrapolation, 147
  solution of by central differences, 135–140, 158
Second-order equations:
  solution of linear complete, by Fox's method, 113–118, 130, 131
  solution of linear incomplete, by Noumerov-Fox's method, 118–121, 130
  starting solution of, 97–101, 124, 125
    non-linear, 97, 125
  step-by-step integration of, by Adams-Störmer's method, 109–112, 127, 128, 129
Separation of the variables, 94, 208, 243
Shear stresses, in elastic torsion, 188
  in plastic torsion, 192
Simpson's rule, double integration by, 176–178, 235
  error in, 177
  single integration by, 72–75, 89, 90
  error in, 74

Simultaneous equations, first-order differential, 108–109, 127
  by Adam's method, 108, 127
  by Runge-Fox's method, 109, 127
Simultaneous equations, linear algebraic, 16–37, 39–44
  matric representation of, 23
  solution of:
    by Cholesky's method, 23, 41, 42
    by Crout's method, 23
    by Doolittle's method, 17
    by error equations, 20, 40
    by Gauss's scheme, 17, 39, 40, 140
    by Gauss-Seidel's iteration method, 28, 42, 43
    by iteration, 29, 42
    by relaxation, 31, 44
  symmetrical systems of, 25, 28
  unit triangular form, 23
Skew coordinates, 220–224, 247, 248
Skew lattices, 221
Skew membrane, deflections of, 248
Skew plates, steady-state temperature of, 247
Square lattices, 168
Step-by-step integration:
  accumulation of error in, 121–124, 132
  by Adams' method, 101, 108, 125, 126
  by Adams-Störmer's method, 109, 111, 127, 128, 129
  by Noumerov-Fox's method, 118, 121, 130
  by Runge-Fox's method, 104, 109, 116, 127
  of boundary value problems, 134, 157
Successive approximations:
  in Fox's method, 114, 116–117, 130
  in Noumerov-Fox's method, 120–121, 130
  in Runge-Fox's method, 106–107, 126
Synthetic division, 3
  backward, 6, 38
  by quadratic factor, 9
    in ascending powers, 11
    in descending powers, 11
  successive applications of, 8
Synthetic substitution, 37

Tabulation:
  of backward differences, 52, 86
  of central differences, 65, 86
  of forward differences, 59, 86
Taylor series, 48, 91, 124–125, 134, 158
  evaluation of derivatives by, 48–51, 81–83, 84, 86

Taylor series (*cont.*):
  starting of integration by, 91–101, 124, 125
  symbolical expansion, 49
Temperature, steady-state:
  in plate with curvilinear boundaries; by unequal differences, 213, 245, 246
  in skew plates, 247
  in square plate, by equal differences, 178, 181, 238–240
  by unequal differences, 213, 245, 246
Temperature, transient, in square plate, 217, 246
Terminal velocity, 125, 126
Torsion, elastic, 188–191
  by membrane analogy, 189
  of square section, by relaxation, 188
  of triangular section, 250
  shear stresses in, 189
Torsion, plastic:
  by membrane analogy, 191–199
  of square section, by relaxation, 191–199, 241
Torsional rigidity, 188, 198–199, 241
Transcendental equations, 13–16, 38, 39
Trapezoidal rule, 70–72, 89, 90, 172–176, 235

Trapezoidal rule (*cont.*):
  error in double integration by, 175
  error in single integration by, 71
Triangular coordinates, 229–234, 249, 250, 251
Truncation error, 121
Twisting moment, of square section:
  elastic, 188
  plastic, 199, 241

Values, pivotal, 45, 81, 82, 83, 168
Vibrations:
  of beams:
    cantilever, 165
    simply-supported, 164
  of elastic sphere, 128
  of membrane:
    annular, 249
    by nonequilateral triangular coordinates, 251
    by unequal differences, 245
    elliptic, 245
    hexagonal, 251
    skew, 248
    triangular, 250
  nonlinear, 129
  of plates, 243

Wire temperature, 135, 159